Prentice Hall

Biology

Teaching Resources
Unit 10

PEARSON
Prentice
Hall

Upper Saddle River, New Jersey
Boston, Massachusetts

Copyright © by Pearson Education, Inc., publishing as Pearson Prentice Hall, Boston, Massachusetts 02116. All rights reserved. Printed in the United States of America. This publication is protected by copyright, and permission should be obtained from the publisher prior to any prohibited reproduction, storage in a retrieval system, or transmission in any form or by any means, electronic, mechanical, photocopying, recording, or likewise. The publisher hereby grants permission to reproduce these pages, in part or in whole, for classroom use only, the number not to exceed the number of students in each class. Notice of copyright must appear on all copies. For information regarding permission(s), write to: Rights and Permissions Department, One Lake Street, Upper Saddle River, New Jersey 07458.

Pearson Prentice Hall™ is a trademark of Pearson Education, Inc.
Pearson® is a registered trademark of Pearson plc.
Prentice Hall® is a registered trademark of Pearson Education, Inc.

ISBN 0-13-203405-0

2 3 4 5 6 7 8 9 10   10 09 08 07

To the Teacher

The Teaching Resources unit booklets have been designed to help you teach *Prentice Hall Biology*. Each unit book consists of materials that have been designed to stimulate students' interest in biology, develop their critical thinking, and teach them basic science skills. The unit books will accommodate a wide range of student abilities and interests.

Each teaching resource unit book contains the following:

- Lesson Plans (for each section)
- Reading and Study Workbook A (includes section summaries, section worksheets, and a chapter vocabulary review written at grade level)
- Adapted Reading and Study Workbook B worksheets (Includes section summaries, key concept worksheets, and a chapter vocabulary review written at a sixth-grade reading level)
- Section Review Worksheets
- Enrichment Worksheets
- Graphic Organizers
- Chapter Tests (Includes two tests for each chapter—Test A for students performing on or above grade level; Test B for students performing on or below grade level)
- Unit Tests (two tests for each unit—Test A and Test B)
- Answer Key (for section review worksheets, enrichment worksheets, graphic organizers, and chapter tests.)
- Graphic Organizer Transparencies (generic reproducible masters)
- Transparency Planner (Full-color preview of all the transparencies that support the unit)

Unit 10 The Human Body
Chapter 35 The Nervous System

Chapter 36 Skeletal, Muscular, and Integumentary Systems

Chapter 37 Circulatory and Respiratory Systems

Chapter 38 Digestive and Excretory Systems

Chapter 39 Endocrine and Reproductive Systems

Chapter 40 The Immune System and Disease

LESSON PLAN 35–1 (pages 891–896)

Human Body Systems

Section Objectives

- **35.1.1 Describe** how the human body is organized.
- **35.1.2 Explain** homeostasis.

Vocabulary specialized cell • epithelial tissue • connective tissue • nervous tissue • muscle tissue • homeostasis • feedback inhibition

Local Standards

1 FOCUS

Vocabulary Preview
Emphasize the word *tissue*, which occurs in four of the Vocabulary words, and remind students that a tissue is a group of similar cells that work together to perform the same function.

Targeted Resources
❏ Transparencies: **507** Section 35–1 Interest Grabber
❏ Transparencies: **508** Section 35–1 Outline

2 INSTRUCT

Build Science Skills: Inferring
Students name the organ systems that they think are involved when people play basketball. **L1 L2**

Use Visuals: Figure 35–2
Students identify structures and functions of the organ systems shown in Figure 35–2. **L1**

Build Science Skills: Using Models
Students create an overlapping model of the human organ systems. **L2 L3**

Demonstration
Students are shown items such as plastic wrap and packaging tape; and, for each item, they decide which type of tissue has a similar function. **L1 L2**

Make Connections: Chemistry
Explain why temperatures within a narrow range are required for most of the body's vital biochemical processes to occur efficiently. **L2**

Build Science Skills: Using Models
Students compare the regulation of body temperature in humans with the regulation of air temperature in a house. **L1 L2**

Targeted Resources
❏ Reading and Study Workbook: Section 35–1
❏ Adapted Reading and Study Workbook: Section 35–1
❏ Teaching Resources: Section Summaries 35–1, Worksheets 35–1
❏ Transparencies: **509** Example of Feedback Inhibition; **510, 511** Figure 35–2 Human Organ Systems (Part I and Part II)

3 ASSESS

Evaluate Understanding
Have students draw a simple diagram to show how the body regulates temperature.

Reteach
State the function of each human organ system, and challenge students to identify the system and name its structures.

Targeted Resources
❏ Teaching Resources: Section Review 35–1
❏ (i)**Text** Section 35–1

Teacher_____ Class_____ Date_____ M T W T F

The Nervous System

Time
1 period
1/2 block

Section Objectives

Local Standards

- **35.2.1 Identify** the functions of the nervous system.
- **35.2.2 Describe** how a nerve impulse is transmitted.

Vocabulary neuron • cell body • dendrite • axon • myelin sheath • resting potential • action potential • threshold • synapse • neurotransmitter

1 FOCUS

Reading Strategy
As students read, they should look for Vocabulary words and Key Concepts in the captions and the text.

Targeted Resources
❑ Transparencies: **512** Section 35–2 Interest Grabber

❑ Transparencies: **513** Section 35–2 Outline

2 INSTRUCT

Demonstration
Demonstrate how quickly cells of the nervous system communicate by having one student perform an action at irregular intervals and another student immediately respond with a different action. **L1 L2**

Build Science Skills: Using Models
Students make a three-dimensional model of a neuron. **L2**

Use Visuals: Figure 35–6
Students explain the difference in concentration of potassium and sodium ions in the drawing of a neuron in Figure 35–6. **L2**

Demonstration
To simulate the movement of an action potential, arrange dominoes in a row and then knock them down by giving the first one a gentle push. **L1 L2**

Make Connections: Health Science
Explain that many mental illnesses, including depression, appear to be associated with abnormal levels of certain neurotransmitters. **L2**

Targeted Resources
❑ Reading and Study Workbook: Section 35–2

❑ Adapted Reading and Study Workbook: Section 35–2

❑ Teaching Resources: Section Summaries 35–2, Worksheets 35–2

❑ Transparencies: **514** A Neuron, **515** Figure 35–6 Resting Potential, **516** Figure 35–7 An Impulse, **517** Figure 35–8 The Synapse

❑ **NSTA** sci*LINKS* Nervous system

3 ASSESS

Evaluate Understanding
Call on students at random to define each of the Vocabulary words, and call on other students to correct any errors.

Reteach
Provide students with copies of Figure 35–5 without the labels, and have them label each part of the neuron.

Targeted Resources
❑ Teaching Resources: Section Review 35–2

❑ **ⓘText** Section 35–2

LESSON PLAN 35–3 (pages 901–905)

Divisions of the Nervous System

Section Objectives

- **35.3.1 Identify** the functions of the central nervous system.
- **35.3.2 Describe** the functions of the two divisions of the peripheral nervous system.

Vocabulary meninges • cerebrospinal fluid • cerebrum • cerebellum • brain stem • thalamus • hypothalamus • reflex • reflex arc

Local Standards

---

1 FOCUS

Vocabulary Preview

Ask students to identify which two of the Vocabulary words do not refer to structures in the brain, and have students predict the meanings of the two words.

Targeted Resources

❑ Transparencies: **518** Section 35–3 Interest Grabber

❑ Transparencies: **519** Section 35–3 Outline

❑ Transparencies: **520** Concept Map

---

2 INSTRUCT

Build Science Skills: Calculating

Students calculate an increase in surface area due to folding to appreciate how greatly the folds of the brain increase its surface area. **L2 L3**

Use Community Resources

Invite a diagnostic imaging technician to visit the class and explain how brain injuries and other abnormalities of the brain are diagnosed. **L2**

Demonstration

With the help of a student volunteer, demonstrate the knee-jerk reflex. **L1 L2**

Build Science Skills: Applying Concepts

Students explain how a person with a healthy peripheral nervous system could lack nervous control of the leg muscles due to a spinal cord injury. **L2**

Use Visuals: Figure 35–11

Students use Figure 35–11 to trace the path of a nerve impulse from the toe to the spinal cord and back to muscles in the leg. **L1 L2**

Build Science Skills: Observing

Demonstrate the pupillary reflex by having students observe the changes in the pupils of the eyes of volunteers adjusting to light after being covered with a blindfold. **L1 L2**

Targeted Resources

❑ Reading and Study Workbook: Section 35–3

❑ Adapted Reading and Study Workbook: Section 35–3

❑ Teaching Resources: Section Summaries 35–3, Worksheets 35–3

❑ Transparencies: **521** Figure 35–9 The Brain, **522** Cross Section of the Spinal Cord

❑ Lab Manual A: Chapter 35 Lab

❑ Lab Manual B: Chapter 35 Lab

❑ **NSTA** *sci*LINKS Human brain

---

3 ASSESS

Evaluate Understanding

Ask students to make a concept map of the divisions and subdivisions of the nervous system.

Reteach

Have each student create a crossword puzzle using the Vocabulary words, and then have students exchange and solve the puzzles.

Targeted Resources

❑ Teaching Resources: Section Review 35–3

❑ *i*Text Section 35–3

LESSON PLAN 35–4 (pages 906–909)

The Senses

Section Objectives

- **35.4.1 Name** the five types of sensory receptors.
- **35.4.2 Identify** the five sense organs.

Vocabulary sensory receptor • pupil • lens • retina • rod • cone • cochlea • semicircular canal • taste bud

Local Standards

1 FOCUS

Reading Strategy
Have students preview the section by studying the figures and reading the captions.

Targeted Resources
❑ Transparencies: **523** Section 35–4 Interest Grabber
❑ Transparencies: **524** Section 35–4 Outline

2 INSTRUCT

Build Science Skills: Applying Concepts
Students identify how the different categories of sensory receptors might be stimulated at a picnic. **L1** **L2**

Make Connections: Physics
Explain that human eyes can detect light only within a very limited range of wavelengths in the electromagnetic spectrum. **L2** **L3**

Use Visuals: Figure 35–14
Students use the diagram of the ear in Figure 35–14 to trace the path of sound waves through the ear and identify the functions of particular structures. **L2**

Make Connections: Health Science
Explain why the middle ear is prone to infections from the throat via the eustachian tube. **L2**

Demonstration
Volunteers taste and try to identify a variety of different fruit juices while wearing a blindfold and pinching their nose shut. **L2**

Build Science Skills: Designing Experiments
Students design an experiment to determine the distribution of temperature receptors on the back of the hand. **L2** **L3**

Targeted Resources
❑ Reading and Study Workbook: Section 35–4
❑ Transparencies: **525** The Senses of Smell and Taste, **526** Figure 35–13 The Eye, **527** Figure 35–14 The Ear
❑ Teaching Resources: Section Summaries 35–4, Worksheets 35–4, Enrichment
❑ Lab Worksheets: Chapter 35 Real-World Lab
❑ **NSTA** *sci*LINKS Senses

3 ASSESS

Evaluate Understanding
Provide students with copies of Figure 35–13 without the labels, and have students label each part of the eye shown in the figure.

Reteach
Have students give examples of each of the five categories of sensory receptors at work.

Targeted Resources
❑ Teaching Resources: Section Review 35–4
❑ **i Text** Section 35–4

LESSON PLAN 35–5 (pages 910–914)

Drugs and the Nervous System

Section Objectives

35.5.1 Name the different classes of drugs that directly affect the nervous system.

35.5.2 Describe the effect of alcohol on the body.

Vocabulary drug • stimulant • depressant • fetal alcohol syndrome • drug abuse • addiction

Local Standards

1 FOCUS

Reading Strategy

Have students read the Key Concepts in the text section to find out the effects of each type of drug on the body.

Targeted Resources

❑ Transparencies: **528** Section 35–5 Interest Grabber

❑ Transparencies: **529** Section 35–5 Outline

2 INSTRUCT

Address Misconceptions

Address the misconception that alcohol and nicotine are not drugs because they are legal. Point out their dangers. **L2**

Build Science Skills: Drawing Conclusions

Students conclude why it is dangerous to combine drugs such as sleep medications and pain relievers with alcohol. **L2**

Use Visuals: Figure 35–18

Students apply the information in Figure 35–18 on commonly abused drugs by describing how people might behave when they take each type of drug. **L2**

Build Science Skills: Making Judgments

Students find newspaper articles relating to alcohol and write a report summarizing the effects of alcohol abuse on society. **L2 L3**

Analyzing Data

Students analyze data in a graph relating blood-alcohol concentration to fatal crashes. **L2 L3**

Use Community Resources

Students investigate drug abuse treatment options available in their community. **L2**

Targeted Resources

❑ Reading and Study Workbook: Section 35–5

❑ Adapted Reading and Study Workbook: Section 35–5

❑ Teaching Resources: Section Summaries 35–5, Worksheets 35–5

❑ Transparencies: **530** Commonly Abused Drugs

❑ **NSTA** *sci*LINKS Drugs and drug abuse

3 ASSESS

Evaluate Understanding

Have students create a flowchart to show how a stimulant or depressant drug affects the synapse.

Reteach

Challenge students to identify one or more harmful effects of each type of drug described in the text.

Targeted Resources

❑ Teaching Resources: Section Review 35–5, Chapter Vocabulary Review, Graphic Organizer, Chapter 35 Tests: Levels A and B

❑ **iText** Section 35–5, Chapter 35 Assessment

❑ **PHSchool.com** Online Chapter 35 Test

Chapter 35   Nervous System

Summary

35–1 Human Body Systems

Cells of multicellular organisms are specialized for certain functions. **The levels of organization in a multicellular organism include cells, tissues, organs, and organ systems.**

- A cell is the basic unit of structure and function in living things. **Specialized cells** are suited to perform a particular function.
- Groups of similar cells work together to form tissues. **Epithelial tissue** covers body surfaces. **Connective tissue** supports the body and connects its parts. **Nervous tissue** carries messages throughout the body. **Muscle tissue** allows movement.
- Groups of tissues that work together to perform complex functions are called organs.
- Organs form organ systems.

Organ systems work together to keep conditions in the body stable. This process is called **homeostasis. Homeostasis is the process by which organisms keep internal conditions relatively constant, despite changes in external environments.** Homeostasis may involve feedback inhibition, or negative feedback. For example, the nervous system senses when the body cools and signals the cells to give off more heat.

35–2 The Nervous System

The nervous system controls and coordinates body functions. It responds to internal and external stimuli. Messages move through the nervous system as electrical signals. The signals are called impulses.

Neurons are nerve cells. Each neuron has a cell body, dendrites, and an axon. The **cell body** is the largest part of a typical neuron. It holds the nucleus. Short branches, called **dendrites,** carry impulses toward the cell body. A long fiber, called the **axon,** carries impulses away from the cell body. A **myelin sheath** covers and insulates parts of some axons. A **synapse** is at the end of an axon. One neuron transfers an impulse to another at the synapse. Chemicals called **neurotransmitters** send impulses across the synapse.

There are three types of neurons: sensory neurons, motor neurons, and interneurons. Sensory neurons carry impulses to the spinal cord. Motor neurons carry impulses from the spinal cord. Interneurons link sensory and motor neurons.

A resting neuron is one that is not carrying an impulse. When a neuron is resting, the inside of the cell has a net negative charge. The outside of the cell has a net positive charge. This charge difference across the cell membrane is called the **resting potential** of the neuron. **When a resting neuron is stimulated by another neuron or by the environment, an impulse starts.** Positive ions flow into the neuron making the inside of the cell temporarily more positive than the outside of the cell. This reversal of charges across the membrane is the impulse, or **action potential.** Once started, the action potential travels quickly down the neuron's axon. At the end of the axon, impulses can be transmitted to the next cell.

35–3 Divisions of the Nervous System

The nervous system has two major divisions: the central nervous system and the peripheral nervous system.

1) <u>The central nervous system</u> is made up of the brain and spinal cord. It is the control center of the body. **It sends messages, processes information, and analyzes information.** The brain and spinal cord are protected by bone and three layers of connective tissue. Fluid between the layers cushions and protects nerve tissue.

The brain has several regions. The **cerebrum** controls voluntary actions. The **cerebellum** coordinates involuntary actions. The **brain stem** controls basic body functions. The **thalamus** receives impulses from the senses and sends them to the cerebrum. The **hypothalamus** connects the nervous and endocrine systems.

The spinal cord connects the brain with the rest of the body. Some reflexes are processed in the spinal cord. A **reflex** is a quick, automatic response to a stimulus. Sneezing is an example. The path of an impulse during a reflex is called the **reflex arc.**

2) <u>The peripheral nervous system</u> has two divisions.
   - The **sensory division** sends impulses from sensory neurons to the central nervous system.
   - The **motor division** sends impulses from the central nervous system to muscles and glands. The motor division is further divided into somatic and autonomic nervous systems.

The somatic nervous system controls voluntary actions. The autonomic nervous system regulates activities that are automatic. These nerves control functions that are not under conscious control.

35–4 The Senses

Sensory receptors are neurons that react to stimuli in the environment. These receptors send impulses to the central nervous system. **There are five types of sensory receptors.** Pain receptors respond to pain. Thermoreceptors respond to temperature. Mechanoreceptors respond to pressure. Chemoreceptors respond to chemicals. Photoreceptors respond to light.

The sensory organ responsible for vision is the eye. Light enters the eye through the pupil. The pupil is a small opening at the front of the eye. Light then moves through the **lens,** which focuses the light on the retina. The retina contains photoreceptors called rods and cones. **Rods** are sensitive to dim light. **Cones** are sensitive to colors.

Ears respond to sound stimuli. Sound vibrations enter the ear and create pressure waves in the fluid-filled cochlea. Sensory receptors in the cochlea send impulses to the brain. Ears also sense balance. Semicircular canals in the ear contain fluid, hair cells, and tiny grains. Movements make the grains bend the hair cells, which send an impulse to the brain.

Chemoreceptors in the nose react to chemicals in the air and send impulses to the brain. **Taste buds** are sense organs that detect taste. Most taste buds are located on a person's tongue. The skin is the largest sense organ. It has receptors that respond to temperature, touch, and pain.

35–5 Drugs and the Nervous System

A **drug** is any substance, other than food, that changes the structure or function of the body. Several types of drugs affect the nervous system.

- Stimulants increase heart rate, blood pressure, and breathing rate.
- Depressants decrease heart rate and breathing rate, lower blood pressure, relax muscles, and relieve tension.
- Opiates act like natural brain chemicals called endorphins. These brain chemicals normally help overcome pain. Opiates are highly addictive.
- Marijuana can cause memory and concentration problems.
- Alcohol is a depressant that slows down the rate at which the central nervous system functions.

Drug abuse can be defined as the intentional misuse of any drug for nonmedical purposes. **Addiction** is an uncontrollable dependence on a drug.

Name_____ Class_____ Date _____

Organization of the Human Body

The human body can be organized into a series of levels: *cells, tissues, organs,* and *organ systems.*

In the first column, fill in the correct level of organization. Then, number the levels in order from simplest (1) to most complex (4) in the last column.

Organization of the Human Body			
Level of Organization	**Description**	**Example**	**Order**
	groups of different types of tissue that function together	brain	
	groups of organs that perform closely related functions	nervous system	
	basic units of structure and function in a living thing	neuron	
	groups of cells that perform a particular function	nervous tissue	

Answer the question.

1. All of the organ systems in the human body work together to maintain homeostasis. What is homeostasis?

_____

_____

2. Name one organ system in the human body.

_____

_____

_____

The Neuron

Neurons are the basic units of the nervous system. They transmit electrical signals called impulses.

Color the neuron according to the prompts below
- Color the structures that receive signals from the environment or another neuron red.
- Color the structure that carries an impulse away from the cell body orange.
- Color the cell body blue.

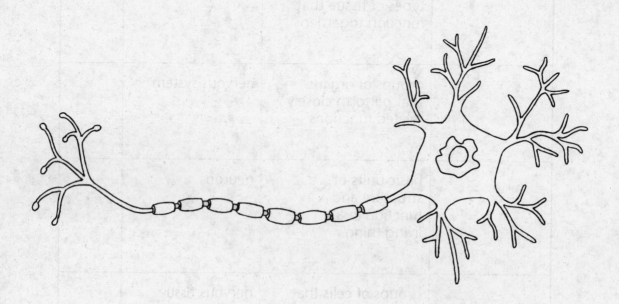

Answer the questions. Circle the correct answer.

1. What is the insulating membrane that surrounds some axons called?

   synapse   myelin sheath

2. What are the structures that carry impulses to the cell body called?

   dendrites   axons

Action Potential

A resting neuron has an overall negative charge. Outside the neuron, the environment has a net positive charge. When a neuron is stimulated, positive ions rush into the cell. The area inside the cell becomes temporarily more positive than the outside. This reversal of charges is called a nerve impulse, or *action potential*. As the action potential passes, positive ions flow out of the cell. This restores the net negative charge inside the cell.

Color the action potential in the appropriate diagrams red. One has been done for you.

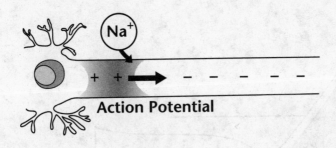

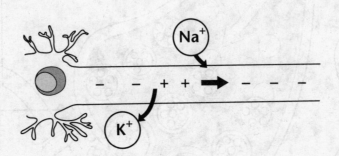

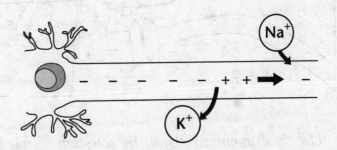

Use the diagram to answer the question. Circle the correct answer.

1. In which direction do potassium ions (K⁺) flow as the action potential passes?

   into the cell   out of the cell

The Synapse

A neuron transfers an impulse to another cell at a synapse. The signals are transferred by neurotransmitters. Neurotransmitters are chemicals released by the neuron that cross the space between the cells and bind to receptors on the neighboring cell.

Label one neurotransmitter, receptor, and two cell membranes on the diagram. Then, color the neuron transmitting the signal red. Color the cell receiving the signal blue.

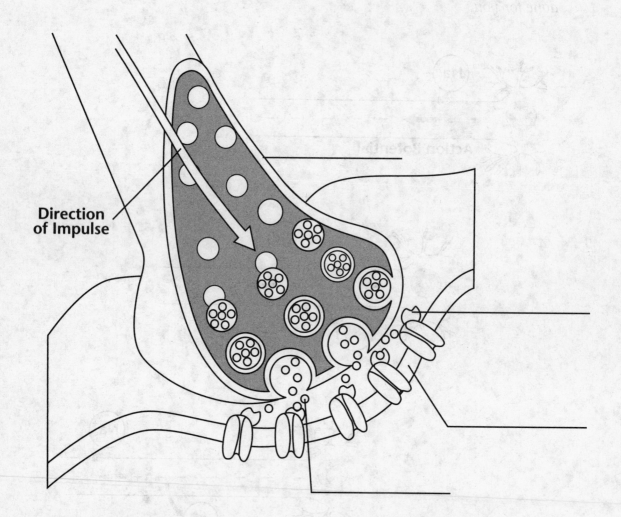

Direction of Impulse

Use the drawing to answer the question. Circle the correct answer.

1. The cell receiving the signal is a neuron. What part of this neuron is pictured above?

dendrite   cell body

The Brain

The brain is a part of the central nervous system. It helps relay messages and processes and analyzes information. Different body functions are controlled by different parts of the brain.

Color different parts of the brain according to the prompts.
- Color the cerebrum brown.
- Color the cerebellum yellow.
- Color the spinal cord green.
- Color the brain stem blue.
- Color the thalamus and hypothalamus red.

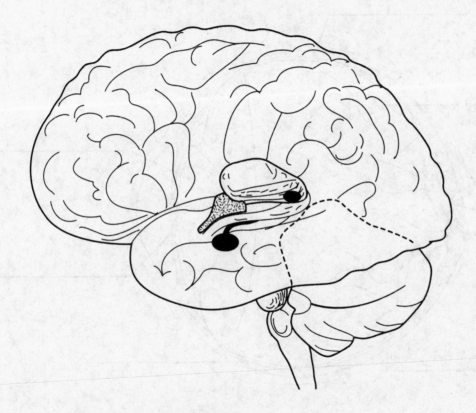

Answer the questions. Circle the correct answer.

1. Which part of the brain controls blood pressure, heart rate, breathing and swallowing?

   brain stem   cerebrum

2. Which part of the brain is the site of intelligence, learning, and judgment?

   thalamus   cerebrum

The Eye

The eye is a sense organ that humans use to see. Different parts of the eye perform different functions. For example, the lens focuses light on the retina.

Use the words below to label the diagram.

lens	pupil	vitreous humor
optic nerve	retina	

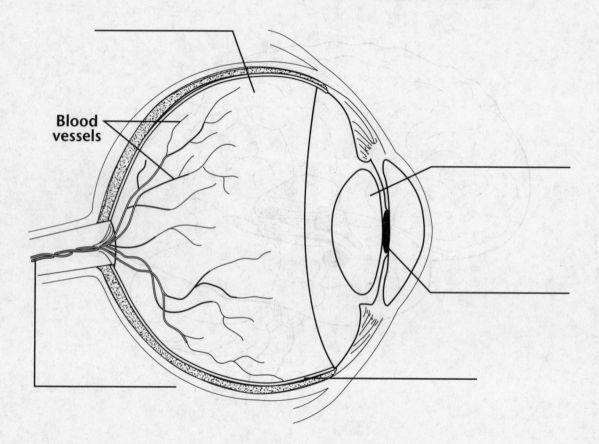

Blood vessels

Answer the question. Circle the correct answer.

1. Rods and cones are two types of cells that can convert light energy into nerve impulses. These cells are located in which structure?

retina   pupil

Hearing

The human ear converts vibrations in the air into nerve impulses that can be interpreted by the brain. This process is called hearing.

The following prompts describe different steps in the hearing process. Use the numbers to label the place in the ear in which each step occurs. Some locations may be labeled with more than one step.

1 Vibrations enter the auditory canal.

2 The vibrations cause the eardrum to vibrate.

3 Vibrations from the eardrum are picked up by the hammer, anvil, and stirrup.

4 Vibrations from the stirrup are transmitted to the oval window.

5 Pressure waves are created in the fluid-filled cochlea. Hair cells respond to pressure waves by producing nerve impulses.

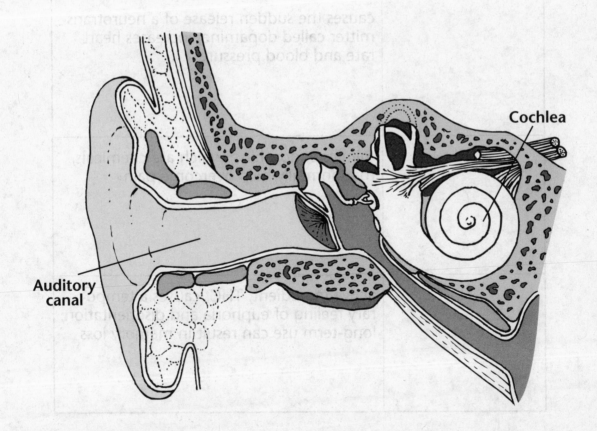

Cochlea

Auditory canal

Answer the question. Circle the correct answer.

1. Which of the following best describes sound?

light waves in the air   vibrations in the air

Drugs

A drug is a substance, other than food, that changes the structure or function of the body.

The following table describes how four different drugs—marijuana, cocaine, opiates, and alcohol—affect the human body. Complete the table by filling in the correct drug. The first one is done for you.

Drug	Effects on the Body
alcohol	slows the rate at which the central nervous system functions; slows reflexes; disrupts coordination; impairs judgment; long-term use harms the liver
	causes the sudden release of a neurotransmitter called dopamine; increases heart rate and blood pressure
	mimics endorphins, which are chemicals that normally help overcome pain
	active ingredient, THC, causes a temporary feeling of euphoria and disorientation; long-term use can result in memory loss

Use the table to answer the questions. Circle the correct answer.

1. Which drug is a depressant?   alcohol   cocaine

2. Which drug is a stimulant?   alcohol   cocaine

Chapter 35   Nervous System

Vocabulary Review

Multiple Choice   *In the space provided, write the letter of the answer that best completes each sentence.*

_____ 1. A drug that increases the actions regulated by the nervous system is a
  a. depressant.
  b. dendrite.
  c. stimulant

_____ 2. The part of a nerve cell that carries impulses toward the cell body is the
  a. axon.
  b. dendrite.
  c. myelin sheath.

_____ 3. The tissue that covers the surface of the body and lines internal organs is
  a. muscle tissue.
  b. nervous tissue.
  c. epithelial tissue.

_____ 4. The process by which the product of a system shuts down or limits the operation of the system is
  a. feedback inhibition.
  b. action potential.
  c. resting potential.

_____ 5. The photoreceptors of the eye that are sensitive to light but do not distinguish color are the
  a. rods.
  b. cones.
  c. pupils.

_____ 6. Neurons that react to light, sound, or other specific stimuli by sending impulses to other neurons are
  a. neurotransmitters.
  b. meninges.
  c. sensory receptors.

_____ 7. The part of the brain that is responsible for coordination and balance is the
  a. cerebrum.
  b. cerebellum.
  c. brain stem.

_____ 8. The control center for the recognition of hunger, thirst, fatigue, and body temperature is the
  a. thalamus.
  b. hypothalamus.
  c. cerebrum.

_____ 9. Chemicals used by a neuron to transmit messages across a synapse are
  a. cerebrospinal fluid.
  b. depressants.
  c. neurotransmitters.

Summary

35-1 Human Body Systems

The levels of organization in a multicellular organism include cells, tissues, organs, and organ systems. Cells are the basic units of structure and function in living things. In multicellular organisms, cells are specialized to perform certain functions. Tissues are groups of similar cells that perform a single function. There are four different types of tissues. Epithelial tissue covers body surfaces. Connective tissue supports the body and connects its parts. Nervous tissue carries messages throughout the body. Muscle tissue enables the body to move. An organ is a group of tissues that work together to perform a complex function. An organ system is a group of organs that perform related functions. Humans have 11 organ systems.

Organ systems work together to maintain stable conditions in the body. The process of maintaining stable internal conditions is called homeostasis. Homeostasis may involve feedback inhibition, or negative feedback. For example, the nervous system senses when the body cools and signals the cells to produce more heat.

35-2 The Nervous System

The nervous system controls and coordinates functions throughout the body and responds to internal and external stimuli. Messages carried by the nervous system are electrical signals called impulses. Cells that transmit impulses are called neurons. A neuron has a cell body containing the nucleus. Short branches, called dendrites, carry impulses toward the cell body. A long fiber, called the axon, carries impulses away from the cell body. A myelin sheath surrounds parts of the axon in some neurons. Impulses can jump over the myelin and travel faster.

A resting neuron is one that is not transmitting an impulse. Resting potential is the difference in electrical charge across the cell membrane of a resting neuron. An impulse begins when a resting neuron is stimulated by another neuron or by the environment. The impulse is a sudden reversal of charge across the cell membrane, called an action potential. The lowest level of stimulus needed to activate a neuron is known as the threshold.

At the end of the axon is a synapse. A synapse is the location at which a neuron can transfer an impulse to another cell. Chemicals called neurotransmitters transmit impulses across the synapse.

35-3 Divisions of the Nervous System

The nervous system has two major divisions: the central nervous system and the peripheral nervous system. The central nervous system is the control center of the body. It relays messages, processes information, and analyzes information. The peripheral nervous system carries messages back and forth between the environment and the central nervous system.

The central nervous system consists of the brain and spinal cord. Both are wrapped in layers of tissue called meninges. Between the meninges and nervous tissue is cerebrospinal fluid, which cushions and protects nervous tissue.

The brain is divided into several regions. The cerebrum controls voluntary actions. The cerebellum controls actions of the muscles. The brain stem controls basic body functions. The thalamus receives impulses from the senses and sends them to the cerebrum. The hypothalamus connects the nervous and endocrine systems.

The spinal cord connects the brain to the rest of the body. Certain kinds of information, including some reflexes, are processed directly in the spinal cord. A reflex is a quick, automatic response to a stimulus. A reflex allows your body to respond to danger immediately, without spending time thinking about a response. Animals rely heavily on reflex behaviors for survival.

The peripheral nervous system has two divisions. The sensory division transmits impulses from sensory neurons to the central nervous system. The motor division transmits impulses from the central nervous system to muscles and glands. The motor division is further divided into somatic and autonomic nervous systems. The somatic nervous system controls voluntary actions. The autonomic nervous system controls involuntary actions.

35–4 The Senses

Sensory receptors are neurons that react to stimuli in the environment and send impulses to the central nervous system. There are five types of sensory receptors. Pain receptors respond to pain. Thermoreceptors respond to temperature. Mechanoreceptors respond to pressure. Chemoreceptors respond to chemicals. Photoreceptors respond to light.

Light enters the eye through the pupil, which is a small opening at the front of the eye. Light then passes through the lens, which focuses the light on the retina. Photoreceptors called rods and cones are located in the retina. Rods are sensitive to dim light. Cones are sensitive to colors.

Sound vibrations enter the ear and create pressure waves in a fluid-filled structure called the cochlea. Sensory receptors in the cochlea send impulses to the brain. Three tiny canals in the ear, called semicircular canals, help the central nervous system maintain balance.

The sense organs that detect taste are the taste buds. Skin—the largest sense organ—contains sensory receptors that respond to temperature, touch, and pain.

35–5 Drugs and the Nervous System

A drug is any substance, other than food, that changes the structure or function of the body. Several types of drugs can affect the nervous system. Stimulants increase actions controlled by the nervous system, such as heart rate. Stimulants also increase the release of neurotransmitters in the brain. Depressants decrease actions, such as heart rate, that are controlled by the brain. Cocaine causes the sudden release in the brain of a neurotransmitter called dopamine. Opiates act like natural brain chemicals called endorphins, which normally help overcome pain. Marijuana can cause memory and concentration problems.

Alcohol is a depressant. It slows down the central nervous system. Drinking alcohol during pregnancy may cause fetal alcohol syndrome (FAS). Babies born with FAS have birth defects. People who are addicted to alcohol have a disease called alcoholism.

Addiction is an uncontrollable dependence on a drug. Drug abuse is the intentional misuse of any drug for nonmedical purposes. The best way to avoid the effects of drugs is to avoid drugs.

Section 35–1 Human Body Systems (pages 891–896)

👄 **Key Concepts**

- How is the human body organized?
- What is homeostasis?

Organization of the Body (pages 891–894)

1. List the levels of organization in a multicellular organism, from smallest to largest.

    a. _____

    b. _____

    c. _____

    d. _____

Match the organ system with its function.

Organ System	Function
_____ **2.** Nervous system	**a.** Stores mineral reserves and provides a site for blood cell formation
_____ **3.** Skeletal system	**b.** Provides oxygen and removes carbon dioxide
_____ **4.** Integumentary system	**c.** Coordinates the body's response to changes in its internal and external environments
_____ **5.** Endocrine system	**d.** Helps produce voluntary movement, circulate blood, and move food
_____ **6.** Lymphatic/immune systems	**e.** Controls growth, development, metabolism, and reproduction
_____ **7.** Muscular system	**f.** Eliminates wastes and maintains homeostasis
_____ **8.** Reproductive system	**g.** Serves as a barrier against infection and injury
_____ **9.** Respiratory system	**h.** Converts food so it can be used by cells
_____ **10.** Excretory system	**i.** Helps protect the body from disease
_____ **11.** Circulatory system	**j.** Produces reproductive cells
_____ **12.** Digestive system	**k.** Brings materials to cells, fights infection, and helps to regulate body temperature

13. What are four types of tissues found in the human body? _____

_____

_____

14. The eye is an example of a(an) _____.

15. Circle the letter of the type of tissue that covers interior and exterior body surfaces.

    a. nervous　　　　　　c. epithelial

    b. connective　　　　 d. muscle

16. Circle the letter of the type of tissue that connects body parts.

    a. nervous   **c.** epithelial

    b. connective   **d.** integumentary

Maintaining Homeostasis (pages 895–896)

17. The process of maintaining a controlled, stable internal environment is called

_____.

18. The process in which a stimulus produces a response that opposes the original stimulus is referred to as _____.

19. Fill in the missing labels in the diagram to show how a thermostat uses feedback inhibition to maintain a stable temperature in a house.

Thermostat senses temperature change and switches off heating system

Thermostat senses temperature change and switches on heating system

20. Is the following sentence true or false? The part of the brain that monitors and controls body temperature is the hypothalamus. _____

21. What happens if nerve cells sense that the core body temperature has dropped below 37°C? _____

_____

_____

22. What happens if the body temperature rises too far above 37°C? _____

_____

_____

Section 35–2 The Nervous System (pages 897–900)

🔑 Key Concepts
- What are the functions of the nervous system?
- How is the nerve impulse transmitted?

Introduction (page 897)

1. What is the function of the nervous system? _____

_____

_____

Neurons (pages 897–898)

2. How are neurons classified? _____

_____

3. What are three types of neurons?

   a. _____

   b. _____

   c. _____

4. Is the following sentence true or false? Sensory neurons carry impulses from the brain and the spinal cord to muscles and glands. _____

5. Label the following features in the drawing of a neuron: cell body, dendrites, and axon.

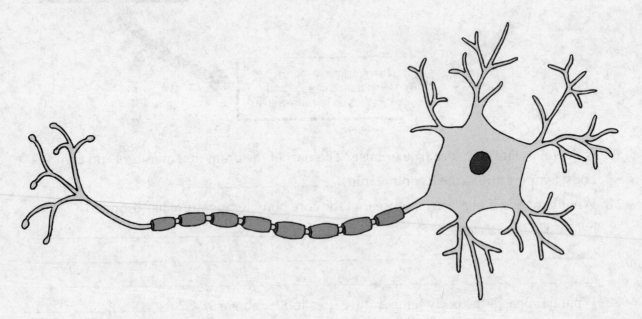

6. What is the function of the myelin sheath? _____

_____

The Nerve Impulse (pages 898–899)

7. The electrical charge across the cell membrane of a neuron in its resting state is called its

_____.

8. How does a nerve impulse begin? _____

_____

_____

_____

9. Circle the letter of the choice that describes an action potential.

   a. Reversal of charges due to the flow of positive ions into a neuron

   b. Increase in negative ions in a neuron due to the flow of potassium out of the cell

   c. Change to a negative charge due to the flow of sodium ions out of a neuron

   d. Reversal of charges due to the flow of negative ions into a neuron

10. The minimum level of a stimulus that is required to activate a neuron is called the

_____.

11. How does a nerve impulse follow the all-or-nothing principle? _____

_____

_____

The Synapse (page 900)

12. What are neurotransmitters? _____

_____

_____

13. Describe what happens when an impulse arrives at an axon terminal.

_____

_____

_____

_____

Reading Skill Practice

When you read about a complex process, representing the process with a diagram can help you understand it better. Make a diagram to show how a nerve impulse is transmitted from one cell to another. Do your work on a separate sheet of paper.

Section 35–3 Divisions of the Nervous System

(pages 901–905)

🔑 Key Concepts

- What are the functions of the central nervous system?
- What are the functions of the two divisions of the peripheral nervous system?

Introduction (page 901)

1. What is the function of the central nervous system? _____

_____

_____

The Central Nervous System (page 901)

2. The central nervous system consists of the _____ and the

_____.

3. Is the following sentence true or false? Three layers of connective tissue known as

meninges protect the brain and spinal cord. _____

4. The brain and spinal cord are bathed and protected by _____.

The Brain (pages 902–903)

Match the part of the brain with its function.

Part of Brain	Function
_____ 5. Cerebrum	a. Coordinates and balances the actions of the muscles
_____ 6. Cerebellum	b. Regulates the flow of information between the brain and the rest of the body
_____ 7. Brain stem	c. Controls voluntary activities of the body
_____ 8. Thalamus	d. Controls hunger, thirst, fatigue, anger, and body temperature
_____ 9. Hypothalamus	e. Receives and relays messages from the sense organs

10. The two hemispheres of the brain are connected by a band of tissue called the

_____.

11. Identify the four lobes of the brain.

a. _____   c. _____

b. _____   d. _____

12. Is the following sentence true or false? The left hemisphere of the cerebrum controls

the body's left side. _____

13. Is the following sentence true or false? The outer layer of the cerebrum is called

the cerebral cortex. _____

14. What is gray matter, and where is it found? _____

_____

15. The two regions of the brain stem are the _____ and the

_____.

The Spinal Cord (page 903)

16. What is the advantage of a reflex? _____

_____

_____

The Peripheral Nervous System (pages 903–904)

17. Circle the letter of each choice that is part of the peripheral nervous system.

    a. cranial nerves   **c.** ganglia

    b. spinal nerves   **d.** spinal cord

18. Complete the concept map.

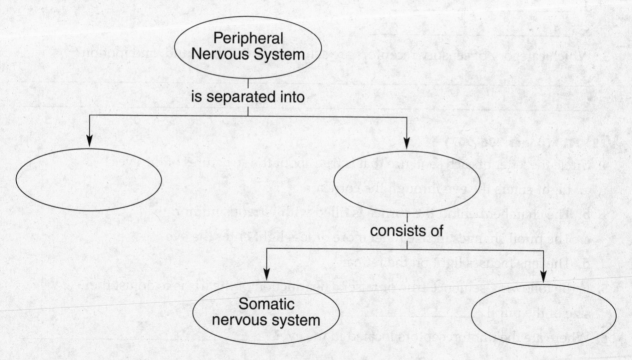

19. Circle the letter of each activity that is controlled by the somatic nervous system.

    a. Beating of the heart   **c.** Wiggling the toes

    b. Lifting a finger   **d.** Pulling foot away from tack

20. What does the autonomic nervous system regulate? _____

_____

_____

21. Why is it important to have two systems that control the same organs?

_____

_____

Section 35–4 The Senses (pages 906–909)

⊂⊃ **Key Concept**
- What are the five types of sensory receptors?

Introduction (page 906)

1. What are sensory receptors? _____

_____

_____

2. List the five general categories of sensory receptors.

   a. _____

   b. _____

   c. _____

   d. _____

   e. _____

3. Which category of sensory receptors are sensitive to touch, sound, and motion?

_____

_____

Vision (pages 906–907)

4. Circle the letter of each sentence that is true about the structures of the eye.

   a. Light enters the eye through the cornea.

   b. The chamber behind the cornea is filled with vitreous humor.

   c. The pupil changes in size to let more or less light enter the eye.

   d. The lens focuses light on the retina.

5. Is the following sentence true or false? The function of the iris is to adjust the

   size of the pupil. _____

6. Where are the photoreceptors located in the eye? _____

_____

7. What do photoreceptors do? _____

_____

8. Is the following sentence true or false? Cones are extremely sensitive to light, but they

   do not distinguish different colors. _____

9. How do impulses travel from the eyes to the brain? _____

_____

10. What are the two types of photoreceptors? _____

Hearing and Balance (pages 908–909)

11. List the two sensory functions of the ear.

a. _____

b. _____

12. Label each of the following structures in the drawing of the ear: auditory canal, tympanum, semicircular canals, and cochlea.

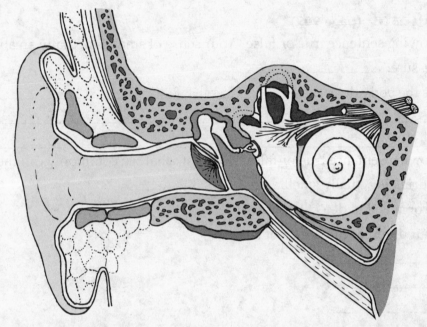

13. Is the following sentence true or false? The tympanum sends nerve impulses to the brain. _____

14. Complete the flowchart.

> Vibrations enter the ear through the _____.

> The vibrations cause the _____ to vibrate.

> These vibrations are picked up by three tiny bones, called the _____, _____, and _____.

> The last bone transmits the vibrations to the _____, creating pressure waves in the _____.

> Tiny hair cells inside the _____ produce nerve impulses that are sent to the brain through the _____ nerve.

15. What is the role of hair cells in the cochlea? _____

_____

_____

16. How do the semicircular canals help maintain balance? _____

_____

_____

Smell and Taste (page 909)

17. Is the following sentence true or false? Your sense of smell is actually an ability to detect pressure. _____

18. How does the body detect smell? _____

_____

19. Is the following sentence true or false? Much of what we commonly call the "taste" of food and drink is actually smell. _____

20. The sense organs that detect taste are the _____.

21. List the four different categories of tastes.

    a. _____

    b. _____

    c. _____

    d. _____

Touch and Related Senses (page 909)

22. What is the largest sense organ? _____

_____

23. Is the following sentence true or false? The skin contains sensory receptors that respond to temperature, touch, and pain. _____

24. Circle the letter of each choice that is true about the sense of touch.

    a. Unlike the other senses, the sense of touch is not found in one particular place.

    b. All parts of the body are equally sensitive to touch.

    c. The greatest density of touch receptors is found on the arms and legs.

    d. Touch is detected by mechanoreceptors.

25. Where is the greatest density of touch receptors found on the body? _____

_____

_____

Section 35–5 Drugs and the Nervous System
(pages 910–914)

⊂⊃ **Key Concepts**
- What are the different classes of drugs that directly affect the central nervous system?
- What is the effect of alcohol on the body?

Introduction (page 910)

1. Is the following sentence true or false? A drug is any illegal substance that changes the structure or function of the body. _____

2. Is the following sentence true or false? Among the most powerful drugs are the ones that cause changes in the nervous system, especially to the brain and the synapses between neurons. _____

3. How can drugs disrupt the functioning of the nervous system? _____

_____

_____

Drugs That Affect the Synapse (pages 910–914)

Match the drug or type of drug with one way that it can affect the body.

	Drug or Type of Drug	Effect on the Body
_____	4. Stimulant	a. Acts on pleasure centers of brain
_____	5. Depressant	b. Destroys liver cells
_____	6. Cocaine	c. Reduces pain
_____	7. Opiate	d. Decreases heart rate
_____	8. Marijuana	e. Increases blood pressure
_____	9. Alcohol	f. Causes lung damage

10. Circle the letter of each choice that is a stimulant drug.
   a. nicotine   c. amphetamine
   b. cocaine   d. codeine

11. Circle the letter of each choice that is a depressant drug.
   a. alcohol   c. tranquilizer
   b. morphine   d. barbiturate

12. Cocaine causes the sudden release in the brain of a neurotransmitter called

   _____.

13. Is the following sentence true or false? The most widely abused illegal drug is marijuana. _____

14. Circle the letter of each choice that is a result of long-term use of marijuana.

   a. Loss of memory   c. Increase in testosterone

   b. Inability to concentrate   d. Cirrhosis of the liver

15. Is the following sentence true or false? Alcohol is one of the most abused legal drugs.

   _____

16. What is fetal alcohol syndrome, or FAS? _____

   _____

   _____

17. People who have become addicted to alcohol suffer from a disease called

   _____.

18. How does long-term alcohol use affect the body? _____

   _____

   _____

Drug Abuse (page 914)

19. The intentional misuse of any drug for nonmedical purposes is referred to as

   _____.

20. An uncontrollable dependence on a drug is known as _____.

21. What is psychological dependence on a drug? _____

   _____

22. When does physical dependence on a drug occur? _____

   _____

   _____

23. How can drug use increase the transmission of HIV, the virus that causes AIDS?

   _____

   _____

   _____

Name_____ Class_____ Date _____

Vocabulary Review

Completion   *Fill in the blanks in the table.*

Tissue Type	Function
Epithelial	1. _____
Connective	2. _____
Nervous	3. _____
Muscle	4. _____

True or False   *Determine whether each statement is true or false. If it is true, write* true *in the space provided. If the statement is false, change the underlined word or words to make the statement true.*

_____ 5. The process by which organisms keep internal conditions relatively constant is called <u>homeostasis</u>.

_____ 6. Cells that transmit nerve impulses are known as <u>meninges</u>.

_____ 7. The long fiber that carries impulses away from the cell body of a nerve cell is the <u>dendrite</u>.

_____ 8. The lowest level of stimulus needed to activate a neuron is called the <u>action potential</u>.

_____ 9. The location at which a neuron can transfer an impulse to another cell is referred to as a(an) <u>synapse</u>.

_____ 10. The part of the brain that controls voluntary actions is the <u>brain stem</u>.

_____ 11. The part of the brain that receives impulses from the senses and sends them to the cerebrum is the <u>hypothalamus</u>.

_____ 12. Light enters the eye through a small opening called the <u>pupil</u>.

_____ 13. Photoreceptors in the eye that are sensitive to colors are known as <u>rods</u>.

_____ 14. Drugs called <u>opiates</u> increase actions controlled by the nervous system.

_____ 15. An uncontrollable dependence on a drug is known as drug <u>abuse</u>.

Answering Questions   *In the space provided, write an answer to each question.*

16. List the levels of organization in a multicellular organism, from smallest to largest.

_____

_____

17. What is resting potential? _____

_____

18. What is the function of the autonomic nervous system? _____

_____

19. How does alcohol affect the central nervous system? _____

_____

20. To which type of stimulus do thermoreceptors react? _____

Chapter 35 Nervous System   **Section Review 35-1**

Reviewing Key Concepts

Completion *On the lines provided, complete the following sentences.*

1. _____ are the basic units of structure and function in living things.

2. _____ consist of groups of similar cells that perform a single function.

3. _____ consist of groups of tissues that work together to perform a single function.

4. _____ consist of groups of organs that perform closely related functions.

5. Homeostasis is the process by which organisms keep internal conditions relatively constant even when _____ conditions do not remain constant.

Reviewing Key Skills

Classifying *On the line provided, write the name of the organ system described.*

_____ 6. includes the brain, spinal cord, and peripheral nerves

_____ 7. serves as a barrier against infection and injury

_____ 8. includes bones, ligaments, cartilage, and tendons

_____ 9. together with the skeletal system, enables the body to move

_____ 10. includes the heart, blood vessels, and blood

_____ 11. brings oxygen to the body and rids the body of carbon dioxide

_____ 12. controls growth, development, and metabolism

_____ 13. converts foods into simple molecules

_____ 14. includes the kidneys, lungs, and urinary bladder

15. **Applying Concepts** One nonliving example of feedback inhibition is the thermostat and how it controls the heating system of a house. Give an example of feedback inhibition in the body, and explain how it maintains homeostasis.

_____

_____

_____

_____

_____

Chapter 35 Nervous System

Reviewing Key Concepts

Short Answer *On the lines provided, answer the following questions.*

1. What role does the nervous system play in the functions of the body?

_____

_____

2. What are the sources of stimulation that start a nerve impulse?

_____

_____

Reviewing Key Skills

Sequencing *On the lines provided, write the correct sequence of events (from 1 through 6) that occur during the transmission of a nerve impulse.*

_____ 3. Action potential continues to move along the axon.

_____ 4. Sodium gates open. Action potential occurs.

_____ 5. Neuron returns to rest.

_____ 6. Neuron is stimulated by another neuron or by the environment.

_____ 7. As the action potential passes, the potassium gates open.

_____ 8. Neuron is at rest.

Interpreting Graphics *On the lines provided, identify the parts of a neuron. Use the following terms:* dendrites, axon, myelin sheath, nodes, cell body, nucleus, *and* axon terminals.

9. _____   10. _____

11. _____   12. _____

13. _____   14. _____

15. _____

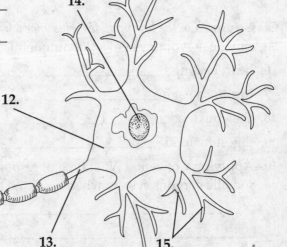

Reviewing Key Concepts

Short Answer *On the lines provided, answer the following questions.*

1. What are the main functions of the central nervous system?

_____

_____

2. What is the function of the sensory division of the peripheral nervous system?

_____

_____

3. What is the function of the motor division of the peripheral nervous system?

_____

_____

Reviewing Key Skills

4. **Using Analogies** In the brain, the thalamus receives messages from sense organs and then relays the messages to the proper region of the cerebrum. Create an analogy that illustrates the role of the thalamus.

_____

_____

_____

5. **Comparing and Contrasting** How are the somatic and autonomic nervous systems different?

_____

_____

_____

Classifying *On the line provided, classify each of the following as a function of the somatic nervous system or the autonomic nervous system.*

6. heart beating _____

7. turning a page _____

8. chewing food _____

9. digesting food _____

10. **Applying Concepts** What type of response occurs in a person's somatic nervous system when he or she touches a pot of boiling water?

_____

_____

_____

Name_____ Class_____ Date _____

Reviewing Key Concepts

Matching *On the line provided, match each sensory receptor with its location(s) in the human body.*

_____ 1. everywhere in the body, except the brain   a. mechanoreceptors

_____ 2. skin, body core, and hypothalamus   b. photoreceptors

_____ 3. skin, skeletal muscles, and inner ears   c. pain receptors

_____ 4. nose and taste buds   d. chemoreceptors

_____ 5. eyes   e. thermoreceptors

Identifying Structures *On the line provided, identify a sense organ that would respond to each of the following stimuli.*

6. a change in temperature _____

7. a flashing light _____

8. being rocked on a ship _____

Reviewing Key Skills

9. **Applying Concepts** Are the tiny hairs in the cochlea mechanoreceptors? Explain your answer.

_____

_____

10. **Comparing and Contrasting** How are rods and cones similar? How are they different?

_____

_____

Interpreting Graphics *On the lines provided, identify the following parts of an eye:* cornea, iris, vitreous humor, pupil, *and* retina.

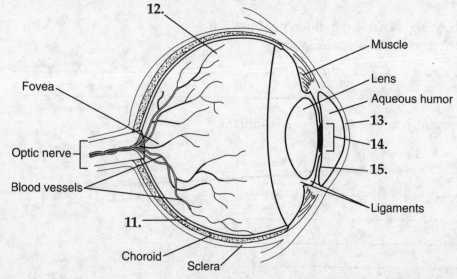

11. _____

12. _____

13. _____

14. _____

15. _____

Chapter 35 Nervous System   Section 35-5

Reviewing Key Concepts

Fill in the Table *In the spaces provided, fill in the table by writing the word* stimulant *or* depressant.

Drug type	Effect on the Body
1.	increases heart rate
2.	increases breathing rate
3.	increases release of neurotransmitters
4.	relaxes muscles
5.	lowers blood pressure
6.	relieves tension

Short Answer *On the lines provided, answer the following questions.*

7. How does cocaine affect the body?

_____

_____

8. What are opiates and how do they relate to endorphins?

_____

_____

9. How does alcohol affect the body?

_____

_____

Reviewing Key Skills

10. **Comparing and Contrasting** What is the difference between a psychological and a physical dependence on a drug?

_____

_____

Classifying *On the line provided, classify each drug as a* stimulant, *a* depressant, *or an* opiate.

11. cocaine _____

12. amphetamine _____

13. barbiturate _____

14. codeine _____

15. morphine _____

Chapter 35 Nervous System — Chapter Vocabulary Review

Completion *On the lines provided, complete the following sentences.*

1. The four basic types of tissue are _____,
   _____, _____, and
   _____.

2. The process by which organisms keep internal conditions relatively
   constant despite changes in their external environments is called
   _____.

3. The process in which a stimulus produces a response that opposes
   the original stimulus is called _____.

4. Short, branched extensions that carry impulses toward the nerve cell
   body are called _____.

5. The difference in electrical charge across the cell membrane of a
   resting neuron is called _____.

6. The minimum level of a stimulus that is required to activate a
   neuron is called the _____.

7. The place where chemicals pass signals from one neuron to the next
   is called a(an) _____.

8. The brain and spinal cord are wrapped in three layers of tissue
   known as _____, between which and the
   nervous tissue is a space filled with _____.

9. The sensory receptor, sensory neuron, motor neuron, and effector
   involved in a reflex form a(an) _____.

10. Neurons that react directly to stimuli from the environment are
    called _____.

11. Light enters the eye through a small opening in the middle of the iris
    called the _____.

12. The two types of photoreceptors arranged in a layer in the retina are
    _____ and _____.

13. Drugs known as _____ increase the action of
    the nervous system, whereas drugs known as _____
    decrease the action of the nervous system.

14. A(An) _____ is an uncontrollable dependence
    on a drug.

15. A group of birth defects caused by the effects of alcohol on an
    unborn child is called _____.

Name_____ Class_____ Date _____

Labeling Diagrams *On the lines provided, label the areas of the brain.*

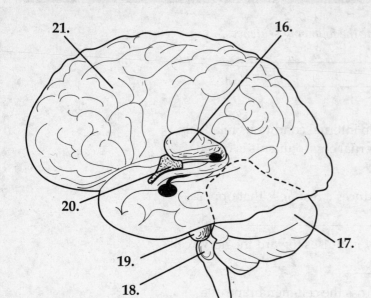

21.

16.

20.

19.

18.

17.

16. _____

17. _____

18. _____

19. _____

20. _____

21. _____

Multiple Choice *On the line provided, write the letter of the answer that best completes each sentence or answers the question.*

_____ **22.** A cell that carries messages through the nervous system is called a

    a. rod.   c. cone.

    b. dendrite.   d. neuron.

_____ **23.** A quick, automatic response to a stimulus is a

    a. reflex.   c. reflex arc.

    b. stimulant.   d. neuron.

_____ **24.** What part of your eye uses small muscles to change its shape so that you can focus on near or distant objects?

    a. retina   c. cornea

    b. lens   d. pupil

_____ **25.** The cochlea and semicircular canals can be found in the

    a. inner ears.   c. taste buds.

    b. eyes.   d. sensory receptors.

Name_____ Class_____ Date _____

Correcting Vision Problems

Many people have vision problems. Some of the most common problems are nearsightedness (myopia), farsightedness (hyperopia), and astigmatism. With myopia, a person can see close objects clearly, but distant objects are blurry. With hyperopia, the opposite is true; a person has difficulty focusing on close objects, but distant ones are clear. Astigmatism causes some parts of an object to be in focus, while other parts are blurry. Another vision problem is presbyopia, a condition that usually occurs later in life. With presbyopia, the lens of the eye becomes more rigid. As the lens changes, it loses the ability to change shape and cannot focus well on close objects.

Myopia, hyperopia, astigmatism, and presbyopia are all problems of focus. These conditions can be treated using eyeglasses or contact lenses to correct the focus. About one half of all Americans wear eyeglasses or contact lenses, and 95 percent of people over the age of 45 have difficulty seeing print or close work.

Each eye condition requires a specific type of lens to correct it. Nearsightedness, for example, can be corrected by placing a concave lens in front of the eye. The lens changes the path of light through the eye, so that the image is focused on the retina instead of in front of it. Farsightedness can be corrected by placing a convex lens in front of the eye. This lens also changes the path of light through the eye, so that the image is focused on the retina instead of behind it. Bifocal lenses are two lenses combined in one set of glasses or contact lenses. One lens corrects for far vision, and the other, a special spherical lens, corrects for near vision.

Eyeglasses or contact lenses can correct most vision problems. Sometimes laser surgery is used for extreme cases of myopia. The operation is known as radial keratotomy, and it alters the shape of the cornea to correct the vision.

Evaluation *Answer the following questions on a separate sheet of paper.*

1. What type of lens would best correct the vision problem shown in the diagram? Explain.

Nearsighted

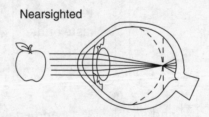

2. What type of lens would best correct the vision problem shown in the diagram? Explain.

Farsighted

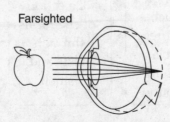

Chapter 35 Nervous System   **Graphic Organizer**

Concept Map

Using information from the chapter, complete the concept map below. If there is not enough room in the concept map to write your answers, write them on a separate sheet of paper.

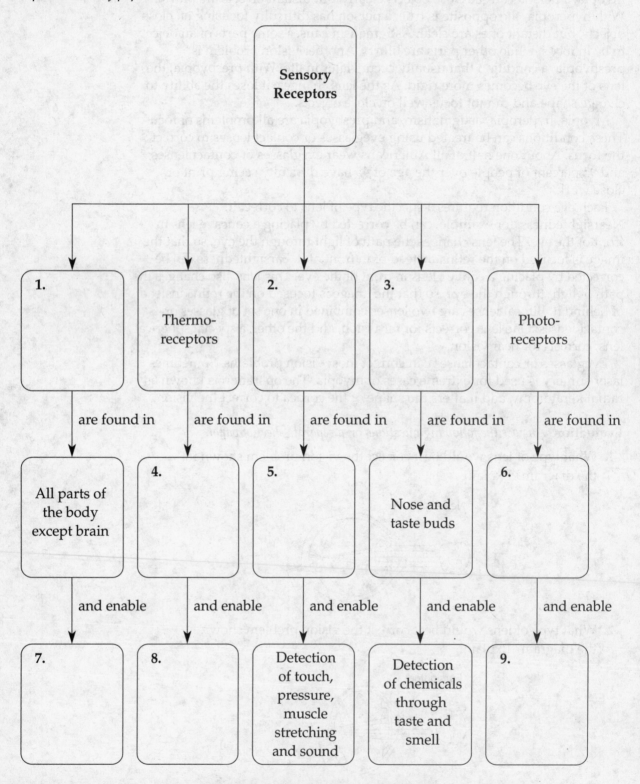

Multiple Choice

Write the letter that best answers the question or completes the statement on the line provided.

_____ 1. The four basic types of tissue in the human body are
   a. cell, organ, and organ system.
   b. sight, smell, and hearing.
   c. thyroid, trachea, adenoid, and bronchus.
   d. muscle, nervous, connective, and epithelial.

_____ 2. The levels of organization in the body include
   a. endocrine, respiratory, digestive, and nervous.
   b. cells, tissues, organs, and organ systems.
   c. cells, tissues, and organs.
   d. lymphatic, respiratory, and circulatory.

_____ 3. Which of the following general categories of sensory receptors are located everywhere in the body except the brain?
   a. thermoreceptors   c. photoreceptors
   b. mechanoreceptors   d. pain receptors

_____ 4. What is the function of neurotransmitters?
   a. to transmit nerve impulses through dendrites
   b. to stimulate the production of epinephrine
   c. to transmit nerve impulses across synapses
   d. none of the above

_____ 5. Which of the following is a function of the cerebrum?
   a. control conscious activities of the body
   b. control heart rate
   c. control blood pressure
   d. control breathing

_____ 6. What types of drugs slow down the activity of the central nervous system?
   a. stimulants
   b. depressants
   c. opiates
   d. cocaine

_____ 7. Which structure of the human ear is filled with fluid and lined with tiny hair cells?
   a. oval window
   b. semicircular canals
   c. cochlear nerve
   d. cochlea

_____ **8.** The region of the brain that recognizes hunger is the

     a. brain stem.   c. hypothalamus.

     b. medulla oblongata.   d. thalamus.

_____ **9.** When an action potential reaches the end of a neuron, it triggers the release of

     a. neurotransmitters.   c. dendrites.

     b. sodium ions.   d. receptors.

_____**10.** Neurons are categorized by the

     a. direction in which they carry impulses.

     b. amount of metabolic activity that takes place.

     c. number of dendrites that branch out.

     d. number of impulses that they carry.

_____**11.** Which process enables the body to maintain a stable temperature?

     a. heating   c. feedback inhibition

     b. circulation   d. cellular activity

_____**12.** What is the smallest structural and functional unit of the nervous system?

     a. receptor   c. organ

     b. neuron   d. tissue

_____**13.** The division of the nervous system that regulates activities that are under conscious control is the

     a. somatic nervous system.

     b. sensory nervous system.

     c. autonomic nervous system.

     d. sympathetic nervous system.

_____**14.** Sense organs are part of the

     a. peripheral nervous system.

     b. central nervous system.

     c. spinal cord.

     d. brain stem.

_____**15.** Alcohol does each of the following EXCEPT

     a. slow reflexes.   c. impair judgment.

     b. stimulate heart rate.   d. disrupt coordination.

Completion

Complete each statement on the line provided.

16. The difference in electrical charge across the cell membrane of a resting neuron is its resting _____ .

17. In most animals, axons and dendrites are clustered into bundles of fibers called _____ .

Name________________ Class________________ Date________________

18. Neurons are classified into three types according to the ________________ in which an impulse travels.

19. ________________ is the process by which organisms maintain a relatively constant internal environment.

20. The myelin sheath that surrounds a single long axon leaves many gaps, called ________________, where the axon membrane is exposed.

Short Answer

In complete sentences, write the answers to the questions on the lines provided.

21. Compare and contrast tissues and organs.

22. What is fetal alcohol syndrome?

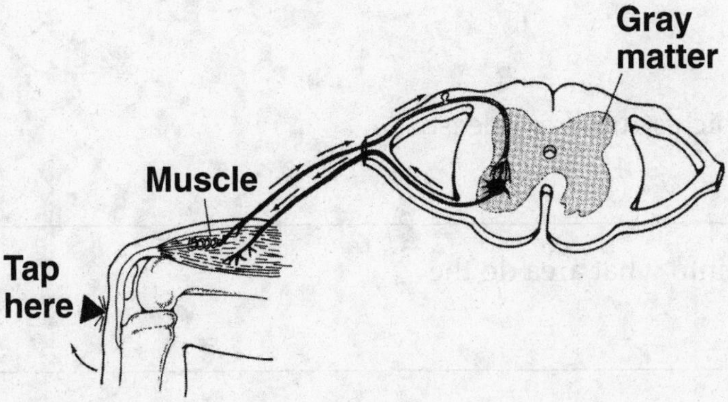

Figure 1

23. Describe the reflex arc shown in Figure 1.

24. Compare and contrast the functions of rods and cones.

25. How is the spinal cord like a major telephone line?

_____

_____

_____

_____

Using Science Skills

Use the diagram below to answer the following questions on the lines provided.

This diagram shows the structure of a synapse between the axon of one neuron and the dendrite of a neighboring neuron.

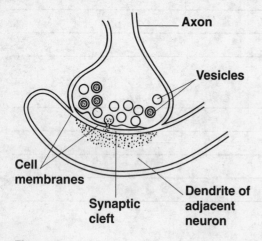

Figure 2

26. Applying Concepts In Figure 2, which structures release neurotransmitters?

_____

27. Interpreting Graphics In Figure 2, into what area do the neurotransmitters diffuse?

_____

28. Predicting Referring to Figure 2, predict the direction of the impulse.

_____

29. Applying Concepts After the neurotransmitters are released from the cell surface, what happens to the neurotransmitters?

_____

_____

_____

30. Applying Concepts If the axon in Figure 2 is part of a motor neuron, to what cell are the impulses being passed?

_____

Essay

Write the answer to each question in the space provided.

31. Compare the effects of the sympathetic and the parasympathetic divisions of the automatic nervous system.

32. What is the function of each of the main regions of the brain?

33. What are the five general categories of sensory receptors? Where are they located in the body?

34. People who must drive long distances sometimes take stimulants. How might this practice be dangerous?

35. Compare resting potential and action potential in a neuron.

Chapter 35 Nervous System

Multiple Choice

Write the letter that best answers the question or completes the statement on the line provided.

_____ 1. The process by which organ systems maintain a relatively constant internal environment is called
  a. circulation.
  b. organization.
  c. homeostasis.

_____ 2. Which system coordinates the body's response to changes in its internal and external environments?
  a. lymphatic system   c. excretory system
  b. nervous system

_____ 3. What begins when a neuron is stimulated by another neuron in its environment?
  a. a threshold   c. an impulse
  b. a resting potential

_____ 4. What is the function of the central nervous system?
  a. to process information
  b. to analyze information
  c. both a and b

_____ 5. Which division(s) of the peripheral nervous system transmit(s) impulses from sense organs to the central nervous system?
  a. sensory division
  b. motor division
  c. sensory and motor division

_____ 6. Which general category of sensory receptors detects variations in temperature?
  a. thermoreceptors
  b. mechanoreceptors
  c. photoreceptors

_____ 7. Which of the five senses contains two types of photoreceptors called rods and cones?
  a. vision   c. smell
  b. hearing

_____ 8. Drugs that increase heart rate, blood pressure, and breathing rate are called
  a. stimulants.   c. opiates.
  b. depressants.

_____ 9. Which illegal drug is most widely abused?

    a. marijuana

    b. tranquilizers

    c. amphetamines

_____10. How many organ systems make up the human body?

    a. 5

    b. 8

    c. 11

_____11. A group of similar cells that perform a single function is called a(an)

    a. nerve.   c. tissue.

    b. organ.

_____12. Which type of tissue lines your internal organs?

    a. epithelial   c. nervous

    b. connective

_____13. Which type of tissue provides support for the body?

    a. epithelial   c. nervous

    b. connective

_____14. What are the two divisions of the peripheral nervous system?

    a. sensory and motor

    b. thalamus and hypothalamus

    c. somatic and autonomic

_____15. What system does alcohol immediately affect?

    a. digestive

    b. circulatory

    c. nervous

Completion

Complete each statement on the line provided.

16. The two major divisions of the human nervous system are the central and the _____ nervous systems.

17. The process by which the product of a system shuts down the system or limits its operation is called _____ inhibition.

18. Sensory receptors called _____ are found in the skin, skeletal muscles, and inner ears and are sensitive to touch, pressure, stretching of muscles, sound, and motion.

19. Sensory neurons and motor neurons are connected by neurons called _____, which carry impulses between them.

20. Cirrhosis of the liver is a possible result of the long-term use of _____.

Name_____ Class_____ Date _____

Short Answer

In complete sentences, write the answers to the questions on the lines provided.

21. Distinguish between the functions of dendrites and axons.

_____

_____

_____

_____

_____

_____

22. How do opiates help people overcome sensations of pain?

_____

_____

_____

_____

_____

_____

23. What are the major regions of the brain?

_____

_____

_____

_____

_____

_____

24. Identify the five main senses.

_____

_____

_____

_____

_____

_____

25. What is homeostasis?

_____

_____

_____

_____

_____

_____

Using Science Skills

Use the diagram below to answer the following questions on the lines provided.

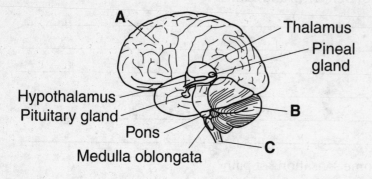

Figure 1

26. **Applying Concepts** What is the name of structure C in Figure 1?

_____

_____

27. **Applying Concepts** Referring to Figure 1, which structure is responsible for the voluntary, or conscious, activities of the body?

_____

_____

28. **Applying Concepts** Referring to Figure 1, which structure is the control center for recognition and analysis of hunger, thirst, fatigue, anger, and body temperature?

_____

_____

29. **Applying Concepts** In Figure 1, which structure is the cerebellum?

_____

_____

30. **Applying Concepts** Referring to Figure 1, what two regions of the brain stem act as neural "switchboards," regulating the flow of information between the brain and the rest of the body?

_____

_____

LESSON PLAN 36–1 (pages 921–925)

The Skeletal System

Section Objectives

- **36.1.1 State** the functions of the skeletal system.
- **36.1.2 Describe** the structure of a typical bone.
- **36.1.3 Explain** how bones develop.
- **36.1.4 Identify** the three different kinds of joints.

Vocabulary periosteum • Haversian canal • bone marrow • cartilage • ossification • joint • ligament

Local Standards

1 FOCUS

Vocabulary Preview

Tell students that words beginning with *os* have something to do with the word *bone,* and challenge students to find and explain the meaning of words that begin with *os.*

Targeted Resources

❏ Transparencies: **531** Section 36–1 Interest Grabber
❏ Transparencies: **532** Section 36–1 Outline

2 INSTRUCT

Demonstration

Show students a three-dimensional model of the human skeleton so they can see how the axial skeleton supports the body and the appendicular skeleton allows movement. **L1 L2**

Address Misconceptions

To overcome the misconception that bone is not living tissue, students learn that a piece of sponge is a better model for bone than a stick of chalk. **L2**

Make Connections: Health Science

Students infer that weight-bearing exercise makes bones stronger by stimulating ossification. **L2**

Build Science Skills: Using Models

Students create models of joints using materials such as craft sticks and modeling clay. **L1 L2**

Make Connections: Health Science

Students distinguish between rheumatoid arthritis and osteoarthritis. **L2 L3**

Targeted Resources

❏ Reading and Study Workbook: Section 36–1
❏ Adapted Reading and Study Workbook: Section 36–1
❏ Teaching Resources: Section Summaries 36–1, Worksheets 36–1
❏ Transparencies: **533** The Skeletal System, **534** Figure 36–3 The Structure of a Bone, **535** Figure 36–4 Freely Movable Joints and Their Movements, **536** Figure 36–5 Knee Joint
❏ Lab Manual A: Chapter 36 Lab
❏ **NSTA** *sci*LINKS Bones and joints

3 ASSESS

Evaluate Understanding

Call on students at random to define each of the Vocabulary words without referring to their textbooks.

Reteach

Work with students to make a table summarizing the similarities and differences among the different types of joints.

Targeted Resources

Teaching Resources: Section Review 36–1
❏ **iText** Section 36–1

LESSON PLAN 36–2 (pages 926–931)

The Muscular System

Section Objectives

- **36.2.1 Describe** the three types of muscle tissue.
- **36.2.2 Explain** how muscles contract.
- **36.2.3 Explain** why exercise is important.

Vocabulary myosin • actin • neuromuscular junction • acetylcholine • tendon

Local Standards

1 FOCUS

Reading Strategy
Suggest that students rewrite the headings as questions before they read the section and then write brief answers to their questions as they read.

Targeted Resources
- ❏ Transparencies: **537** Section 36–2 Interest Grabber
- ❏ Transparencies: **538** Section 36–2 Outline
- ❏ Transparencies: **539** Cycle Diagram

2 INSTRUCT

Build Science Skills: Inferring
Students infer that muscles become larger through an increase in the size of existing muscle cells rather than through an increase in the number of muscle cells. **L2 L3**

Use Visuals: Figure 36–7
Students use the drawing of muscle components in Figure 36–7 to demonstrate an understanding of muscle structure. **L1 L2**

Build Science Skills: Inferring
Students infer whether cardiac and smooth muscles contract in the same way as skeletal muscles, based on a comparison of their structures. **L2**

Demonstration
Students take part in a simple demonstration that illustrates the role of the central nervous system in muscle contraction. **L1 L2**

Use Community Resources
Invite a physical therapist or other exercise specialist to speak to the class about exercising to increase and maintain muscle size and strength. **L2**

Targeted Resources
- ❏ Reading and Study Workbook: Section 36–2
- ❏ Adapted Reading and Study Workbook: Section 36–2
- ❏ Teaching Resources: Section Summaries 36–2, Worksheets 36–2
- ❏ Transparencies: **540** Figure 36–7 Skeletal Muscle Structure, **541** Figure 36–8 Muscle Contraction, **542** Figure 36–11 Opposing Muscle Pairs
- ❏ Lab Manual B: Chapter 36 Lab
- ❏ **NSTA** *sci*_{LINKS} Muscle contraction

3 ASSESS

Evaluate Understanding
Have students make Venn diagrams comparing and contrasting skeletal muscle tissue, smooth muscle tissue, and cardiac muscle tissue.

Reteach
Work with the class to make a flowchart showing how a motor neuron stimulates a muscle cell.

Targeted Resources
- ❏ Teaching Resources: Section Review 36–2
- ❏ *i*Text Section 36–2

LESSON PLAN 36–3 (pages 933–936)

Time
1 period
1/2 block

The Integumentary System

Section Objectives

Local Standards

- **36.3.1 State** the functions of the integumentary system.
- **36.3.2 Describe** the structures of hair and nails.

Vocabulary epidermis • keratin • melanin • dermis • hair follicle

1 FOCUS

Reading Strategy
Have students preview the Key Concept and Figure 36–13 and then predict which structures are involved in each function of the integumentary system.

Targeted Resources
❏ Transparencies: **543** Section 36–3 Interest Grabber
❏ Transparencies: **544** Section 36–3 Outline
❏ Transparencies: **545** Concept Map

2 INSTRUCT

Demonstration
Students observe how plastic wrap protects the exposed surface of a cut apple and infer from their observations how human skin protects the body. **L1 L2**

Use Visuals: Figure 36–13
Students use the information in Figure 36–13 to make a chart comparing and contrasting the dermis and epidermis. **L1 L2**

Build Science Skills: Using Models
Students sketch a series of models of the epidermis to show how cells in the epidermis are replaced. **L2**

Address Misconceptions
Correct the misconception that dark skin does not need protection from ultraviolet radiation. **L2**

Analyzing Data
Students analyze data on the UV index to learn how much sun exposure causes sunburn and how to protect themselves from UV damage. **L2**

Build Science Skills: Designing Experiments
Students design an experiment to measure the effects of a variable such as age or gender on the pattern and rate of hair growth. **L2**

Targeted Resources
❏ Reading and Study Workbook: Section 36–3
❏ Adapted Reading and Study Workbook: Section 36–3
❏ Transparencies: **546** Figure 36–13 The Structure of Skin
❏ Teaching Resources: Section Summaries: 36–3, Worksheets 36–3, Enrichment
❏ Lab Worksheets: Chapter 36 Real-World Lab

3 ASSESS

Evaluate Understanding
Call on several students at random to name the functions of the skin.

Reteach
Have students define or describe the function of each of the structures of the skin that are shown in Figure 36–13.

Targeted Resources
❏ Teaching Resources: Section Review 36–3, Chapter Vocabulary Review, Graphic Organizer, Chapter 36 Tests: Levels A and B
❏ *iText* Section 36–3, Chapter 36 Assessment
❏ **PHSchool.com** Online Chapter 36 Test

Chapter 36   Skeletal, Muscular, and Integumentary Systems

Summary

36–1 The Skeletal System

The skeletal system has several jobs. **It supports the body, protects internal organs, allows movement, stores mineral reserves, and provides a site for blood cell formation.** The skeleton is divided into two parts.

- The axial skeleton is made up of the skull, ribs, and spine.
- The appendicular skeleton is made up of all of the bones related to the arms and legs. This includes the bones of the shoulders, hips, hands, and feet.

Bones are living tissue. **Bones are a solid network of cells and protein fibers surrounded by deposits of calcium salts.** The **periosteum** is a layer of connective tissue that surrounds a typical bone. Under the periosteum is a thick layer of compact bone. A network of tubes called **Haversian canals** runs through compact bone. These canals hold blood vessels and nerves. Cavities that hold **bone marrow** are inside the bone. Yellow bone marrow is made up of fat cells. Red bone marrow makes blood cells.

The skeleton of an embryo is made mostly of cartilage. **Cartilage** is a tough but flexible connective tissue. Cartilage is replaced by bone in a process called **ossification.** Ossification starts before birth and continues until adulthood.

A **joint** is a place where one bone attaches to another. Joints allow bones to move without damaging each other. **Depending on its type of movement, a joint is classified as immovable, slightly movable, or freely movable.**

- **Immovable joints** allow no movement. Immovable joints are found in the skull.
- **Slightly movable joints,** such those in the spine, allow a small amount of movement.
- **Freely movable joints** permit movement in one or more directions. Four common freely movable joints are: ball-and-socket joints, hinge joints, pivot joints, and saddle joints.

Ligaments are strips of tough connective tissue that hold bones together in a joint. The bony surfaces of the joint are covered with cartilage. A substance called synovial fluid forms a thin film on the cartilage, making the joint surfaces slippery.

Excessive strain or disease can damage bones and joints.

- Arthritis is a disorder that involves inflammation of the joints.
- Osteoporosis is a condition in which bones weaken. Weak bones are prone to fracture, or breaking.

36–2 The Muscular System

Working together with the skeletal system, the muscular system produces movement. **There are three different types of muscle tissue.**

- **Skeletal muscles** most often attach to bones. Skeletal muscles allow voluntary movements such as dancing.
- **Smooth muscles** line blood vessels and the digestive tract. They are not under conscious control. Smooth muscles move food through the digestive tract and control the flow of blood through the circulatory system.
- **Cardiac muscle** is found only in the heart. Cardiac muscle is not under voluntary control.

Skeletal muscle cells are called muscle fibers. Muscle fibers are made up of smaller structures called myofibrils. Each myofibril is made up of even smaller structures called filaments. Filaments can be thick or thin. Thick filaments are made of the protein **myosin.** Thin filaments are made of the protein **actin.** Thick and thin filaments are arranged in units called sarcomeres. When the muscle is relaxed, there are no thin filaments in the middle of the sarcomere.

A muscle contracts when the thin filaments in the muscle fiber slide over the thick filaments. During muscle contraction, knoblike heads of myosin filaments attach to binding sites on actin molecules. Each attachment is called a cross-bridge. ATP then causes the myosin cross-bridge to change shape. This change in shape pulls the actin filament toward the center of the sarcomere. The myosin head detaches and the cycle repeats.

Tendons join muscles to bones. Tendons pull on bones, making them work like levers. Muscles supply the force that moves bones.

Most skeletal muscles work in opposing pairs. When one muscle contracts, the other muscle relaxes. For example, in order to bend the arm at the elbow, the biceps contract and the triceps relax. This creates the force necessary to bend the elbow joint. To extend the arm, the triceps contract and the biceps relax.

Regular exercise is important in maintaining muscle strength and flexibility. Regular exercise also strengthens bones. Strong bones and muscles are less likely to be injured.

36–3 The Integumentary System

The integumentary system has several jobs. It covers the body and protects against infection, injury, and ultraviolet radiation. It helps regulate body temperature and removes wastes from the body.

The skin is made up of two main layers.

- The **epidermis** is the outer layer of the skin. The epidermis is composed of two layers. The inner layer of the epidermis is made up of living cells. These cells quickly divide and push older cells up toward the surface of the skin. Eventually, the older cells die. The outside layer of the epidermis is made up of dead cells. It provides a tough, flexible, waterproof outer covering for the body. The epidermis also contains cells that produce melanin. **Melanin** is a dark brown pigment. It helps protect the skin from ultraviolet radiation in sunlight.

- The **dermis** is the inner layer of skin. The dermis contains many different types of structures such as blood vessels, nerve endings, hair follicles, and glands. There are two main types of glands in the dermis: sweat glands and sebaceous glands. Sweat glands produce sweat. Sweat evaporates off of the surface of skin and helps keep the body cool. Sebaceous glands produce sebum. This oily substance helps keep the epidermis flexible and waterproof.

Hair and nails are also parts of the integumentary system. Hair and nails are made mainly of keratin. Hair is made by structures called **hair follicles.** Nails grow from an area called the nail root. Nails protect the tips of the fingers and toes.

Structure of a Bone

Most human bones are composed of compact bone and spongy
bone. Spongy bone provides strength and support to the bone
while limiting mass. Compact bone contains Haversian canals,
which contain blood vessels. The bone is covered by a tough layer
of tissue called the periosteum.

Color the spongy bone *yellow. Color the* compact bone *red. Then label
the* Haversian canals *and* periosteum.

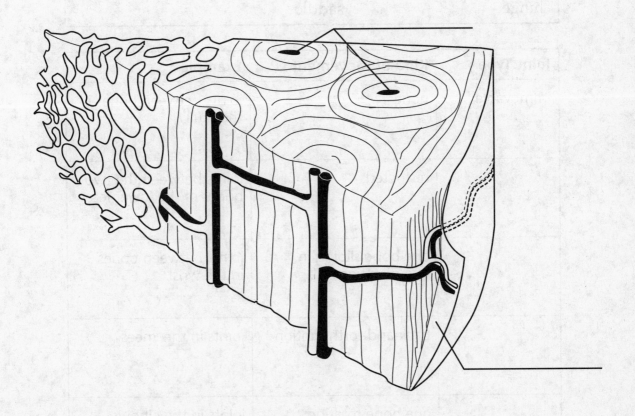

Use the diagram to answer the questions.

1. Where in long bones is spongy bone found? Circle the
   correct answer.

   in the middle   at the ends

2. What do the Haversian canals contain?

   _____

Types of Joints

Any place where two bones attach to each other is called a joint. There are three major categories of joints: immovable, slightly movable, and freely movable. The four most common kinds of freely movable joints, named for how they work, are: ball-and-socket joints, hinge joints, pivot joints, and saddle joints.

Use the words below to fill in the table. One row has been completed for you.

ball-and-socket hinge	pivot saddle	slightly movable

Joint Type	Kind of Movement	Example
immovable	none	joints between bones in the skull
	restricted	joints between the two bones of the lower leg
	one bone sliding in two directions	joints between bones in the wrist
	back-and-forth motion	joints in the knees
	one bone rotating around another	joints in the elbows
	movement in many directions	joints in the shoulders

Use the table to answer the question.

1. Which type of joint allows the greatest range of movement?

_____

Types of Muscle Tissue

Use the words below to identify each of the three types of muscle found in the human body.

cardiac muscle	skeletal muscle	smooth muscle

Muscle Type	Structure and Function	Example
	Cells are spindle-shaped with one nucleus and no striation; muscles are usually not under voluntary control.	muscles that move food through the digestive tract
	Cells are striated, with one or two nuclei; muscle is found in only one place in the body; it is generally not under voluntary control.	heart muscle
	Cells are large and striated and have many nuclei; muscles are used for voluntary motion.	muscles attached to bones

Use the table to answer the questions. Circle the correct answer.

1. Which muscles can you consciously control?

    smooth   skeletal

2. Where in the body is cardiac muscle found?

_____

Muscle Contraction

Skeletal muscle fibers are made up of thick and thin filaments arranged in units called sarcomeres. The thick filaments contain the protein myosin, and the thin ones contain the protein actin. When a muscle contracts, cross-bridges form between the myosin and actin fibers. The myosin fibers pull on the actin fibers. This motion, repeated in many sarcomeres, causes a muscle to contract.

Use the words below to label the diagrams.

actin	cross-bridges	myosin	sarcomere

Relaxed Muscle

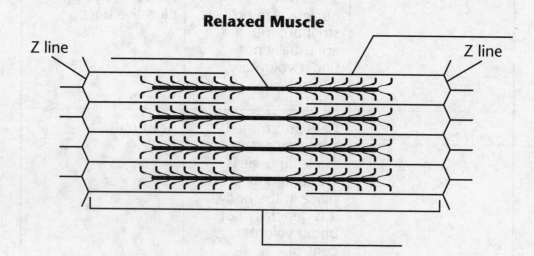

Z line   Z line

Contracted Muscle

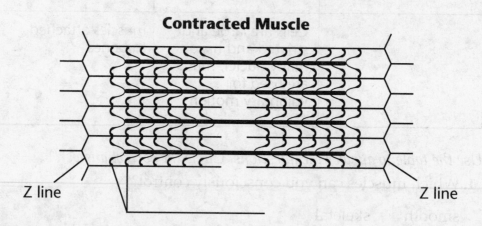

Z line   Z line

Use the diagram to answer the question.

1. Describe how the position of the actin filaments changes during muscle contraction.

_____

_____

Opposing Pairs

When you straighten or bend your arm, two muscles work together: the biceps and triceps. The biceps is located on the inside of your upper arm. The triceps is on the outside of your upper arm. When one muscle is contracted, the other muscle is relaxed.

Label whether each muscle is contracted or relaxed.

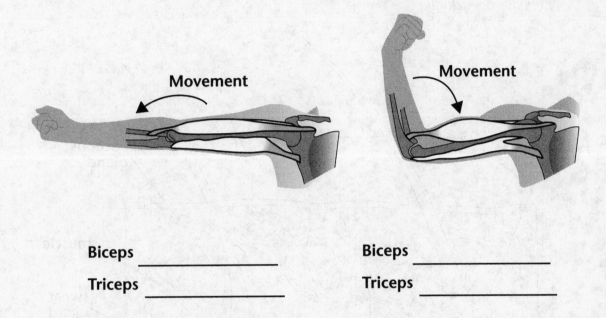

Biceps _____   Biceps _____

Triceps _____   Triceps _____

Use the diagram to answer the questions.

1. Which muscle contracts when you bend your arm? Circle the correct answer.

   biceps   triceps

2. Which muscle relaxes when you extend your arm? Circle the correct answer.

   biceps   triceps

3. Which muscles are used in the controlled movement of holding a tennis racket?

   _____

Structures of the Skin

Human skin has three layers: the epidermis, dermis, and hypodermis. The epidermis is the outer layer. The dermis is the inner
layer that contains blood vessels, nerve endings, muscles, hair
follicles, and other structures. The hypodermis is a layer of fat
and connective tissue.

*Color the epidermis red. Color the dermis orange. Color the
hypodermis yellow.*

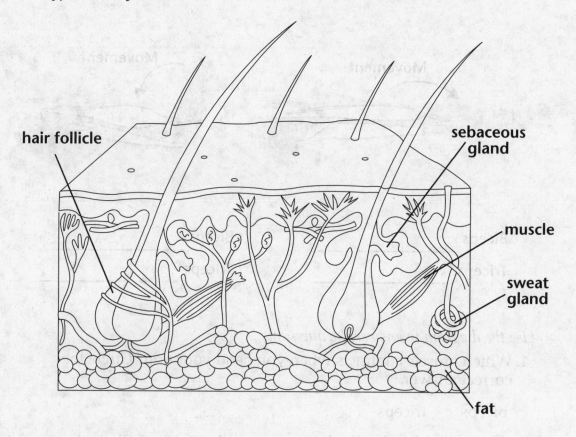

Use the diagram to answer the questions.

1. In which layer are sweat glands found? Circle the
   correct answer.

   dermis   epidermis

2. In which layer are hair follicles found? Circle the correct answer.

   hypodermis   dermis

3. What is the function of the hypodermis?

   _____

Chapter 36   Skeletal, Muscular, and Integumentary Systems

Vocabulary Review

Matching   *In the space provided, write the letter of the definition that best matches each term.*

_____ 1. cartilage

_____ 2. joint

_____ 3. melanin

_____ 4. ossification

_____ 5. tendon

a. place where one bone is attached to another

b. process in which cartilage is replaced with bone

c. dark brown pigment found in skin

d. connective tissue that supports the body and is more flexible than bone

e. tough connective tissue that joins skeletal muscles to bones

Matching   *In the space provided, write the letter of the definition that best matches each term.*

_____ 6. keratin

_____ 7. epidermis

_____ 8. actin

_____ 9. Haversian canal

_____ 10. ligament

a. outer layer of skin

b. network of tubes in bones that contains blood vessels and nerves

c. protein that makes up most of the thin filaments of muscle fibers

d. connective tissue that holds bones together at a joint

e. tough, fibrous protein made by skin cells

Completion   *Fill in the blanks with the correct term. Use the words listed below.*

bone marrow	dermis	myosin

11. The inner layer of skin is called the _____.

12. The protein that makes up the thick filaments in muscle

is called _____.

13. _____ is the soft tissue contained in the cavities of bones.

Summary

36–1 The Skeletal System

The skeletal system supports the body, protects internal organs, provides for movement, stores mineral reserves, and provides a site for blood cell formation. The skeleton is divided into two parts: the axial skeleton and the appendicular skeleton. The axial skeleton includes the skull, ribs, and spine. The appendicular skeleton includes all the bones associated with the arms and legs, including bones of the shoulders, hips, hands, and feet.

The bones that make up the skeletal system are living tissue. Bones are a solid network of living cells and protein fibers that are surrounded by deposits of calcium salts. A typical bone is surrounded by a tough layer of connective tissue called the periosteum. Beneath the periosteum is a thick layer of compact bone. Running through compact bone is a network of tubes called Haversian canals. These canals contain blood vessels and nerves. Inside the layer of compact bone is spongy bone. Spongy bone is quite strong and adds strength to bones without adding mass. Within bones are cavities that contain a soft tissue called bone marrow. Bone marrow can be yellow or red. Yellow marrow is made up of fat. Red marrow produces blood cells.

The skeleton of an embryo is composed almost entirely of cartilage. Cartilage is a type of connective tissue that is tough but flexible. Cartilage is replaced by bone during the process of bone formation, or ossification. Ossification starts before birth and continues until adulthood.

A place where one bone attaches to another bone is called a joint. Joints permit bones to move without damaging each other. Depending on its type of movement, a joint is classified as immovable, slightly movable, or freely movable.

Immovable joints, such as the joints in the skull, allow no movement. Slightly movable joints, such as the joints in the spine, allow a small amount of restricted movement. Freely movable joints permit movement in one or more directions. Freely movable joints are classified by the type of movement they permit.

Ball-and-socket joints, such as the shoulder, allow the widest range of movement of any joint. Hinge joints, such as the knee, permit only back-and-forth movement. Pivot joints, such as the elbow, allow one bone to rotate around another. Saddle joints, such as those in the hand, allow one bone to slide in two directions.

Strips of tough connective tissue, called ligaments, hold bones together in a joint. The bony surfaces of the joint are covered with cartilage. A substance called synovial fluid forms a thin film on the cartilage and makes the joint surfaces slippery.

Bones and joints can be damaged by excessive strain or disease. Arthritis is a disorder that involves inflammation of the joints. Osteoporosis is a condition in which bones weaken. Weak bones are likely to fracture, or break.

36–2 The Muscular System

Muscle tissue is found everywhere in the body. There are three different types of muscle tissue: skeletal, smooth, and cardiac. Skeletal muscles are usually attached to bones. They appear to be striped, so they are also called striated muscles. Skeletal muscles are responsible for voluntary movements such as dancing.

Smooth muscles line blood vessels and the digestive tract. They are not striated or under conscious control. Smooth muscles move food through the digestive tract and control the flow of blood through the circulatory system. Cardiac muscle is found only in the heart. Like smooth muscle, it is not under conscious control.

Skeletal muscle cells are called muscle fibers. Muscle fibers are composed of smaller structures called myofibrils. Each myofibril is made up of even smaller structures called filaments. Filaments can be thick or thin. Thick filaments are made of a protein called myosin. Thin filaments are made of a protein called actin. A muscle contracts when the thin filaments in the muscle fiber slide over the thick filaments.

Impulses from motor neurons control the contraction of skeletal muscles. The point of contact between a motor neuron and a muscle fiber is called a neuromuscular junction. A neurotransmitter named acetylcholine is released by the motor neuron into the synapse. Acetylcholine transmits the impulse across the synapse to the skeletal muscle cell. The more muscle cells that are stimulated to contract, the stronger the contraction.

Skeletal muscles are joined to bones by tough connective tissues called tendons. Tendons pull on bones and make them work like levers. Muscles provide the force to move the bones. Most skeletal muscles work in opposing pairs. When one muscle contracts, the other relaxes.

Regular exercise is important in maintaining the strength and flexibility of muscles. Regular exercise also strengthens bones. Strong bones and muscles are less likely to become injured.

36–3 The Integumentary System

The skin is the single largest organ of the body. It is also the largest component of the integumentary system. The integumentary system has many functions. It serves as a barrier against infection and injury, helps to regulate body temperature, removes waste products from the body, and provides protection against ultraviolet radiation from the sun.

The skin is made up of two main layers: the epidermis and the dermis. The epidermis is the outer layer of the skin. Cells of the epidermis produce keratin. Keratin is a tough, fibrous protein that helps keep the epidermis flexible and waterproof. The epidermis also contains cells, called melanocytes, that produce melanin. Melanin is a dark drown pigment that helps protect the skin from ultraviolet rays.

The dermis is the inner layer of skin. It contains nerves, blood vessels, glands, and other structures not found in the epidermis. The dermis works with other organs to maintain homeostasis. It helps to regulate body temperature. Sweat glands in the dermis produce sweat when the body gets too hot. When the sweat evaporates from the skin, it cools the body.

Too much sunlight can produce skin cancer. You can protect against skin cancer by wearing a hat, sunglasses, and protective clothing. You also should use sunscreen with a sun protection factor (SPF) of at least 15.

In addition to the skin, the integumentary system includes the hair and nails. Both hair and nails are composed mainly of keratin. Hair on the head protects the scalp from sunlight and cold. Hair in the nostrils and around the eyes prevents dirt from entering the body. Hair is produced by structures called hair follicles. Hair follicles are located in the dermis. Nails grow from an area called the nail root. Nails protect the tips of the fingers and toes.

Chapter 36 Skeletal, Muscular, and Integumentary Systems

Section 36–1 The Skeletal System (pages 921–925)

🔑 **Key Concepts**
- What are the functions of the skeletal system?
- What is the structure of a typical bone?
- What are the three different kinds of joints?

Introduction (page 921)

1. What forms the skeletal system? _____

_____

The Skeleton (page 921)

2. List the functions of the skeletal system.

a. _____   d. _____

b. _____   e. _____

c. _____

3. Is the following sentence true or false? Most bones act like levers on which muscles act

to produce movement. _____

4. How many bones are there in the adult human skeleton? _____

5. Complete the concept map.

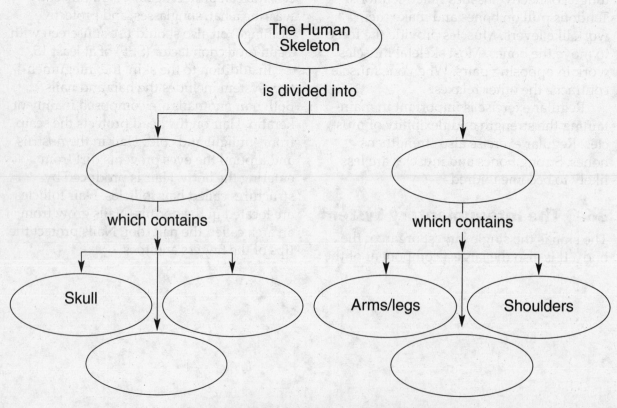

6. What is the general function of the axial skeleton? _____
_____

Structure of Bones (page 922)

7. The two minerals that make up most of the mass of bone are _____ and _____.

8. Is the following sentence true or false? Bones are living tissue. _____

Match each structure in a bone with its description.

	Structure	Description
_____	**9.** Periosteum	**a.** Network of tubes running through bone
_____	**10.** Compact bone	**b.** Soft tissue contained in bone cavities
_____	**11.** Haversian canals	**c.** Tough layer of connective tissue surrounding bone
_____	**12.** Spongy bone	**d.** Thick layer of dense bone beneath the periosteum
_____	**13.** Bone marrow	**e.** Bone with a latticework structure

14. Cells that produce bone are called _____.

Development of Bones (pages 922–923)

15. The skeleton of an embryo is composed almost entirely of a type of connective tissue called _____.

16. The network of fibers in cartilage is made from two proteins called _____ and _____.

17. Circle the letter of each sentence that is true about cartilage.

   a. It contains blood vessels.   **c.** It cannot support weight.

   b. It is dense and fibrous.   **d.** It is extremely flexible.

18. Cartilage is replaced by bone during the process of bone formation called

   _____.

19. Is the following sentence true or false? By adulthood, all the cartilage in the body has been replaced by bone. _____

Types of Joints (page 924)

20. What is a joint? _____
_____

21. List the three classifications of joints, based on their type of movement.

   a. _____

   b. _____

   c. _____

22. What are examples of immovable joints? _____

_____

_____

23. Is the following sentence true or false? The joints between the two bones of the lower leg are slightly movable joints. _____

24. Identify the type of freely movable joint represented in each of the drawings below.

 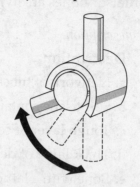 

_____   _____   _____

25. Is the following sentence true or false? Ball-and-socket joints permit the widest range of movement. _____

Structure of Joints (pages 924–925)

26. Circle the letter of each sentence that is true about the structure of joints.

   a. Cartilage protects the ends of bones as they move against each other at joints.

   b. Ligaments hold bones together at joints.

   c. Synovial fluid prevents the ends of bones from slipping past each other at joints.

   d. A bursa is a swelling caused by inflammation of a joint.

Skeletal System Disorders (page 925)

27. Inflammation of a bursa is called _____.

28. A serious disorder that involves inflammation of one or more joints is

_____.

Section 36–2 The Muscular System (pages 926–931)

⊂⊃ **Key Concepts**
- What are the three types of muscle tissue?
- How do muscles contract?
- Why is exercise important?

Types of Muscle Tissue (pages 926–927)

1. List the three different types of muscle tissue.

   a. _____   b. _____   c. _____

2. Is the following sentence true or false? Each type of muscle has the same function.

   _____

3. Is the following sentence true or false? Skeletal muscles are usually attached to bones.

   _____

4. Circle the letter of each sentence that is true about skeletal muscles.

   a. They have striations.

   b. Most of them are consciously controlled by the central nervous system.

   c. Their cells have just one nucleus.

   d. Their cells are long and slender.

5. Circle the letter of each sentence that is true about smooth muscle cells.

   a. They are spindle-shaped.

   b. They can function without nervous stimulation.

   c. They have two or more nuclei.

   d. They are connected by gap junctions.

6. What are three functions of smooth muscles? _____

   _____

   _____

   _____

7. Is the following sentence true or false? Cardiac muscle cells always have two nuclei.

   _____

8. Complete the table that compares and contrasts the three types of muscle tissue.

TYPES OF MUSCLE TISSUE

Muscle Tissue Type	Striated/Not Striated	What It Controls
Skeletal	Striated	
	Not striated	Involuntary movements
Cardiac		

Muscle Contraction (page 928)

9. Circle the letter of the choice that lists the muscle structures from largest to smallest.

a. Myofibrils, filaments, muscle fibers

b. Muscle fibers, myofibrils, filaments

c. Muscle fibers, filaments, myofibrils

d. Myofibrils, muscle fibers, filaments

Match each type of muscle filament with the protein it contains.

Type of Filament	Protein It Contains
_____ **10.** thick	**a.** Actin
_____ **11.** thin	**b.** Myosin

12. The filaments are arranged along the muscle fiber in units called _____.

13. Is the following sentence true or false? When a muscle is relaxed, there are only thin filaments in the center of a sarcomere. _____

14. How does a muscle contract according to the sliding-filament model of muscle contraction? _____

15. The energy for muscle contraction is supplied by _____.

Control of Muscle Contraction (page 929)

16. Complete the flowchart to show the missing steps in the stimulation of a muscle cell by a neuron.

```
┌─────────────────────────────────────────┐
│  Diffusion of acetylcholine across synapse │
└─────────────────────────────────────────┘
                  produces
                     ↓
┌─────────────────────────────────────────┐
│     Impulse in membrane of muscle cell    │
└─────────────────────────────────────────┘
                   causes
                     ↓
┌─────────────────────────────────────────┐
│                                           │
└─────────────────────────────────────────┘
                  affects
                     ↓
┌─────────────────────────────────────────┐
│            Regulatory proteins            │
└─────────────────────────────────────────┘
                   allow
                     ↓
┌─────────────────────────────────────────┐
│                                           │
└─────────────────────────────────────────┘
```

17. Is the following sentence true or false? Impulses from motor neurons control the contraction of skeletal muscles. _____

18. The point of contact between a motor neuron and a skeletal muscle cell is a(an) _____.

19. What terminates a muscle contraction? _____

_____

_____

20. Is the following sentence true or false? A single motor neuron can form synapses with many muscle cells. _____

21. What is the difference between a strong muscle contraction and a weak muscle contraction? _____

_____

_____

How Muscles and Bones Interact (page 930)

22. Is the following sentence true or false? Individual muscles can pull in only one direction. _____

23. Circle the letter of the term that refers to the tough connective tissue joining skeletal muscle to bone.

    a. cartilage   b. ligament   c. tendon   d. bursa

24. If bones are like levers, what functions as a fulcrum? _____

25. What does it mean for muscles to "work in opposing pairs"? _____

_____

Exercise and Health (page 931)

26. Why is regular exercise important? _____

_____

Reading Skill Practice

When you read a section with many details, writing an outline may help you organize and remember the material. Outline Section 36–2 by first writing the section headings as major topics in the order in which they appear in the book. Then, beneath each major topic, list important details about it. Title your outline *The Muscular System.* Do your work on a separate sheet of paper.

Section 36–3 The Integumentary System
(pages 933–936)

⊂━━ Key Concept
- What are the functions of the integumentary system?

Introduction (page 933)

1. Circle the letter of each choice that is part of the integumentary system.

   a. skin   c. cartilage

   b. bones   d. nails

The Skin (pages 933–936)

2. The most important function of the skin is _____.

3. List the four functions of the integumentary system.

   a. _____

   b. _____

   c. _____

   d. _____

4. The largest component of the integumentary system is the _____.

5. The outer layer of skin is called the _____.

6. Is the following sentence true or false? The inner layer of the epidermis is made up of dead cells. _____

7. Label the structures of the skin.

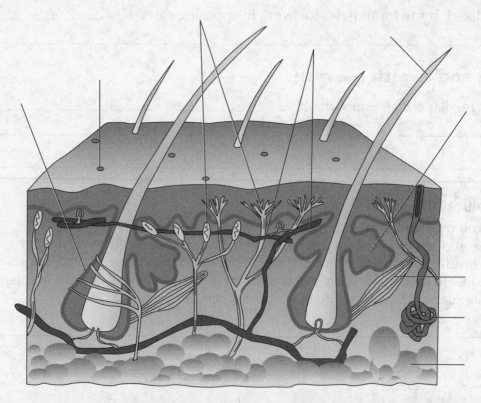

Match each term with its definition.

	Term	Definition
_____	**8.** keratin	**a.** Tough, fibrous protein
_____	**9.** melanin	**b.** Inner layer of the skin
_____	**10.** dermis	**c.** Dark brown pigment

11. Circle the letter of each sentence that is true about melanocytes.

   a. Melanocytes are cells that produce melanin.

   b. Most people have roughly the same number of melanocytes in their skin.

   c. All melanocytes produce about the same amount of melanin.

   d. Most people have the same distribution of melanocytes in their skin.

12. Is the following sentence true or false? The epidermis contains blood vessels.

   _____

13. Circle the letter of each type of structure that is found in the dermis.

   a. blood vessels   **c.** glands

   b. nerve endings   **d.** hair follicles

14. How does the dermis help regulate body temperature? _____

   _____

   _____

   _____

   _____

   _____

15. List the two types of glands contained in the dermis.

   a. _____

   b. _____

16. How does sweat help keep you cool? _____

   _____

17. What is the function of sebum? _____

   _____

Hair and Nails (page 936)

18. The basic structure of human hair and nails is _____.

19. List the two functions of head hair.

    a. _____

    b. _____

20. How does hair in the nose and ears and around the eyes help protect the body?

    _____

    _____

    _____

21. Hair is produced by cells called _____.

22. Is the following sentence true or false? Hair is composed of cells that have died.

    _____

23. What causes hair to grow? _____

    _____

24. What is the nail root? _____

    _____

    _____

Chapter 36 Skeletal, Muscular, and Integumentary Systems

Vocabulary Review

Crossword Puzzle *Complete the puzzle by entering the term that matches each numbered description.*

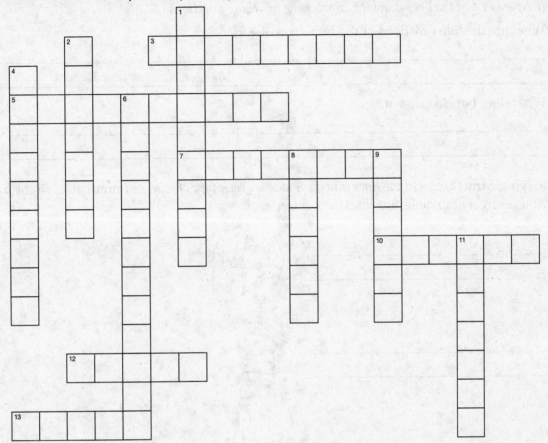

Across

3. type of canals in bone that contain blood vessels and nerves
5. tough layer of connective tissue that surrounds bone
7. tough connective tissue that holds bones together in a joint
10. layer of skin that contains glands and blood vessels
12. place where one bone attaches to another bone
13. protein found in thin muscle filaments

Down

1. type of connective tissue that is replaced by bone as a person grows
2. protein found in hair and nails
4. layer of skin where melanocytes are located
6. process in which cartilage is replaced by bone
8. protein found in thick muscle filaments
9. tough connective tissue that joins skeletal muscle to bone
11. dark brown pigment in skin

Completion *Fill in the blanks with terms from Chapter 36.*

The three different types of muscle tissue are _____,

_____, and _____. Skeletal muscles are controlled

by motor neurons. A motor neuron and a skeletal muscle cell meet at a point called

a(an) _____. The motor neuron releases a neurotransmitter,

called _____, which transmits the impulse to the muscle cell.

**Chapter 36 Skeletal, Muscular, and
Integumentary Systems**
Section Review 36-1

Reviewing Key Concepts

Short Answer *On the lines provided, answer the following questions.*

1. What are the five functions of the human skeleton?

   _____

   _____

2. What does bone consist of?

   _____

   _____

Identifying Structures *On the lines provided, identify each type of joint as* immovable, slightly movable, *or* freely movable, *and describe its movement.*

3. _____

   _____

4. _____

   _____

5. _____

   _____

Reviewing Key Skills

Classifying *On the line provided, classify each bone as part of the* axial skeleton *or the* appendicular skeleton.

6. skull _____

7. femur _____

8. rib cage _____

9. **Comparing and Contrasting** How are bone and cartilage similar? How are they different?

   _____

   _____

10. **Drawing Conclusions** After you injure your knee in a bike accident, your doctor says that you have a torn ligament. Describe the injury in terms of the bones and muscles surrounding your knee.

    _____

    _____

Chapter 36 Skeletal, Muscular, and Integumentary Systems

Reviewing Key Concepts

Short Answer *On the lines provided, answer the following questions.*

1. Name the three different types of muscle tissue.

_____

_____

2. Describe the sliding-filament model of muscle contraction.

_____

_____

3. What supplies the energy for muscle contraction?

_____

_____

Identifying Structures *On the line provided, label each characteristic with the type of muscle tissue that it describes.*

4. spindle-shaped, no striations _____

5. found in the heart _____

6. found in blood vessels _____

7. attached to bones _____

Reviewing Key Skills

8. **Predicting** What would occur if the body did not produce the enzyme that breaks down acetylcholine?

_____

_____

_____

9. **Applying Concepts** Explain how the skeletal and muscular systems work together to produce movement in the lower leg.

_____

_____

_____

10. **Inferring** What will happen to the muscles in the arm when a cast is worn on it to allow a broken bone to heal? Explain your answer.

_____

_____

_____

Chapter 36 Skeletal, Muscular, and Integumentary Systems

Section Review 36-3

Reviewing Key Concepts

Identification *On the line provided, write* Yes *if the phrase describes a function of the integumentary system. Write* No *if it does not.*

_____ 1. serves as a barrier against infection and injury

_____ 2. helps to regulate body temperature

_____ 3. provides a site for blood cell formation

_____ 4. removes waste products from the body

_____ 5. stores mineral reserves

_____ 6. provides protection against ultraviolet radiation from the sun

Reviewing Key Skills

7. **Comparing and Contrasting** How are sebaceous glands and sweat glands similar? How are they different?

_____

_____

_____

8. **Inferring** If a cut on your arm has begun to bleed, which layer of skin must have been penetrated for the cut to be bleeding? Explain your answer.

_____

_____

_____

9. **Predicting** Using your knowledge of the relationship between melanin production and skin color, how do you think sun exposure affects melanin production?

_____

_____

_____

10. **Formulating Hypotheses** Humidity is the amount of water vapor in the air. How does the humidity of the air around you affect how well your skin cools your body? Explain your answer.

_____

_____

_____

Chapter 36 Skeletal, Muscular, and Integumentary Systems

Chapter Vocabulary Review

Defining Terms *On the lines provided, write a definition for each of the following terms.*

1. periosteum _____

_____

2. ligament _____

_____

3. myosin _____

_____

4. actin _____

_____

5. tendon _____

_____

6. epidermis _____

_____

7. melanin_____

_____

8. dermis _____

_____

Matching. *On the line provided, write the letter of the term that correctly matches the description.*

   a. bone marrow
   b. acetylecholine
   c. joint
   d. neuromuscular junction
   e. keratin
   f. cartilage

_____ 9. Soft tissue contained in bone cavities

_____ 10. The place where two bones come together

_____ 11. Connective tissue that is extremely flexible and does not contain blood vessels

_____ 12. The point of contact between a motor neuron and skeletal muscle cell

_____ 13. Neurotransmitter released by motor neurons

_____ 14. A tough, fibrous protein in skin

Short Answer *On the lines provided, answer the following questions.*

15. What are hair follicles?

_____

_____

16. What is ossification?

_____

_____

Labeling Diagrams *On the lines provided, write the names of the bone structures that correspond to the numbers in the diagram.*

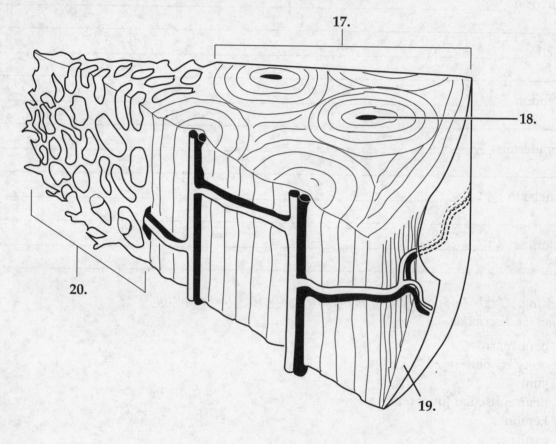

17. _____

18. _____

19. _____

20. _____

Acne

Contrary to one popular belief, pimples are not caused by chocolate. Pimples *are* caused by acne, a disorder of the sebaceous glands in the skin. Sebaceous glands secrete a fatty lubricant, known as sebum, through the pores and hair follicles. Humans have sebaceous glands all over the body, except the palms of the hands and soles of the feet. Acne occurs when sebum from the sebaceous glands clogs the pores. Blackheads are external plugs made of sebum and dead cells. If the plugs are invaded by bacteria, they become pimples, or pus-filled inflammations.

Hormones trigger the production of sebum. Hormone cycles change throughout adolescence, so adolescents are most likely to suffer from acne. The exact cause of acne is not clear. Genetic factors, as well as hormonal changes, seem to trigger the disorder. While they do not cause acne, poor skin care, lack of sunlight, and lack of exercise may aggravate it. In some people, certain foods may also irritate symptoms of the disorder.

Most adolescents, and many adults, suffer from some form of mild acne; a few people have more severe cases. Treatments vary greatly. For minor cases, gently cleansing the skin with mild soap and warm—not hot—water can help irritations heal more quickly. For more severe cases, antibiotics, especially tetracycline, can reduce infection and prevent new infections. When antibiotics are used over a long period of time, however, bacteria often become resistant to them.

Two drugs have been developed for treating acne, both related to vitamin A. Tretinoin (brand name: Retin-A) and isotretinoin (brand name: Accutane) have successfully been used to treat acne. Both drugs, however, may have side effects.

Evaluation *On the lines provided, answer the following questions.*

1. Do different types of food cause pimples? Explain your answer.

   _____

   _____

   _____

   _____

   _____

2. What are some possible factors that cause acne?

   _____

   _____

   _____

   _____

   _____

Compare/Contrast Table

Complete the following compare/contrast matrix using the words Yes *or* No *to
determine whether the description applies to the specific type of muscle.*

	Skeletal Muscle	Smooth Muscle	Cardiac Muscle
Voluntary Control	Yes	1.	2.
Striated	3.	No	4.
Individual Nucleus in Cells	5.	6.	No
Attached to Bone	Yes	7.	8.
Can Contract	9.	Yes	10.
Spindle Shaped	11.	12.	No

Chapter 36 Skeletal, Muscular, and Integumentary Systems   Chapter Test A

Multiple Choice

Write the letter that best answers the question or completes the statement on the line provided.

____ **1.** Which of the following is NOT part of the axial skeleton?

   a. skull   c. pelvis

   b. vertebral column   d. rib cage

____ **2.** How many bones are found in an adult human skeleton?

   a. 150   c. 206

   b. 200   d. 212

____ **3.** Which of the following contains nerves and blood vessels and runs through the compact bone?

   a. osteocytes   c. bone marrow

   b. Haversian canals   d. periosteum

____ **4.** Which of the following is true about red marrow?

   a. It makes blood cells.

   b. It stores fat.

   c. It produces new bone.

   d. It is found in compact bones of adults.

____ **5.** What is the function of cells called osteoclasts?

   a. build and maintain bone

   b. break down bone

   c. support the skin

   d. produce blood cells

Diagram A

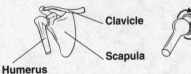

Diagram C

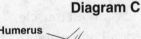

Diagram B

Diagram D

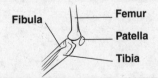

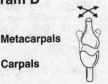

Figure 1

____ **6.** Which diagram in Figure 1 is an example of a ball-and-socket joint?

   a. Diagram A   c. Diagram C

   b. Diagram B   d. Diagram D

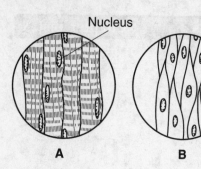

Nucleus   Nucleus   Nucleus

A   B   C

Figure 2

____ 7. Which diagram(s) in Figure 2 show(s) muscles that are striated?
   a. A and B   c. C
   b. B   d. A and C

____ 8. About what percent of the mass of the human body is made up of muscle?
   a. under 10 percent   c. 30 percent
   b. 20 percent   d. over 40 percent

____ 9. Where is the protein called actin located in the body?
   a. ATP molecules   c. myosin filaments
   b. thin filaments   d. acetylcholine neurotransmitters

____10. In addition to myosin, what other protein is involved in skeletal muscle contraction?
   a. collagen   c. keratin
   b. actin   d. melanin

____11. Which of the following types of muscle generally remain in a state of partial contraction when you are keeping your legs straight?
   a. skeletal muscle   c. smooth muscle
   b. cardiac muscle   d. all of the above

____12. The top layer of the epidermis is made of
   a. flat, dead cells.   c. collagen.
   b. melanin.   d. healthy, living cells.

____13. Which of the following is NOT a function of skin?
   a. helps regulate body temperature
   b. removes body wastes
   c. contracts and relaxes muscles
   d. helps prevent infection

____14. Which of the following is NOT part of the integumentary system?
   a. skin   c. nails
   b. cartilage   d. hair

_____15. From which of the following does the basic structure of hair and nails form?

a. sweat

c. collagen

b. melanin

d. keratin

Completion

Complete each statement on the line provided.

16. A less dense tissue known as _____ is found in the ends of long bones and in the middle part of short, flat bones.

17. The joints between adjacent vertebrae are slightly _____ joints.

18. The concept used to explain the action of filaments in muscle contraction is the _____ .

19. The point of contact between a motor neuron and a skeletal muscular cell is called a(an) _____ .

20. A slight scratch of the skin does not cause bleeding because the epidermis lacks _____ .

Short Answer

In complete sentences, write the answers to the questions on the lines provided.

21. Name and describe the two major parts of the skeletal system.

_____

_____

_____

_____

22. Where is cartilage located in an adult human? Why is cartilage necessary?

_____

_____

_____

_____

_____

23. In Figure 3, identify and explain the function of the structure labeled A.

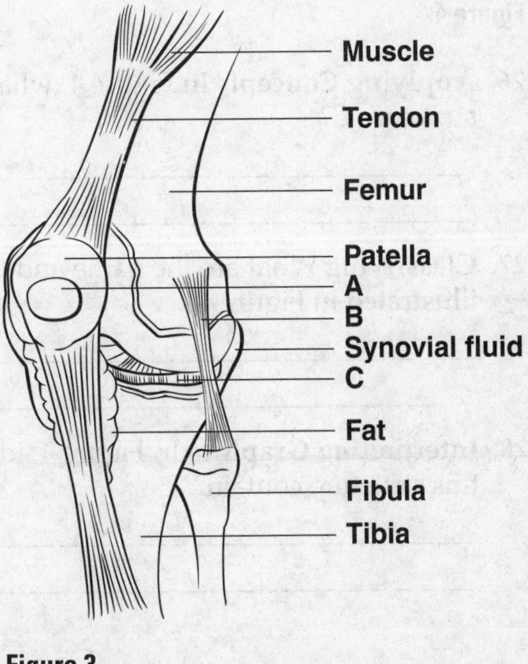

_____

_____

_____

_____

_____

Muscle

Tendon

Femur

Patella

A

B

Synovial fluid

C

Fat

Fibula

Tibia

Figure 3

24. In a left-handed person, which hand would probably have more strength? Why?

_____
_____
_____
_____

25. Compare and contrast keratin and melanin.

_____
_____
_____
_____

Using Science Skills

Use the diagram below to answer the following questions on the lines provided.

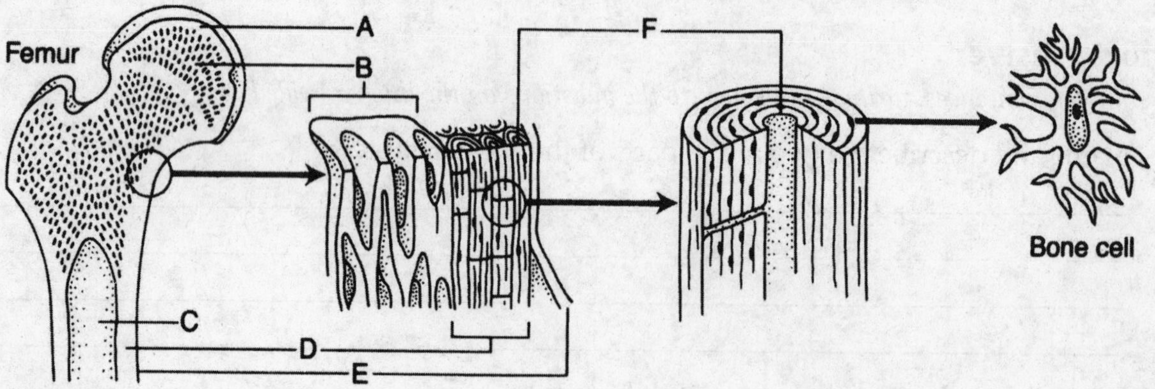

Figure 4

26. Applying Concepts In Figure 4, what two tissues might make up structure C?

_____
_____

27. Classifying What are the name and the function of the bone cell illustrated in Figure 4?

_____
_____

28. Interpreting Graphics In Figure 4, identify structure F. What does this structure contain?

_____
_____

29. Applying Concepts What are the name and the function of structure E in Figure 4?

_____

_____

30. Interpreting Graphics What structures are found inside the compact bone of the femur illustrated in Figure 4?

_____

_____

Essay

Write the answer to each question in the space provided.

31. Compare and contrast spongy bone and compact bone.

32. Name the three types of joints. Give an example of each type.

33. Name and compare the three types of muscle tissue.

34. Why is regular exercise important for the body?

35. How is hair produced, and how does it grow?

Chapter 36 Skeletal, Muscular, and Integumentary Systems — Chapter Test B

Multiple Choice

Write the letter that best answers the question or completes the statement on the line provided.

____ 1. Which of the following provides support for the body, attachment sites for muscles, and protection for internal organs?

    a. skin

    b. spinal cord

    c. skeleton

____ 2. Which of the following is NOT a function of bones in the human skeletal system?

    a. storing minerals

    b. regulating body temperature

    c. moving body parts

____ 3. The main function of the skull is to

    a. produce blood cells.

    b. protect the heart and lungs.

    c. protect the brain.

Diagram A

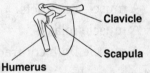
Clavicle
Scapula
Humerus

____ 4. The periosteum is a

    a. place for storing fat cells.

    b. location for red blood cell production.

    c. tough layer of connective tissue surrounding a bone.

Diagram B

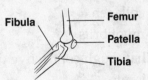
Fibula
Femur
Patella
Tibia

____ 5. Of what is the skeleton of a newborn baby mainly composed?

    a. bone

    b. cartilage

    c. bone marrow

Diagram C

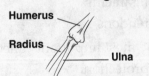
Humerus
Radius
Ulna

____ 6. Ligaments connect

    a. bone to bone.

    b. muscle to muscle.

    c. bone to muscle.

Diagram D

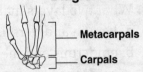
Metacarpals
Carpals

____ 7. A saddle joint is represented in which diagram in Figure 1?

    a. Diagram A

    b. Diagram C

    c. Diagram D

Figure 1

Name_____ Class_____ Date _____

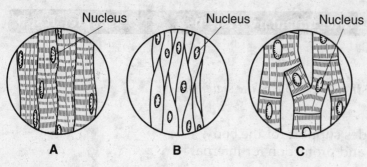

Figure 2

_____ 8. In Figure 2, diagram B is an example of
   a. cardiac muscle.
   b. skeletal muscle.
   c. smooth muscle.

_____ 9. Where is cardiac muscle tissue located in the body?
   a. heart
   b. ribs
   c. skull

_____10. What happens when the thin filaments in a muscle fiber slide over the thick filaments?
   a. A muscle contracts.
   b. A muscle relaxes.
   c. A muscle both contracts and relaxes.

_____11. Myosin and actin make up
   a. osteoblasts.
   b. collagen.
   c. myofibrils.

_____12. What tough connective tissue joins skeletal muscles to bones?
   a. joints
   b. ligaments
   c. tendons

_____13. The most important function of the skin is
   a. protection.   c. sweating.
   b. storing fat.

_____14. What two layers make up skin?
   a. keratin and dermis
   b. epidermis and melanin
   c. epidermis and dermis

_____15. Which of the following are tubelike pockets of epidermal cells that extend into the dermis?
   a. hair follicles   c. melanin cells
   b. keratin layers

Completion

Complete each statement on the line provided.

16. The vertebral column and skull are part of the _____ skeleton.

17. The _____ form a cage that protects the heart and lungs.

18. The process by which cartilage is replaced by bone is _____ .

19. The dark pigment in the skin is called _____ .

20. Hair and nails are part of the _____ system.

Short Answer

In complete sentences, write the answers to the questions on the lines provided.

21. What are three functions of the human skeleton?

_____

_____

_____

_____

22. Of what are bones made?

_____

_____

_____

_____

_____

23. What type of freely movable joint is found in the knee?

_____

_____

24. What are the three different types of muscles?

_____

_____

_____

_____

25. What are the four functions of the integumentary system?

_____

_____

_____

_____

_____

Using Science Skills

Use the diagram below to answer the following questions on the lines provided.

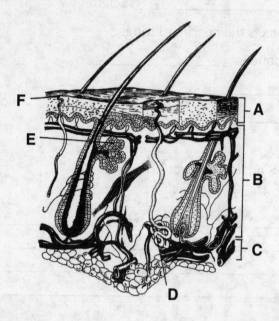

Figure 3

26. **Interpreting Graphics** In Figure 3, what letter is used to label the part of the skin that contains the melanin?

_____

27. **Drawing Conclusions** Explain why a slight scratch will probably not bleed.

_____

_____

_____

28. **Interpreting Graphics** In Figure 3, what is the part of the skin labeled B?

_____

29. **Comparing and Contrasting** In Figure 3, how are the structures labeled F and D related?

_____

_____

30. **Interpreting Graphics** What is the function of the structure labeled E in Figure 3?

_____

_____

LESSON PLAN 37–1 (pages 943–950)

Time
2 period
1 block

The Circulatory System

Section Objectives

Local Standards

- **37.1.1 Identify** the functions of the human circulatory system.
- **37.1.2 Describe** the structures of the circulatory system.
- **37.1.3 Name** the three types of blood vessels in the circulatory system.
- **37.1.4 Describe** blood pressure.

Vocabulary myocardium • atrium • ventricle • pulmonary circulation • systemic circulation • valve • pacemaker • aorta • artery • capillary • vein • atherosclerosis

1 FOCUS

Vocabulary Preview
Challenge students to explain which Vocabulary words refer to structures of the heart and which words refer to types of blood vessels.

Targeted Resources
❏ Transparencies: **547** Section 37–1 Interest Grabber
❏ Transparencies: **548** Section 37–1 Outline

2 INSTRUCT

Build Science Skills: Calculating
Students calculate how much blood the heart pumps in an average lifespan. **L2**

Demonstration
Students use a model of the heart to identify the parts of the heart and to trace the route of blood through the heart. **L1 L2**

Use Visuals: Figure 37–5
Use Figure 37–5 to help students identify the differences among types of blood vessels. **L1 L2**

Build Science Skills: Using Tables and Graphs
Students use library sources to find tables and graphs that relate behavioral variables, such as smoking, to the risk of high blood pressure and other circulatory disorders. **L2 L3**

Targeted Resources
❏ Reading and Study Workbook: Section 37–1
❏ Adapted Reading and Study Workbook: Section 37–1
❏ Teaching Resources: Section Summaries 37–1, Worksheets 37–1
❏ Transparencies: **549** The Sinoatrial Node, **550** Figure 37–2 The Circulatory System, **551** Figure 37–3 The Structures of the Heart, **552** Figure 37–5 The Three Types of Blood Vessels
❏ Teaching Resources: Section Summaries: 37–1, Worksheets 37–1, Enrichment
❏ Lab Manual B: Chapter 37 Lab
❏ **NSTA** *sciLINKS* Cardiovascular system

3 ASSESS

Evaluate Understanding
Call on students at random to define each of the vocabulary terms, and call on other students to correct any errors.

Reteach
Students explain the flow of blood through the heart and name each structure through which blood passes.

Targeted Resources
❏ Teaching Resources: Section Review 37–1
❏ *i*Text Section 37–1

LESSON PLAN 37–2 (pages 951–955)

Blood and the Lymphatic System

Time
1 period
1/2 block

Section Objectives

- **37.2.1 Describe** blood plasma.
- **37.2.2 Explain** the functions of red blood cells, white blood cells, and platelets.
- **37.2.3 Describe** the role of the lymphatic system.

Vocabulary plasma • hemoglobin • lymphocyte • platelet • lymph

Local Standards

---

1 FOCUS

Reading Strategy
Students preview section content by studying the figures and reading the captions.

Targeted Resources
❑ Transparencies: **553** Section 37–2 Interest Grabber
❑ Transparencies: **554** Section 37–2 Outline

---

2 INSTRUCT

Use Community Resources
Students contact their local chapter of the American Red Cross to learn about blood donations and then share what they learn with the class. **L2**

Build Science Skills: Calculating
Students calculate the number of white blood cells in a milliliter of blood and explain why some blood might have more white blood cells. **L2** **L3**

Demonstration
Students observe prepared slides of red blood cells, white blood cells, and platelets, and sketch and describe the appearance of each structure. **L1** **L2**

Analyzing Data
Students analyze data on blood transfusions to predict and explain the success of blood transfusions by blood type of donor and recipient. **L2** **L3**

Use Visuals: Figure 37–11
Use Figure 37–11 to help students understand how the lymphatic and circulatory systems are related. **L2**

Targeted Resources
❑ Reading and Study Workbook: Section 37–2
❑ Adapted Reading and Study Workbook: Section 37–2
❑ Teaching Resources: Section Summaries 37–2, Worksheets 37–2
❑ Transparencies: **555** Blood Transfusions, **556** Figure 37–7 Centrifuged Blood Sample, **557** Types of White Blood Cells, **558** Figure 37–10 Blood Clotting, **559** Figure 37–11 The Lymphatic System
❑ Investigations in Forensics: Investigation 10
❑ **NSTA** *sci*LINKS Blood cells

---

3 ASSESS

Evaluate Understanding
Call on students to name and describe the components of blood.

Reteach
Help students create a concept map of the functions of blood, and have them identify the parts of the blood involved in each function.

Targeted Resources
❑ Teaching Resources: Section Review 37–2
❑ **iText** Section 37–2

LESSON PLAN 37–3 (pages 956–963)

The Respiratory System

Time
1 period
1 block

Section Objectives
- **37.3.1 Describe** respiration.
- **37.3.2 Identify** the function of the respiratory system.
- **37.3.3 Describe** gas exchange and breathing.
- **37.3.4 Explain** how smoking affects the respiratory system.

Vocabulary pharynx • trachea • larynx • bronchus • alveolus
• diaphragm • nicotine • emphysema

Local Standards

1 FOCUS

Reading Strategy
Have students predict how respiration, gas exchange, and breathing are related.

Targeted Resources
❏ Transparencies: **560** Section 37–3 Interest Grabber
❏ Transparencies: **561** Section 37–3 Outline
❏ Transparencies: **562** Flowchart

2 INSTRUCT

Address Misconceptions
Help students understand how breathing is related to respiration. **L1 L2**

Use Visuals: Figure 37–13
Use Figure 37–13 to review with students the structures through which air passes as it travels through the respiratory system. **L1**

Quick Lab
Students do a simple experiment to formulate a hypothesis about how breathing is controlled. **L2**

Demonstration
Demonstrate to students the toxicity of tobacco by spraying a tobacco solution on a plant infected with aphids. **L1 L2**

Targeted Resources
❏ Reading and Study Workbook: Section 37–3
❏ Adapted Reading and Study Workbook: Section 37–3
❏ Teaching Resources: Section Summaries 37–3, Worksheets 37–3
❏ Transparencies: **563** Figure 37–13 The Respiratory System, **564** Figure 37–14 Gas Exchange in the Lungs, **565** Figure 37–15 The Mechanics of Breathing
❏ Lab Worksheets: Chapter 37 Design an Experiment
❏ Lab Manual A: Chapter 37 Lab
❏ **PHSchool.com** Career links

3 ASSESS

Evaluate Understanding
Call on students at random to describe the function of respiratory system structures.

Reteach
Work with students to create a diagram showing the process of gas exchange in the alveoli.

Targeted Resources
❏ Teaching Resources: Section Review 37–3, Chapter Vocabulary Review, Graphic Organizer, Chapter 37 Tests: Levels A and B
❏ **iText** Section 37–3, Chapter 37 Assessment
❏ **PHSchool.com** Online Chapter 37 Test

Chapter 37 Circulatory and Respiratory Systems

Summary

37–1 The Circulatory System

Working with the respiratory system, the circulatory system supplies the body's cells with oxygen and nutrients and removes carbon dioxide and other wastes. **The circulatory system includes the heart, blood vessels, and blood.**

The Heart. The heart is located near the center of the chest. The thick layer of muscle that forms the heart's walls is called the **myocardium.** Contractions of the myocardium pump blood through the body. A contraction begins in a group of cells called the **pacemaker.** The impulse travels through the rest of the heart, causing it to contract.

The heart is divided into right and left halves by the septum. The septum prevents the mixing of oxygen-poor and oxygen-rich blood. Each half of the heart has two chambers. The upper two chambers, or **atria** (singular: atrium), receive blood entering the heart. The lower two chambers, or **ventricles,** pump blood out of the heart. Flaps called **valves** lie between chambers. The valves keep blood from flowing backward in the heart.

Pumping of the heart produces pressure. Blood pressure is the force of the blood on artery walls. Blood pressure moves blood through the body.

The human body has a double-loop circulatory system. Blood moves through two basic pathways.

- In **pulmonary circulation,** oxygen-poor blood flows from the heart to the lungs. In the lungs, carbon dioxide is released from the blood and oxygen is absorbed. This oxygen-rich blood then returns back to the heart.
- In **systemic circulation,** oxygen-rich blood is pumped throughout the body. In the body, oxygen is delivered to body cells and carbon dioxide is picked up by the blood. This oxygen-poor blood returns to the heart.

Blood Vessels. **As blood flows through the circulatory system, it moves through three types of vessels.**

- **Arteries** are large vessels that carry blood away from the heart.
- From arteries, blood flows into **capillaries,** the smallest vessels. In capillaries, materials such as carbon dioxide, oxygen and nutrients are exchanged between the blood and body tissues.
- From the capillaries, blood flows into **veins.** Veins carry blood to the heart. Large veins have valves that keep blood moving forward.

Cardiovascular diseases, such as atherosclerosis and high blood pressure, are diseases of the circulatory system. **Atherosclerosis** is a condition in which fatty deposits build up in arteries. Both high blood pressure and atherosclerosis make the heart work harder. Both can lead to heart attack and stroke. You can prevent these diseases by exercising regularly, eating a low-fat diet, controlling your weight, and not smoking.

37–2 Blood and the Lymphatic System

Blood is a type of connective tissue that contains both dissolved substances and specialized cells. Blood regulates body temperature and pH. It protects the body from disease. In addition, blood can form clots to repair damaged blood vessels.

Just over half of blood is a watery fluid called **plasma.** Proteins in plasma help to clot blood and fight infections.

The cellular portion of blood is made up of red blood cells, white blood cells, and platelets.

- **Red blood cells carry oxygen.** A protein called **hemoglobin** in red blood cells binds to oxygen and carries it throughout the body.
- **White blood cells guard against infection, fight parasites, and attack bacteria.** There are many types of white blood cells. White blood cells called lymphocytes make antibodies. Antibodies are proteins that help fight infection.
- **Blood clotting is made possible by plasma proteins and platelets. Platelets** are cell fragments. Platelets cluster around a wound and release proteins called clotting factors, leading to the formation of a clot.

As blood circulates, some fluid called **lymph** leaks from the blood into surrounding tissues. **The lymphatic system collects the fluid that is lost by the blood and returns it back to the circulatory system.** The lymphatic system is a network of lymph vessels, lymph nodes, and organs. Lymph nodes act as filters and produce certain white blood cells that protect body cells. The lymphatic system also helps absorb nutrients and fight infection.

37–3 The Respiratory System

The respiratory system allows for the exchange of oxygen and carbon dioxide between the blood, the air, and tissues. The nose, pharynx, larynx, trachea, bronchi, and lungs are organs of the respiratory system.

Air enters the body through the nose (or mouth) and passes to the **pharynx,** a tube in the throat. The air then moves into the **trachea,** or windpipe. The **larynx,** which contains the vocal cords, is at the top of the trachea. From the trachea, air moves into two large tubes in the chest called **bronchi** (singular: bronchus). Each bronchus enters a lung.

Within each lung, the bronchus divides into smaller tubes, called bronchioles. The bronchioles keep subdividing until they end in millions of tiny air sacs called **alveoli** (singular: alveolus). Capillaries surround each alveolus. Oxygen crosses the thin capillary walls from the alveolus into the blood. Carbon dioxide in the blood crosses in the opposite direction into the alveolus.

Breathing. Breathing is the movement of air into and out of the lungs. During inhalation, air is pulled into the lungs, delivering oxygen. During exhalation, air is pushed out of the lungs, removing carbon dioxide.

The **diaphragm** is a muscle at the bottom of the chest cavity. When the diaphragm contracts, the chest cavity gets larger. This forms a partial vacuum in the chest. This draws in air that fills the lungs. When the diaphragm relaxes, the chest cavity gets smaller. Pressure rises inside the chest forcing air back out of the lungs.

Breathing is an involuntary action. Carbon dioxide levels in the blood control breathing rate. When carbon dioxide levels rise, the medulla oblongata in the brain sends impulses to the lungs to take a breath.

Dangers of Smoking. Tobacco smoke contains dangerous substances that harm the respiratory system. **Nicotine** increases heart rate and blood pressure. Carbon monoxide is a toxic gas that blocks the transport of oxygen by blood. Tar contains substances that cause cancer.

Smoking can cause such respiratory diseases as chronic bronchitis, emphysema, and lung cancer. Emphysema is a loss of elasticity in lung tissues. Smoking also can cause heart disease. Passive smoking is inhaling the smoke of others. Passive smoking can harm nonsmokers, especially young children. Quitting smoking can improve a smoker's health. The best way to protect your health is to not begin smoking.

The Human Heart

The human heart has four chambers: right atrium, right ventricle, left atrium, and left ventricle. Blood flows from the body into the right atrium. Valves keep blood flowing in only one direction.

Follow the prompts to identify parts of the human heart. The diagram shows the heart as if viewed from the front, so left and right are switched.

- Color the left atrium orange.
- Color the left ventricle red.
- Color the right atrium yellow.
- Color the right ventricle blue.

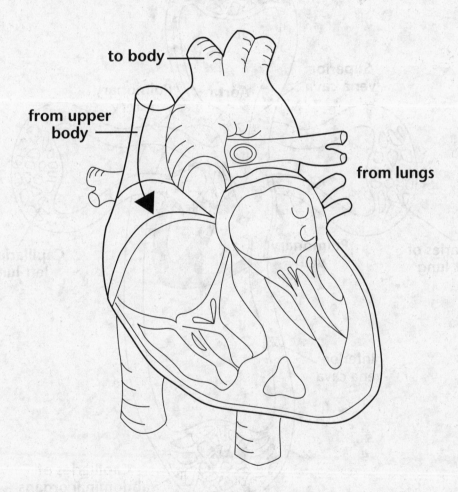

Use the diagram to answer the question.

1. A valve is located between the right atrium and the right ventricle. What is the role of valves in the heart?

_____

_____

The Circulatory System

The human circulatory system moves blood through two primary pathways. One connects the heart and lungs, and the other connects the heart and the rest of the body.

Draw arrows to show how blood moves through the circulatory system. One has been drawn for you.

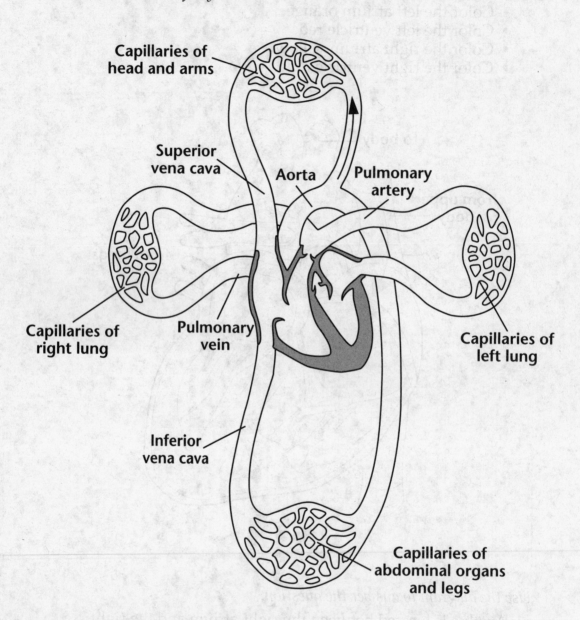

Use the diagram to answer the question.

1. Through which blood vessel does blood return to the heart from the head and arms?

_____

Blood Vessels

As blood flows through the body, it passes through three types of blood vessels—arteries, veins, and capillaries.

Complete the table. Fill in the missing information.

Blood Vessels	Structure	Function
arteries	thick walls containing connective tissue, endothelium, and smooth muscle	
	walls containing connective tissue, endothelium, and smooth muscle; large ones also have valves to control the direction of blood flow	carry blood toward the heart
capillaries		bring nutrients and oxygen to cells and remove carbon dioxide and waste

Use the table to answer the questions.

1. Which are the smallest blood vessels? Circle the correct answer.

   capillaries   veins

2. How does exercise help veins function?

   _____

   _____

Blood Clot Formation

When a blood vessel is injured, platelets release proteins that start a series of chemical reactions. These reactions lead to the formation of filaments called fibrin. The fibrin forms a clot that stops the bleeding.

Color the red blood cells *in the diagrams red. Color the* platelets *blue. Color the* fibrin *yellow.*

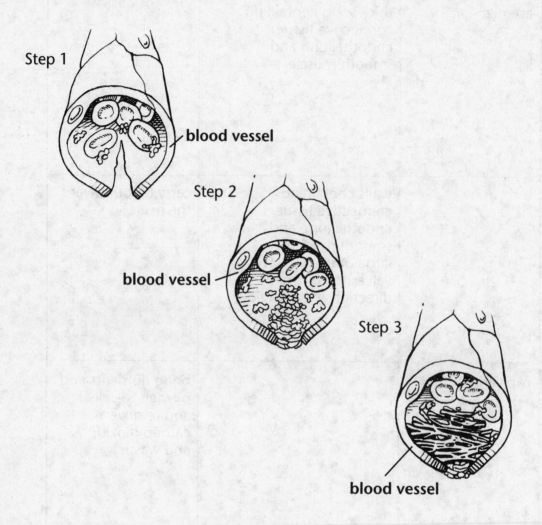

Step 1

blood vessel

Step 2

blood vessel

Step 3

blood vessel

Use the diagrams to answer the questions.

1. In step 2, what is clumped at the site of injury? Circle the correct answer.

   platelets   fibrin

2. Why is it important for blood to form clots?

   _____

The Lymphatic System

The lymphatic system collects fluid that leaks out of blood vessels and returns it to the circulatory system.

Color the lymphatic system. Then label the thymus *and* spleen.

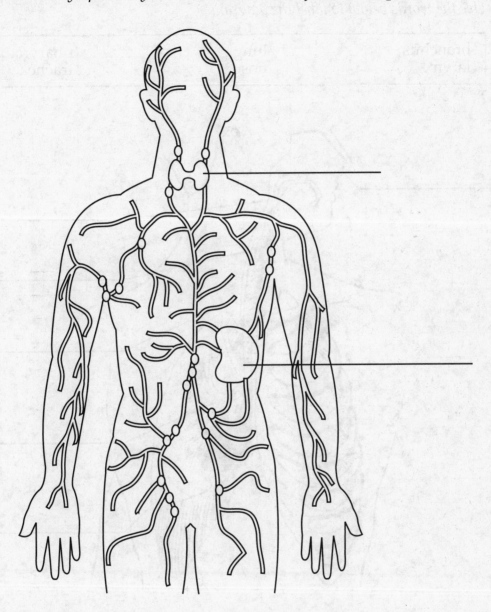

Answer the question.

1. What happens when large numbers of pathogens are trapped in lymph nodes?

_____

The Respiratory System

Air enters the body through the mouth and nose. It passes through air passages and fills the lungs. In the lungs, oxygen enters the bloodstream and carbon dioxide leaves the bloodstream.

Use the words below to label the diagram.

bronchus	lung	pharynx
larynx	nose	trachea

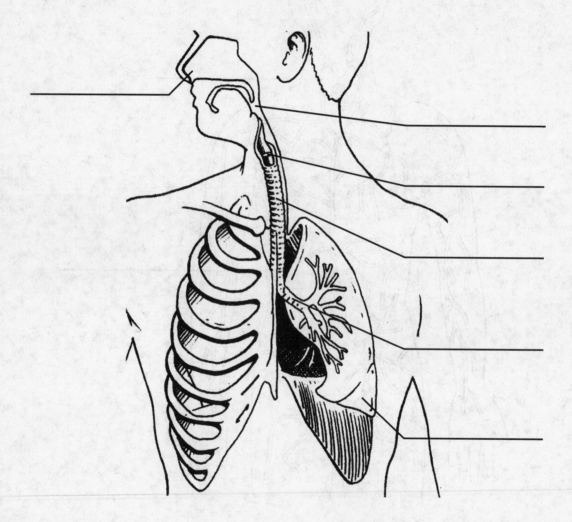

Use the diagram to answer the question. Circle the correct answer.

1. Which structure does air enter after the nose?

bronchus   pharynx

Gas Exchange

In the lungs, gas exchange takes place in millions of tiny air sacs called alveoli. Oxygen diffuses from the alveoli through the capillary walls into the blood. Carbon dioxide diffuses in the opposite direction.

Follow the prompts to identify important parts of the diagram.
- Color the areas containing oxygen-poor blood blue.
- Color the areas containing oxygen-rich blood red.
- Color the areas in which gas exchange takes place purple.

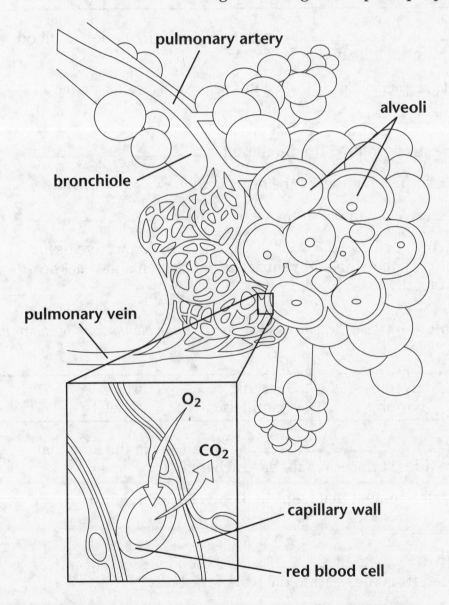

Use the diagram to answer the question. Circle the correct answer.

1. What diffuses from red blood cells into the alveoli?

carbon dioxide   oxygen

Chapter 37   Circulatory and Respiratory Systems

Vocabulary Review

Completion   *Use the words below to fill in the blanks with terms from the chapter.*

atrium	systemic	diaphragm
valve	plasma	ventricle

1. _____ circulation is the circulation of blood throughout the body.

2. A large flat muscle in the chest that helps with breathing is the

   _____.

3. The straw-colored fluid in blood is _____.

4. The upper chamber of the heart is the _____.

5. The lower chamber of the heart is the _____.

6. A(An) _____ is a flap of connective tissue between the atria and ventricles that prevents the backflow of blood.

Completion   *Use the words below to fill in the blanks with terms from the chapter.*

alveolus	larynx	artery
lymph	capillaries	platelet

6. A(An) _____ is an air sac in the lung that provides surface area for gas exchange.

7. A cell fragment that helps in blood clotting is a(an)

   _____.

8. A(An) _____ is a blood vessel that carries blood from the heart to the rest of the body.

9. _____ are the smallest blood vessels.

10. Fluid that is lost by blood and that collects in lymph capillaries

   is called _____.

Summary

37–1 The Circulatory System

The human circulatory system consists of the heart, blood vessels, and blood. Together with the respiratory system, the circulatory system supplies the body's cells with nutrients and oxygen and removes carbon dioxide and other wastes from the body.

The heart is located near the center of the chest. It is composed almost entirely of muscle. The thick layer of muscle that forms the walls of the heart is called the myocardium. Contractions of the myocardium pump blood through the circulatory system.

The heart is divided into right and left halves by a wall called the septum. Each half of the heart has two chambers, for a total of four chambers. The upper two chambers, or atria (singular: atrium), receive blood entering the heart. The lower two chambers, or ventricles, pump blood out of the heart. The right side of the heart pumps blood from the heart to the lungs. This pathway is the pulmonary circulation. The left side of the heart pumps blood to the rest of the body. This pathway is the systemic circulation. Flaps of connective tissue, called valves, between chambers prevent blood from flowing backward in the heart.

Each heart contraction begins in a small group of cardiac muscle cells called the pacemaker. From the pacemaker, the impulse travels through the rest of the heart, causing the heart to contract.

When blood leaves the heart for the body, it passes into a large blood vessel called the aorta. As blood flows through the rest of the circulatory system, it moves through three types of vessels: arteries, capillaries, and veins. Arteries are large vessels that carry blood away from the heart.

From arteries, blood flows into capillaries, the smallest vessels. Capillaries bring nutrients and oxygen to the cells and absorb carbon dioxide and other wastes. From the capillaries, blood flows into veins and is returned to the heart. Large veins contain valves that keep blood moving toward the heart.

The pumping of the heart produces pressure. The force of the blood on artery walls is called blood pressure. Blood pressure keeps blood flowing through the body. Blood pressure is controlled by the autonomic nervous system and the kidneys.

Diseases of the circulatory system, called cardiovascular diseases, are leading causes of death. Two causes of these diseases are high blood pressure and atherosclerosis, in which fatty deposits build up in arteries. Both high blood pressure and atherosclerosis force the heart to work harder and can lead to heart attack and stroke. Cardiovascular diseases are easier to prevent than cure. Prevention includes exercising regularly, eating a low-fat diet, controlling weight, and not smoking.

37–2 Blood and the Lymphatic System

Blood is a type of connective tissue containing dissolved substances and specialized cells. Blood is almost half cells and just over half fluid. The fluid portion of blood is called plasma. Plasma is mostly water. Proteins in plasma help to clot blood and fight infections.

Cells in blood include red blood cells, white blood cells, and platelets. Red blood cells transport oxygen. A protein called hemoglobin in red blood cells binds to oxygen and carries it throughout the body. White blood cells guard against infection, fight parasites, and attack bacteria. There are many types of white blood cells. White blood cells known as lymphocytes produce antibodies. Antibodies are proteins that help fight infection. Platelets—along with plasma proteins—make blood clotting possible. Platelets cluster around a wound and release proteins called clotting factors, leading to the formation of a clot.

As blood circulates, some fluid leaks from the blood into surrounding tissues. This fluid is called lymph. The lymphatic system consists of a network of vessels, lymph nodes, and organs. This system collects lymph and returns it to the circulatory system. The lymphatic system also helps absorb nutrients and fight infection.

37–3 The Respiratory System

In biology, the word *respiration* is used in two ways. Cellular respiration, as you may recall, is the release of energy from the breakdown of food molecules in the presence of oxygen. The other meaning of respiration is the exchange of gases between an organism and the environment. The human respiratory system brings about the exchange of oxygen and carbon dioxide between the blood, the air, and tissues.

The respiratory system consists of the nose, pharynx, larynx, trachea, bronchi, and lungs. Air from the nose enters the pharynx, a tube in the throat. Air moves from the pharynx into the trachea. At the top of the trachea is the larynx, which contains the vocal cords. From the trachea, air passes into two large passageways in the chest called bronchi (singular: bronchus). Each bronchus leads into one of the lungs. Within each lung, the bronchus subdivides into smaller passageways, called bronchioles. The bronchioles continue to subdivide until they reach millions of tiny air sacs called alveoli (singular: alveolus). Each alveolus is surrounded by capillaries. Oxygen crosses the thin capillary walls from the alveolus into the blood. Carbon dioxide in the blood crosses in the opposite direction into the alveolus.

Breathing is the movement of air into and out of the lungs. At the bottom of the chest cavity is a muscle called the diaphragm. When the diaphragm contracts, the chest cavity becomes larger. This creates a partial vacuum in the chest. Air pressure causes air to rush in and fill the lungs. When the diaphragm relaxes, the chest cavity becomes smaller. Increased pressure inside the chest forces air back out of the lungs.

The rate of breathing is controlled by the level of carbon dioxide in the blood. This level is monitored by the medulla oblongata in the brain. As the carbon dioxide level rises, the medulla oblongata sends nerve impulses to the diaphragm, causing it to contract. This results in breathing.

Tobacco smoke harms the respiratory system. Three of the most dangerous substances in tobacco smoke are nicotine, carbon monoxide, and tar. Nicotine is a stimulant that increases heart rate and blood pressure. Carbon monoxide is a poisonous gas that blocks the transport of oxygen by blood. Tar contains substances that cause cancer. Smoking can cause emphysema, which is loss of elasticity in the tissues of the lungs. Smoking can also cause lung cancer and heart disease. Passive smoking means inhaling the smoke of others. Passive smoking is damaging to nonsmokers, especially young children. Quitting smoking can improve a smoker's health. The best solution, however, is not to begin smoking.

Name_____ Class_____ Date_____

Section 37–1 The Circulatory System (pages 943–950)

⊂⊃ **Key Concepts**
- What are the structures of the circulatory system?
- What are the three types of blood vessels in the circulatory system?

Functions of the Circulatory System (page 943)

1. Why do large organisms require a circulatory system? _____

_____

_____

_____

2. What is a closed circulatory system? _____

_____

3. List the three components of the circulatory system.

a. _____ b. _____ c. _____

The Heart (pages 944-946)

4. Is the following sentence true or false? The heart is composed almost entirely of muscle.

_____

Match each heart structure with its description.

	Structure	Description
_____	5. pericardium	a. Thick layer of muscle in the walls of the heart
_____	6. myocardium	b. Sac of tissue that encloses and protects the heart
_____	7. atrium	c. Upper chamber of the heart
_____	8. ventricle	d. Lower chamber of the heart

9. Dividing the right side of the heart from the left side is a wall called a(an) _____.

10. Is the following sentence true or false? The heart functions as four separate pumps. _____

11. Complete the table about the circulatory system.

THE CIRCULATORY SYSTEM

Name of Circulatory Pathway	Side of Heart Involved	Route Blood Follows
Pulmonary circulation		From heart to lungs
	Left side	

12. What happens to blood when it reaches the lungs? _____

_____

13. Why is the blood that enters the heart from the systemic circulation oxygen-poor?

_____

_____

14. Circle the letter of each sentence that is true about blood flow through the heart.

    a. Blood enters the heart through the right and left atria.

    b. Blood enters the heart through the right and left ventricles.

    c. Blood flows from the ventricles to the atria.

    d. Blood flows out of the heart through the right and left atria.

15. Flaps of connective tissue called _____ prevent blood from flowing backward in the heart.

16. Each heart contraction begins in a small group of cardiac muscle cells called the _____ node.

17. Cells that "set the pace" for the beating of the heart as a whole are also called the _____.

Blood Vessels (pages 946–947)

18. Complete the concept map.

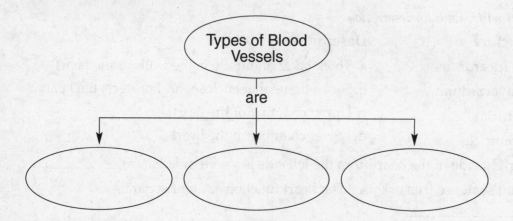

19. Circle the letter of each sentence that is true about arteries.

    a. Most carry oxygen-poor blood.   **c.** They have thin walls.

    b. They can expand under pressure.   **d.** The largest is the aorta.

20. The smallest blood vessels found in the body are the _____.

21. What work is done in the capillaries? _____

_____

22. What keeps blood flowing toward the heart in the largest veins? _____

Blood Pressure (pages 948–949)

23. The force of blood on the walls of arteries is known as _____.

24. Is the following sentence true or false? Blood pressure increases when the heart relaxes.

_____

Match each type of blood pressure with the force it measures.

Type of Pressure	Force It Measures
_____ **25.** systolic	**a.** Force of the blood when the ventricles relax
_____ **26.** diastolic	**b.** Force of the blood when the ventricles contract

27. A typical blood pressure reading for a healthy person is _____.

28. How does the autonomic nervous system regulate blood pressure?

_____

_____

_____

29. How do the kidneys regulate blood pressure? _____

_____

_____

Diseases of the Circulatory System (pages 949–950)

30. A condition in which fatty deposits build up on the walls of arteries is called

_____.

31. High blood pressure also is called _____.

32. Is the following sentence true or false? High blood pressure increases the risk of heart attack and stroke. _____

33. Circle the letter of each sentence that is true about heart attack.

   a. It is caused by atherosclerosis in the coronary arteries.

   b. It occurs when part of the heart muscle begins to die.

   c. Its symptoms include nausea and chest pain.

   d. It requires immediate medical attention.

34. Is the following sentence true or false? A stroke may be caused by a clot in a blood vessel leading to the brain. _____

35. List three ways of avoiding cardiovascular diseases.

   a. _____

   b. _____

   c. _____

Section 37–2 Blood and the Lymphatic System
(pages 951–955)

🔑 Key Concepts
- What is the function of each type of blood cell?
- What is the function of the lymphatic system?

Blood Plasma (page 951)

1. The straw-colored fluid portion of blood is called _____.

2. Plasma is about 90 percent water and 10 percent _____
_____

Match each type of plasma protein with its function.

	Type of Protein	Function
_____	**3.** albumin	**a.** Helps blood clot
_____	**4.** globulin	**b.** Regulates osmotic pressure and blood volume
_____	**5.** fibrinogen	**c.** Fights viral and bacterial infections

Blood Cells (pages 952–954)

6. List the three components of the cellular portion of blood.

   a. _____ b. _____ c. _____

7. What is the role of red blood cells? _____

8. What is hemoglobin? _____
_____

9. Is the following sentence true or false? Mature red blood cells have two nuclei.

   _____

10. Circle the letter of each sentence that is true about white blood cells.

    a. They contain nuclei.

    b. They attack foreign substances.

    c. They contain hemoglobin.

    d. They are also called leukocytes.

11. Is the following sentence true or false? Most white blood cells live for an average of
120 days. _____

12. White blood cells that engulf and digest foreign cells are called _____.

13. What does a sudden increase in the number of white cells tell a physician?
_____

14. List the two components of blood that make clotting possible.

a. _____ b. _____

15. Number the drawings below to show the correct sequence in which a blood clot forms when a blood vessel is injured.

 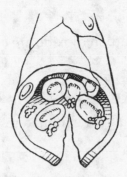 

_____ _____ _____

16. A genetic disorder that results from a defective protein in the clotting pathway is

_____.

The Lymphatic System (pages 954–955)

17. What is the lymphatic system? _____

_____

_____

18. The fluid lost by blood is called _____.

19. What is the function of lymph nodes? _____

_____

Reading Skill Practice

When you read a section with difficult material, writing a summary can help you identify and remember the main ideas and supporting details. Write a concise paragraph summing up the material under each heading in Section 37–2. Each of your paragraphs should be much shorter than the text under that heading in your book. Include each of the highlighted, boldface vocabulary terms in your summary. Do your work on a separate sheet of paper.

Section 37–3 The Respiratory System (pages 956–963)

Key Concepts
- What is the function of the respiratory system?
- How does smoking affect the respiratory system?

What Is Respiration? (page 956)

1. The process by which oxygen and carbon dioxide are exchanged between the lungs and the environment is known as _____.

The Human Respiratory System (pages 956–958)

2. What is the basic function performed by the human respiratory system? _____
_____
_____

3. Label each of the following structures in the drawing of the human respiratory system: nose, pharynx, larynx, trachea, bronchus, and lung.

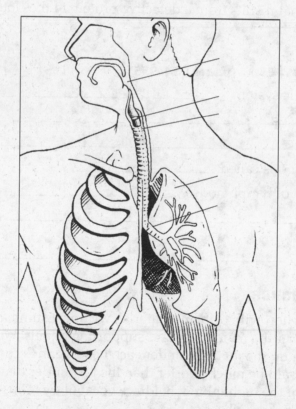

4. Circle the letter of the choice that lists the respiratory structures from largest to smallest.

   a. Alveoli, bronchioles, bronchi   **c.** Bronchi, bronchioles, alveoli

   b. Bronchioles, bronchi, alveoli   **d.** Bronchi, alveoli, bronchioles

5. What prevents food from entering your trachea? _____
_____

Match each structure of the respiratory system with its description.

Structure	Description
_____ 6. pharynx	**a.** Tiny air sacs where gas exchange occurs
_____ 7. trachea	**b.** Tiny projections that sweep trapped particles and mucus away from the lungs
_____ 8. cilia	**c.** Tube that serves as a passageway for both air and food
_____ 9. larynx	**d.** Large passageways in the chest that lead to the lungs
_____ 10. bronchi	**e.** Structure at the top of the trachea that contains the vocal cords
_____ 11. alveoli	**f.** Passageway between the pharynx and bronchi

Gas Exchange (page 958)

12. Gas exchange occurs in the _____.

13. Describe the process of gas exchange. _____

_____

_____

14. Circle the letter of each sentence that is true about gas exchange.

   a. It is a very efficient process.

   b. Exhaled air usually contains no oxygen.

   c. The lungs remove about half of the oxygen of inhaled air.

   d. The lungs increase the carbon dioxide content of inhaled air by a factor of 100.

15. Why is hemoglobin needed? _____

_____

_____

Breathing (pages 959–960)

16. The movement of air into and out of the lungs is called _____.

17. The large, flat muscle at the bottom of the chest cavity is the _____.

18. Is the following sentence true or false? The force that drives air into the lungs comes from air pressure. _____

19. What happens when you inhale? _____

_____

_____

20. What happens when pressure in the chest cavity becomes greater than atmospheric pressure? _____

How Breathing Is Controlled (pages 960–961)

21. The part of the brain that controls breathing is the _____.

22. Is the following sentence true or false? Cells in the breathing center monitor the amount of oxygen in the blood. _____

23. Why do airplane passengers in emergency situations often have to be told to begin breathing pressurized oxygen? _____

_____

_____

Tobacco and the Respiratory System (pages 961–963)

24. List three of the most dangerous substances in tobacco smoke.

    a. _____

    b. _____

    c. _____

25. Is the following sentence true or false? Nicotine is a stimulant drug that increases pulse rate and blood pressure. _____

26. Why is carbon monoxide dangerous? _____

_____

_____

27. List three respiratory diseases caused by smoking.

    a. _____

    b. _____

    c. _____

28. Circle the letter of each sentence that is true about chronic bronchitis.

    a. It is characterized by swollen bronchi.

    b. It occurs only in heavy smokers.

    c. It can make stair climbing and similar activities difficult.

    d. It is unrelated to smoking.

29. What is emphysema? _____

30. Circle the letter of each sentence that is true about lung cancer.

    a. Its most important cause is smoking.

    b. It is often deadly.

    c. It cannot spread to other parts of the body.

    d. It is usually detected early enough for a cure.

31. Circle the letter of each way that smoking affects the cardiovascular system.

    a. It constricts the blood vessels.

    b. It causes blood pressure to rise.

    c. It makes the heart work harder.

    d. It causes heart disease.

32. Inhaling the smoke of others is called _____.

33. Why is passive smoking particularly harmful to young children? _____

_____

34. Why is it so hard to quit smoking? _____

_____

35. What is the best solution for dealing with tobacco? _____

_____

Reading Skill Practice

When you read a section with many details, writing an outline may help you organize and remember the material. Outline Section 37–3 by first writing the section headings as major topics in the order in which they appear in the book. Then, beneath each major topic, list important details about it. Title your outline *The Respiratory System*. Do your work on a separate sheet of paper.

Vocabulary Review

Matching   *In the space provided, write the letter of the definition that best matches each term.*

_____ **1.** pulmonary circulation

_____ **2.** systemic circulation

_____ **3.** aorta

_____ **4.** capillary

_____ **5.** atherosclerosis

_____ **6.** plasma

_____ **7.** hemoglobin

_____ **8.** platelet

_____ **9.** pharynx

_____ **10.** larynx

_____ **11.** artery

_____ **12.** vein

_____ **13.** lymph

a. path of blood from heart to body

b. fluid part of blood

c. cell fragment that helps blood to clot

d. path of blood from heart to lungs

e. smallest type of blood vessel

f. protein in blood that carries oxygen

g. structure containing vocal cords

h. buildup of fat deposits on artery walls

i. tube in throat through which air passes

j. largest artery

k. fluid that is lost by the blood

l. blood vessel that carries blood away from the heart

m. blood vessel that carries blood toward the heart

True or False   *Determine whether each statement is true or false. If it is true, write* **true** *in the space provided. If the statement is false, change the underlined word or words to make the statement true.*

_____ **14.** Air moves from the pharynx into the <u>bronchus</u>.

_____ **15.** The tiny sacs where gas exchange takes place are the <u>lymphocytes</u>.

_____ **16.** The <u>diaphragm</u> is a muscle that enables breathing.

_____ **17.** Loss of elasticity in the lungs is called <u>lung cancer</u>.

_____ **18.** The stimulant drug in tobacco smoke is known as <u>tar</u>.

Writing Descriptions   *In the space provided, describe each structure of the heart.*

19. myocardium _____

_____

20. atrium _____

_____

21. ventricle _____

_____

22. valve _____

_____

23. pacemaker _____

_____

Chapter 37 Circulatory and Respiratory Systems   **Section Review 37-1**

Reviewing Key Concepts

Short Answer *On the lines provided, answer the following questions.*

1. What is the function of the heart?

_____

2. What does blood carry throughout the body?

_____

3. In what direction do all arteries carry blood?

_____

4. In what direction do all veins carry blood?

_____

5. What role do capillaries play in the circulatory system?

_____

Reviewing Key Skills

Completion *On the lines provided, complete the paragraph using the terms*
lungs, pulmonary veins, aorta, pulmonary arteries, superior vena cava,
left atrium, right atrium, left ventricle, *and* right ventricle.

A large vein called the _____ brings the blood from
                                    6.

the upper part of the body to the heart, where it enters the _____.
                                                                      7.

The blood is pumped out of the right atrium into the _____ and
                                                              8.

travels through the _____ to the _____, where
                            9.   **10.**

it picks up oxygen. From the lungs, blood travels through the _____
                                                                        11.

and returns to the heart, where it enters the _____. Finally, the
                                                        12.

blood is forced from the _____ into
                                  13.

the _____, which carries it to the tissues of the body.
            14.

15. **Comparing and Contrasting** A stroke may also be referred to as a
    "brain attack". In what ways is a stroke similar to a heart attack?

    _____

    _____

    _____

Chapter 37 Circulatory and Respiratory Systems   Section Review 37-2

Reviewing Key Concepts

Short Answer *On the lines provided, answer the following questions.*

1. What do red blood cells carry throughout the body?

   _____

2. How does the body depend on white blood cells?

   _____

3. How do platelets protect against blood loss?

   _____
   _____

Completion *On the lines provided, complete the following sentences.*

4. The lymphatic system consists of a network of nodes, organs, and

   _____.

5. The lymphatic system collects fluid called _____
   that is lost from the circulatory system.

6. Fluid collected by the lymphatic system is returned to the

   _____ system.

Reviewing Key Skills

7. **Predicting** How will lymph nodes change in response to an
   infection?

   _____
   _____
   _____

8. **Predicting** What might happen if your lymphatic vessels became
   blocked?

   _____
   _____
   _____

9. **Applying Concepts** How would a low level of hemoglobin affect
   the function of red blood cells?

   _____
   _____
   _____

10. **Using Analogies** Explain why white blood cells are described as the
    "army" of the circulatory system.

    _____
    _____
    _____

Chapter 37 Circulatory and Respiratory Systems   **Section Review 37-3**

Reviewing Key Concepts

Labeling Diagrams *On the lines provided, label the organs of the respiratory system that correspond to the numbers in the diagram.*

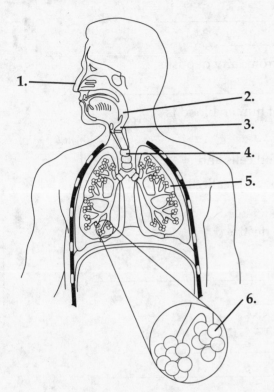

1. _____
2. _____
3. _____
4. _____
5. _____
6. _____

Short Answer *On the lines provided, answer the following question.*

7. What are bronchioles?

_____

8. What are some diseases caused by smoking?

_____
_____

Reviewing Key Skills

9. **Inferring** Imagine that years of smoking have caused you to develop emphysema. Why would this make it harder for your body to get the oxygen it needs?

_____
_____
_____

10. **Applying Concepts** Explain how the respiratory system and the circulatory system work together to respond to your body's needs during vigorous exercise.

_____
_____
_____

Name_____ Class_____ Date _____

Completion *On the lines provided, complete the following sentences.*

1. The heart pumps blood into two pathways, called _____ circulation and _____ circulation.

2. The three basic types of blood vessels are _____, _____, and _____.

3. The disorder of the circulatory system that results from fatty deposits building up within the walls of arteries is called _____.

4. The straw-colored fluid that makes up 55 percent of human blood is called _____.

5. The iron-containing protein that is found in red blood cells and carries oxygen from the lungs to the tissues of the body is called _____.

6. White blood cells that produce antibodies that help destroy pathogens are called _____.

7. The fluid collected by the lymphatic system is called _____.

8. The windpipe is also called the _____.

9. The vocal chords are a part of the _____.

10. Each lung is connected to the trachea by a(an) _____.

11. Gas exchange occurs in the lungs in tiny sacs called _____.

12. The loss of elasticity in the tissues of the lungs is called _____.

Labeling Diagrams *On the lines provided, label the parts of the heart that correspond to the numbers in the diagram.*

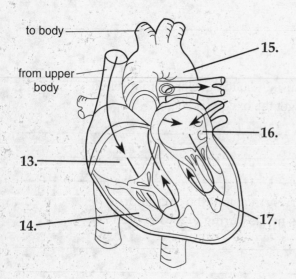

to body

from upper body

13.

14.

15.

16.

17.

13. _____

14. _____

15. _____

16. _____

17. _____

Name_____ Class_____ Date _____

Multiple Choice *On the line provided, write the letter of the answer that best answers the question or completes the sentence.*

_____ 18. What structure serves as a passageway for both air and food?
  a. pharynx   c. larynx
  b. trachea   d. bronchi

_____ 19. The largest layer of the walls of the heart is the
  a. pericardium.
  b. myocardium.
  c. atrium.
  d. ventricle.

_____ 20. What prevents blood from flowing backward in blood vessels?
  a. valves
  b. capillaries
  c. veins
  d. pumps

_____ 21. What is another name for the sinoatrial node?
  a. pacesetter
  b. aorta
  c. pacemaker
  d. atherosclerosis

_____ 22. Blood clotting is made possible by the action of cell fragments called
  a. hemoglobin.
  b. phagocytes.
  c. red blood cells.
  d. platelets.

_____ 23. Inside the chest, each bronchus divides into smaller and smaller passageways known as
  a. bronchi.
  b. bronchioles.
  c. emphysema.
  d. atherosclerosis.

_____ 24. The large flat muscle at the bottom of the chest cavity is called the
  a. diaphragm.
  b. pharynx.
  c. bronchus.
  d. lung.

_____ 25. The stimulant drug found in tobacco is called
  a. tar.
  b. hemoglobin.
  c. nicotine.
  d. carbon monoxide.

Chapter 37 Circulatory and Respiratory Systems   Enrichment

Artificial Pacemakers

Your heart has a natural pacemaker that initiates a rhythmic heartbeat. This natural pacemaker is made of specialized muscle tissue with characteristics of both muscles and nerves. It contracts like a muscle. When it contracts, it also generates electrical impulses, like a nerve. Each time the pacemaker contracts, it sends an impulse, a wave of energy, through the heart. This impulse causes the heart to contract.

Some heart diseases can prevent the natural pacemaker in the heart from functioning properly. Until 1958, problems with a natural pacemaker could not be effectively treated. That year, an American biomedical engineer, Wilson Greatbatch, invented an artificial pacemaker. The artificial pacemaker, a small flat disk made of plastic, is powered by a tiny battery. People whose natural pacemakers do not function properly often have an artificial pacemaker inserted.

The artificial pacemaker is implanted in the body, usually in the subcutaneous fat layer. It is connected to the heart with wires during surgery. Just as a natural pacemaker would, the pacemaker sends electrical impulses to the heart to trigger action. Unlike a natural pacemaker, however, the artificial pacemaker can be controlled and adjusted.

The artificial pacemaker has resolved the breathlessness and inability to exercise suffered by many heart patients. Researchers are still working to improve the device. Older models of pacemakers were sensitive to electromagnetic devices such as microwave ovens and automatic doors. Exposure to those devices could cause malfunction of the pacemaker. The modern pacemaker is shielded from interference. Someday, pacemakers may be sensitive to body temperature and to increases in oxygen need. They may adjust automatically to changing needs.

Evaluation *On the lines provided, answer the following questions.*

1. What does an artificial pacemaker do?

_____

_____

_____

_____

_____

2. What are some shortcomings of modern artificial pacemakers?

_____

_____

_____

_____

_____

Flowchart

*In the following flowchart, enter the steps of inhalation and exhalation listed
below in the order in which they occur.*

Diaphragm relaxes; Volume of the chest cavity expands; Diaphragm contracts;
Air fills the lungs; Air rushes out of the lungs; Pressure decreases in the chest cavity

1.

2.

3.

4.

5.

6.

Chapter 37 Circulatory and Respiratory Systems　　　　Chapter Test A

Multiple Choice

Write the letter that best answers the question or completes the statement on the line provided.

_____ 1. Which of the following is NOT a part of the circulatory system?
　　　a. heart　　　　　　　　c. blood vessels
　　　b. air passageway　　　d. blood

_____ 2. Which of the following pathways is the largest of the circulatory system?
　　　a. systemic circulation
　　　b. pulmonary circulation
　　　c. lymphatic circulation
　　　d. coronary circulation

_____ 3. Where are the cells that make up the sinoatrial node, or pacemaker, located?
　　　a. right atrium　　　　c. right ventricle
　　　b. left atrium　　　　　d. left ventricle

_____ 4. Compared with the walls of arteries, the walls of veins
　　　a. are thicker.　　　　c. lack valves.
　　　b. are thinner.　　　　d. have more resistance.

_____ 5. The function of valves in the human circulatory system is to
　　　a. stimulate the heartbeat.
　　　b. accelerate the flow of blood.
　　　c. prevent the backward flow of blood.
　　　d. serve as a cushion to prevent friction.

_____ 6. Which helps regulate blood pressure?
　　　a. spleen　　　　　　　c. bronchus
　　　b. kidney　　　　　　　d. alveolus

_____ 7. Which of the following activities is(are) key(s) to avoiding cardiovascular disease?
　　　a. exercise　　　　　　c. weight control
　　　b. low-fat diet　　　　d. all of the above

_____ 8. How much blood does the human body contain?
　　　a. 1–2 liters　　　　　c. 8–10 liters
　　　b. 4–6 liters　　　　　d. 12–14 liters

_____ 9. In Figure 1, what does step B show?
　　　a. clot forming
　　　b. capillary wall breaking
　　　c. clumping of platelets
　　　d. conversion of fibrinogen into fibrin

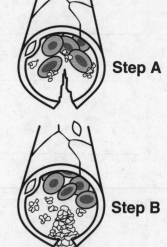

Step A

Step B

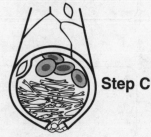

Step C

Figure 1

Name________________________________ Class __________________ Date ______________

____**10.** Into what substance is fibrinogen converted?

a. thrombin c. platelets
b. fibrin d. thromboplastin

____**11.** Which of the following is NOT a function of the lymphatic system?

a. collects and returns lost fluid to the circulatory system
b. traps bacteria
c. absorbs protein
d. carries fat-soluble vitamins to the blood

____**12.** Which of the following are signs that a person is breathing?

a. hearing or feeling air being exhaled from the nose
b. chest rising and falling
c. hearing or feeling air being exhaled from the mouth
d. all of the above

____**13.** Air is filtered, warmed, and moistened in the

a. nose. c. lungs.
b. alveoli. d. bronchioles.

____**14.** Air is forced into the lungs by the contraction of the

a. alveoli. c. diaphragm.
b. bronchioles. d. heart.

____**15.** What gas, found in cigarette smoke, blocks the transport of oxygen by hemoglobin in the blood?

a. hydrogen peroxide
b. carbon monoxide
c. carbon dioxide
d. sodium bicarbonate

Completion

Complete each statement on the line provided.

16. In Figure 2, the pathway for pulmonary circulation is labeled ________________.

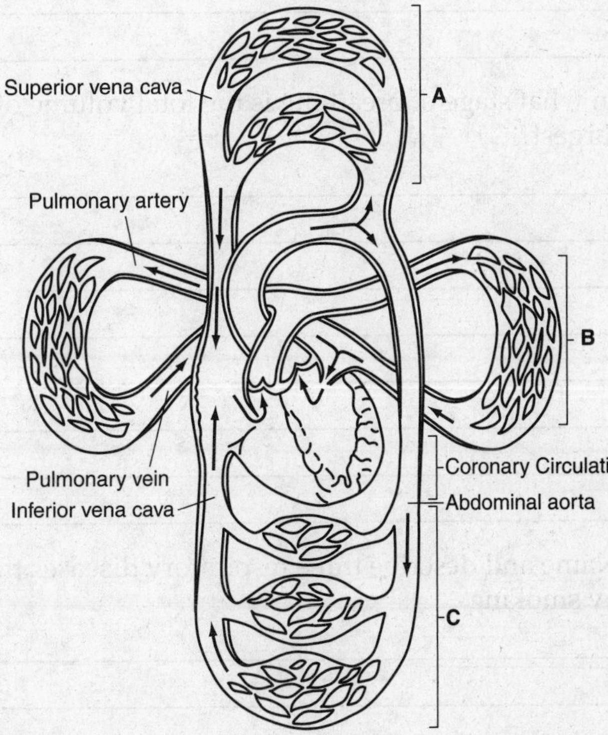

Superior vena cava
A
Pulmonary artery
B
Pulmonary vein
Inferior vena cava
Coronary Circulation
Abdominal aorta
C

Figure 2

Name_____ Class_____ Date _____

17. Medical workers use a sphygmomanometer to measure _____ .

18. Fatty deposits called plaque build up on the inner walls of arteries, causing a condition known as _____ .

19. Plasma consists mostly of _____ .

20. A genetic disorder called _____ results from a defective protein in the clotting pathway.

Short Answer

In complete sentences, write the answers to the questions on the lines provided.

21. Are the ribs raised or lowered after you exhale?
_____

22. List the main functions of the three types of blood cells.
_____
_____
_____
_____

23. List in order the structures of the respiratory system through which air passes from the outside environment to the alveoli.
_____
_____
_____

24. In what stage of breathing is the total volume of the chest cavity largest?
_____
_____
_____
_____
_____
_____
_____

25. Name and describe three respiratory diseases that can be caused by smoking.
_____
_____
_____
_____

Using Science Skills

Use the diagram below to answer the following questions on the lines provided.

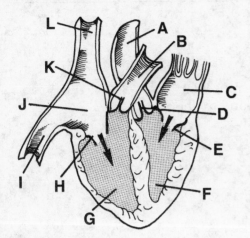

Figure 3

26. **Interpreting Graphics** Name and describe the function of the structure labeled I in Figure 3.

_____

_____

_____

27. **Drawing Conclusions** What is the function of the structures labeled D, E, H, and K in Figure 3?

_____

_____

_____

_____

_____

28. **Interpreting Graphics** In Figure 3, what label shows the vessel in which oxygen-rich blood leaves the heart and goes to the rest of the body?

_____

_____

_____

_____

29. **Drawing Conclusions** In Figure 3, what happens to valves E and H when the ventricles contract?

_____

30. Interpreting Graphics In Figure 3, what is the function of the structure labeled B?

_____

_____

Essay

Write the answer to each question in the space provided.

31. Describe the function of each of the following: (a) the muscular walls of the large arteries, (b) the valves in the veins, and (c) the valves in the heart.

32. How does the body regulate blood pressure?

33. How do white blood cells guard against infection, fight parasites, and attack bacteria?

34. What is the lymphatic system, and what are its functions?

35. Compare the two types of biological respiration.

Chapter 37 Circulatory and Respiratory Systems | Chapter Test B

Multiple Choice

Write the letter that best answers the question or completes the statement on the line provided.

____ 1. Which body system acts as a transportation system?
  a. circulatory
  b. respiratory
  c. nervous

____ 2. In the walls of the heart, there are two thin layers that form a sandwich around a thick layer of muscle called the
  a. epithelial tissue layer.
  b. pericardium.
  c. myocardium.

____ 3. Which of the following are the smallest of the blood vessels?
  a. arteries
  b. veins
  c. capillaries

____ 4. Which of the following is NOT a type of blood vessel?
  a. artery
  b. vein
  c. lymphatic cell

____ 5. When the heart contracts, it produces a wave of fluid pressure in the
  a. veins.   c. capillaries.
  b. arteries.

____ 6. When the pressure of blood pumping through the blood vessels is constantly too high, the condition is known as
  a. a heart attack.   c. atherosclerosis.
  b. hypertension.

____ 7. Which of the following is correct about the composition of plasma?
  a. 90 percent water   c. 10 percent water
  b. 50 percent water

____ 8. Which plasma proteins help to regulate osmotic pressure and blood volume?
  a. albumins   c. fibrinogens
  b. globulins

____ 9. Which of the following blood cells contain hemoglobin?
  a. red blood cells   c. platelets
  b. white blood cells

____**10.** Which body system collects the fluid that is lost by the blood and returns it to the body's transport system?

    a. circulatory

    b. lymphatic

    c. respiratory

____**11.** What is the term used to describe a swelling of the tissues due to the accumulation of excess fluid, which can occur when lymphatic vessels are blocked because of injury or disease?

    a. hemophilia

    b. stroke

    c. edema

____**12.** The process by which oxygen and carbon dioxide are exchanged between cells, the blood, and air in the lungs is one type of

    a. systemic circulation.

    b. respiration.

    c. emphysema.

____**13.** What structure serves as a passageway for both air and food?

    a. pharynx

    b. trachea

    c. larynx

____**14.** Generally speaking, what controls breathing?

    a. the brain

    b. the lungs

    c. the diaphragm

____**15.** Which of the following is NOT contained in tobacco smoke?

    a. carbon monoxide

    b. caffeine

    c. nicotine

Completion

Complete each statement on the line provided.

16. A circulating fluid called _____ is pumped through a system of vessels in the body.

17. Gas exchange takes place in the _____ .

18. The iron-containing protein called _____ binds to oxygen in the lungs and transports it to tissues throughout the body, where the oxygen is released.

19. Inhaled air passes from the trachea to one of the two _____ .

20. Breathing is such an important function that your _____ system will not let you have complete control over it.

Short Answer

In complete sentences, write the answers to the questions on the lines provided.

21. What are the three structures of the circulatory system?

_____

_____

_____

22. Identify and compare the functions of the three types of blood vessels of the circulatory system.

_____

_____

_____

_____

23. What is blood pressure?

_____

_____

_____

24. Describe blood plasma.

_____

_____

_____

_____

25. What is the basic function of the human respiratory system?

_____

_____

Name_____ Class_____ Date _____

Using Science Skills

Use the diagram below to answer the following questions on the lines provided.

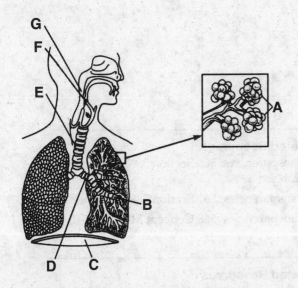

Figure 1

26. **Interpreting Graphics** In Figure 1, which labeled structure is the diaphragm?

_____

_____

27. **Interpreting Graphics** In Figure 1, what are two names for the structure labeled E?

_____

_____

28. **Interpreting Graphics** What is the name of the structures in which the exchange of gases takes place?

_____

29. **Interpreting Graphics** What is the name of the structure in Figure 1 that prevents the passage of food from the pharynx into the lungs?

_____

30. **Interpreting Graphics** In Figure 1, what is the label and name of the structure that carries air from the trachea to a lung?

_____

_____

LESSON PLAN 38–1 (pages 971–977)

Food and Nutrition

Section Objectives   **Local Standards**

- **38.1.1 Explain** how food provides energy.
- **38.1.2 Describe** the nutrients your body needs.
- **38.1.3 State** why water is such an important nutrient.
- **38.1.4 Explain** how to use the food pyramid.

Vocabulary Calorie • carbohydrate • fat • protein
• vitamin • mineral

1 FOCUS

Reading Strategy
Suggest that students create a table as they read to compare and contrast the nutrients the body needs.

Targeted Resources
- ❏ Transparencies: **566** Section 38–1 Interest Grabber
- ❏ Transparencies: **567** Section 38–1 Outline
- ❏ Transparencies: **568** Concept Map

2 INSTRUCT

Make Connections: Chemistry
Students explain how ATP releases energy so the cells can use it. **L2**

Demonstration
Demonstrate how much water is contained in a variety of foods by weighing the foods before and after they have been left to dry out. **L1** **L2**

Build Science Skills: Designing Experiments
Students design an experiment to relate diet to incidence of colon cancer. **L3**

Build Science Skills: Inferring
Students infer the health consequences of diets lacking sufficient carbohydrates, fats, or proteins. **L2**

Make Connections: Environmental Science
Relate the foods in the different levels of the Food Guide Pyramid to the organisms found at the different levels of a food chain. **L2**

Targeted Resources
- ❏ Reading and Study Workbook: Section 38–1
- ❏ Adapted Reading and Study Workbook: Section 38–1
- ❏ Teaching Resources: Section Summaries 38–1, Worksheets 38–1
- ❏ Transparencies: **569** Figure 38–6 Types of Vitamins, **570** Figure 3–7 Types of Minerals, **571** Figure 38–8 Food Guide Pyramid
- ❏ **NSTA** *sci*$_{LINKS}$ Nutrition

3 ASSESS

Evaluate Understanding
Call on students to name the six types of nutrients and to describe their roles in the body.

Reteach
Have students review the Food Guide Pyramid and name the nutrients that foods in each group are rich in.

Targeted Resources
- ❏ Teaching Resources: Section Review 38–1
- ❏ **iText** Section 38–1

LESSON PLAN 38–2 (pages 978–984)

The Process of Digestion

Time
2 periods
1 block

Section Objectives

Local Standards

■ **38.2.1 Identify** the organs of the digestive system.

■ **38.2.2 Describe** the function of the digestive system.

Vocabulary amylase • esophagus • peristalsis • stomach • chyme • small intestine • pancreas • liver • villus • large intestine

---

1 FOCUS

Vocabulary Preview
Read each of the Vocabulary words to the class, and have students repeat them after you so they know how to pronounce them correctly.

Targeted Resources
❏ Transparencies: **572** Section 38–2 Interest Grabber
❏ Transparencies: **573** Section 38–2 Outline

---

2 INSTRUCT

Build Science Skills: Using Models
Students identify tools that perform mechanical functions similar to the mechanical functions of the different types of teeth. **L2**

Use Visuals: Figure 38–10
Students locate each of the digestive organs and related structures in Figure 38–10. **L1 L2**

Demonstration
Demonstrate with a simple model how peristalsis pushes food through the esophagus. **L1 L2**

Make Connections: Chemistry
Students observe how sodium bicarbonate neutralizes hydrochloric acid and then relate their observations to the function of sodium bicarbonate in the digestive system. **L2**

Make Connections: Mathematics
Students estimate the surface area of the large intestine and compare it with the surface area of the small intestine. **L2 L3**

Targeted Resources
❏ Reading and Study Workbook: Section 38–2
❏ Adapted Reading and Study Workbook: Section 38–2
❏ Transparencies: **574** Digestive Enzymes, **575** Figure 38–10 The Digestive System, **576** Figure 38–13 The Liver and Pancreas, **577** Figure 38–14 The Small Intestine
❏ Teaching Resources: Section Summaries 38–2, Worksheets 38–2, Enrichment
❏ Lab Worksheets: Chapter 38 Design an Experiment
❏ Lab Manual B: Chapter 38 Lab
❏ **NSTA** *sci*$_{LINKS}$ Digestion

---

3 ASSESS

Evaluate Understanding
Have students make a table listing the enzymes found in or produced by each organ of the digestive system and the nutrients that the enzymes help break down.

Reteach
Describe the functions of the digestive organs, and have students identify them from their functions.

Targeted Resources
❏ Teaching Resources: Section Review 38–2
❏ **iText** Section 38–2

LESSON PLAN 38–3 (pages 985–989)

The Excretory System

Time
1 period
1/2 block

Section Objectives

- **38.3.1 Identify** the functions of the kidneys.
- **38.3.2 Explain** how blood is filtered.

Vocabulary kidney • ureter • urinary bladder • nephron • filtration • glomerulus • Bowman's capsule • reabsorption • loop of Henle • urethra

Local Standards

1 FOCUS

Reading Strategy
Suggest that students outline the section by first writing the headings and subheadings and then filling in important details as they read.

Targeted Resources
- ❑ Transparencies: **578** Section 38–3 Interest Grabber
- ❑ Transparencies: **579** Section 38–3 Outline

2 INSTRUCT

Demonstration
Use a balloon filled with water as a model of a cell to demonstrate why cells must be able to eliminate waste products. **L1 L2**

Use Visuals: Figure 38–17
Students compare the sizes of the nephron and kidney in Figure 38–17 with the actual sizes to increase their understanding of how the two structures are related. **L2**

Build Science Skills: Using Models
Students consider a coffee filter as a model of a kidney and state how the two are similar and how they are different. **L1 L2**

Demonstration
Students observe a beef or lamb kidney, identify its structures, and suggest how it might be different from a human kidney. **L2**

Make Connections: Health Science
Relate the kidney's ability to maintain homeostasis to health issues. **L2 L3**

Targeted Resources
- ❑ Reading and Study Workbook: Section 38–3
- ❑ Adapted Reading and Study Workbook: Section 38–3
- ❑ Teaching Resources: Section Summaries 38–3, Worksheets 38–3
- ❑ Transparencies: **580** The Urinary System, **581** Figure 38–17 Structure of the Kidneys, **582** The Nephron, **583** Figure 38–19 Kidney Dialysis
- ❑ Lab Manual A: Chapter 38 Lab
- ❑ **NSTA** *sciLINKS* Excretory system

3 ASSESS

Evaluate Understanding
Call on students at random to state the function of the different parts of the kidney and nephron, and call on other students to correct any errors.

Reteach
Have students use Figure 38–17 to trace the path of blood into and out of the kidney and to trace the path of urine from the kidney to the urethra.

Targeted Resources
- ❑ Teaching Resources: Section Review 38–3, Chapter Vocabulary Review, Graphic Organizer, Chapter 38 Tests: Levels A and B
- ❑ **iText** Section 38–3, Chapter 38 Assessment
- ❑ **PHSchool.com** Online Chapter 38 Test

Chapter 38   Digestive and Excretory Systems

Summary

38–1 Food and Nutrition

One calorie is equal to the amount of energy needed to raise the temperature of one gram of water by one degree Celcius. The energy in food is measured in dietary Calories (with a capital C). One **Calorie** is equal to 1000 calories. The number of Calories you need each day depends on your age, sex, and activity level.

Nutrients are substances in food that supply the body with energy and raw materials needed for growth, repair, and maintenance. **The nutrients that the body needs are water, carbohydrates, fats, proteins, vitamins, and minerals.**

Every cell in the human body needs water because many of the body's processes take place in water. Water makes up a large part of blood and other body fluids. Sweating removes water in order to cool the body by evaporation. Water must be replaced regularly.

Simple and complex **carbohydrates** are the body's main source of energy. Simple carbohydrates do not have to be digested or broken down. They provide quick energy for the body. Complex carbohydrates must be broken down into simple sugars to be used for energy.

Fats are formed from fatty acids and glycerol. Saturated fats are usually solid at room temperature. Unsaturated fats are usually liquid at room temperature. Fats protect organs and joints. They help make up cell membranes, and insulate the body.

Proteins supply raw materials for growth and repair of the body. Amino acids form proteins. The human body can produce twelve of the twenty amino acids. The other eight must be obtained from food. These amino acids are called essential amino acids.

Vitamins are organic molecules that help regulate body processes. Fat-soluble vitamins can be stored in fatty tissues. Water-soluble vitamins cannot be stored and should be in the foods that a person eats every day. Some diseases result when the body does not receive a sufficient supply of vitamins. Vitamins can have serious effects on a person's health.

Minerals are inorganic nutrients. Your body usually needs minerals in small amounts. Examples of minerals include calcium and iron. The body loses minerals in sweat, urine, and other waste products, so they must be replaced by eating foods.

The new food pyramid—MyPyramid—can help you choose a balanced diet. MyPyramid is designed to help you make smart food choices from every food group, get the most nutrition out of your calories, and emphasize the importance of daily exercise.

38–2 The Process of Digestion

The digestive system breaks down food into simpler molecules that can be absorbed and used by cells. The human digestive system is a one-way tube. It includes the mouth, pharynx, esophagus, stomach, small intestine, and large intestine. Other structures—salivary glands, pancreas, and liver—add secretions to the digestive system.

1. Digestion starts in the mouth. Teeth tear and crush food to begin mechanical digestion. Mechanical digestion is the physical breakdown of large chunks of food into smaller pieces. Salivary glands in the mouth secrete saliva, which contains enzymes that break down starches into sugars. This begins the process of chemical digestion. Chemical digestion breaks down large food molecules into smaller food molecules.

2. The swallowed clump of food passes through the pharynx and into the **esophagus.** A flap of skin, the epiglottis, keeps the food from entering the trachea. Muscle contractions, called **peristalsis,** squeeze food through the esophagus to the stomach.

3. Chemical and mechanical digestion take place in the **stomach.** Glands in the stomach lining make hydrochloric acid and the enzyme pepsin. The hydrochloric acid and pepsin start the chemical digestion of protein. Stomach muscles contract to churn and mix the stomach contents. This mechanical digestion forms a liquid mixture.

4. Most chemical digestion and absorption of food occurs in the **small intestine.** Enzymes from the **pancreas** help digest starch, protein, and fat. A liquid called bile from the **liver** dissolves and breaks up fat droplets. Several enzymes help break down carbohydrates and proteins. Tiny fingerlike projections called **villi** (singular: villus) increase the surface area of the small intestine. Cells at the small intestine's surface absorb nutrients.

5. The **large intestine** removes water from the undigested material. The remaining waste passes out of the body.

Peptic ulcers, diarrhea, and constipation are digestive system disorders. Bacteria cause most peptic ulcers. Diarrhea occurs when too little water is removed from waste in the large intestine. Constipation occurs when too much water is removed.

38–3 The Excretory System

During metabolism, cells make wastes such as carbon dioxide and urea. Excretion is the process in which the body eliminates wastes. The main organs of excretion are the **kidneys. The kidneys play an important role in maintaining homeostasis. They remove waste products from blood, maintain blood pH, and control the water content of blood.**

Two **kidneys** are located in the lower back. Blood containing wastes enters the kidneys. The kidneys remove urea, excess water, and other substances from the blood. This cleaned blood returns to circulation. The wastes are excreted. The wastes are removed and passed to the ureter.

The basic unit of function in a kidney is the **nephron.** Each nephron is a small self-sufficient processing unit. **As blood enters a nephron, impurities are filtered out and emptied into the collecting duct.** The purified blood exits the nephron through the venule. The processes of filtration and reabsorption take place in the nephrons.

- <u>Filtration</u> removes wastes from the blood. It occurs in a part of the nephron called the glomerulus. The **glomerulus** is enclosed within a structure called **Bowman's capsule.**
- <u>Reabsorption</u> returns some of the filtered materials back to the blood. These materials include nutrients and water.

Fluid that remains in the kidneys is called urine. Urine contains urea, excess salts, and other substances. After some water is removed the urine leaves each kidney through a tube called the **ureter.** The ureters carry urine to the urinary bladder, where urine is stored. Urine leaves the body through a tube called the **urethra.**

The kidney's activity is controlled by hormones and by the composition of blood. Drinking excess water increases the amount of water in the blood. This causes the kidneys to decrease the amount of water they reabsorb and return to the blood. Similarly, salty foods result in excess salt in the blood. To keep the composition of blood the same, the kidneys excrete the excess salt in urine.

A person can live with only one kidney. If both kidneys fail, the person must receive a kidney transplant or undergo dialysis. Dialysis purifies the blood by passing it through a filtering machine.

Nutrients

Carbohydrates, fats, proteins, vitamins, minerals, and water are all nutrients that are important to body functions. Each serves a different function in the body.

Use the words below to complete the table. The first one has been done for you.

carbohydrates	minerals	vitamins
fats	proteins	

Nutrient	Function in Body
water	essential for many body processes; makes up the bulk of blood, lymph, and other fluids; helps with temperature regulation
	main energy source for the body; some help food and wastes move through digestive system
	material for producing membranes and hormones; help the body absorb some vitamins; protect body organs; insulate the body; store energy
	raw materials for growth and repair; used for regulation and transport
	organic molecules that help regulate body processes
	inorganic nutrients used for making bones, teeth, and hemoglobin; essential in small amounts for other body processes

Use the table to answer the question.

1. Which nutrients are needed for growth and repair?

_____

MyPyramid

MyPyramid is a guide to healthful eating. It divides food into six groups. It also suggests how many servings from each group make up a healthful diet.

MyPyramid.gov
STEPS TO A HEALTHIER YOU

Use what you know as well as the information in MyPyramid to write the letter of the description that best matches the food group.

Description   Food Group

_____ **1.** This group contains calcium-rich foods.   **a.** vegetables
Calcium is needed for bone density and   **b.** fruits
helps maintain normal blood pressure.   **c.** milk

_____ **2.** This group provides the best source of   **d.** meat and
protein but also contains fat.   beans

_____ **3.** This group contains a wide variety of
vegetables and minerals that can reduce
the risk of heart disease and cancer.

_____ **4.** This group contains a variety of nutrients,
including vitamin C.

The Digestive System

When you eat food, digestion begins in your mouth. Food then travels through the digestive tract. Other organs, such as the liver and salivary glands, produce secretions that help with digestion but are not part of the digestive tract.

Use the words below to label the diagram.

esophagus	mouth	stomach
large intestine	small intestine	

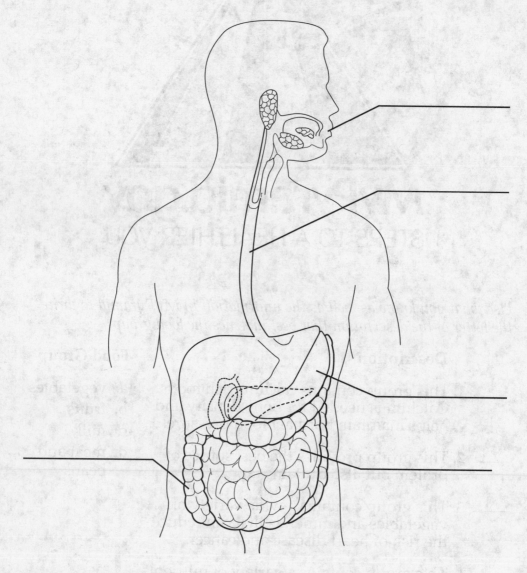

Use the diagram to answer the questions.

1. Through which organ does food pass first? Circle the correct answer.

esophagus   stomach

The Small Intestine

The inner surface of the small intestine is covered with circular folds. The folds are covered with fingerlike projections called villi (singular villus). Each villus holds blood and lymph vessels that absorb nutrients and carry them to the body.

Use the words below to label the diagram.

capillaries	lymph vessel	villi

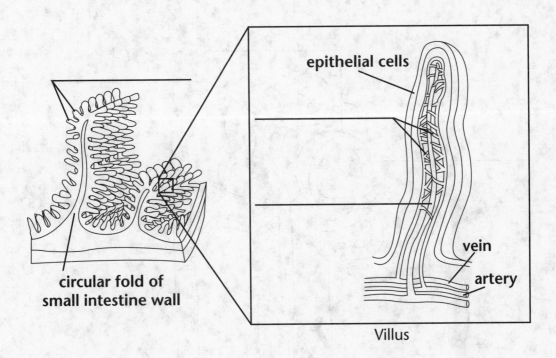

circular fold of
small intestine wall

epithelial cells

vein

artery

Villus

Use the diagram to answer the questions.

1. Where do nutrients enter the bloodstream?

_____

_____

2. How is the surface of the small intestine wall adapted for its function?

_____

_____

_____

Structure of the Nephron

Nephrons are structures within the kidneys that filter wastes out of blood. Most of the filtration occurs in the glomerulus, a network of capillaries inside a structure called Bowman's capsule. Some of the material filtered out is reabsorbed into the blood.

Use the words below to label the diagram.

Bowman's capsule	collecting duct	loop of Henle
capillaries	glomerulus	

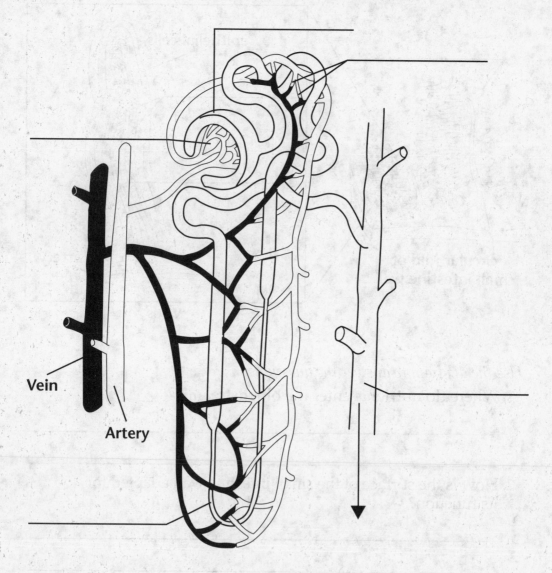

Vein

Artery

Answer the question. Circle the correct answer.

1. Which of the following is reabsorbed into the bloodstream?

water   urine

Chapter 38   Digestive and Excretory Systems

Vocabulary Review

Completion   *Use the words below to fill in the blanks with terms from the chapter.*

minerals	kidneys	stomach
small intestine	large intestine	

1. In the body, most chemical digestion takes place in the

   _____.

2. Food from the esophagus empties into a large muscular sac

   called the _____.

3. _____ are inorganic nutrients that the body needs.

4. The primary job of the _____ is to remove
   water from undigested material before it is excreted by
   the body.

5. The _____ are the organs that remove waste
   materials from the blood.

Completion   *Use the words below to fill in the blanks with terms from the chapter.*

filtration	nephrons
urethra	peristalsis

6. The removal of water, urea, salts, and amino acids from the

   blood involves the process of _____.

7. Urine is released from the body through the

   _____.

8. _____ are the small, functional units of
   the kidneys.

9. Food is moved through the esophagus by the process

   of_____.

Summary

38–1 Food and Nutrition

Cells use the chemical energy stored in food to meet their energy needs. The amount of energy in food is measured in calories. Scientists refer to the energy stored in food as dietary Calories with a capital C. The number of Calories you need each day depends on your size and level of activity.

Nutrients are substances in food that supply the energy and raw materials the body uses for growth, repair, and maintenance. Nutrients include water, carbohydrates, fats, proteins, vitamins, and minerals.

Every cell in the human body needs water, because many of the body's processes take place in water. Simple and complex carbohydrates are the main source of energy for the body. Carbohydrates include sugars, starches, and fiber. Fats are formed from fatty acids. The body needs fatty acids to make cell membranes and certain hormones. Deposits of fat protect body organs and insulate the body. Proteins are formed from amino acids. Proteins supply raw materials for growth and repair of the body. In addition, many hormones are proteins. Vitamins are organic molecules that help regulate body processes. They include water-soluble vitamins and fat-soluble vitamins. A diet lacking certain vitamins can have serious consequences. Minerals are inorganic nutrients that the body needs, usually in small amounts. Examples of minerals are calcium and iron.

The new food pyramid—MyPyramid—classifies foods into six categories: grains; vegetables; fruits; milk; meat and beans; and fats, sugar, and salts. The pyramid can be used to illustrate the main characteristics of a balanced diet. Each color in the pyramid represents a different food category. Grains, especially whole grains, should make up the largest part of your diet, while fats, sugar, and salts should be used sparingly. In addition to a balanced diet, you should try to get at least 30 minutes of exercise each day.

38–2 The Process of Digestion

The function of the digestive system is to break down food into simpler molecules that can be absorbed and used by the cells. The human digestive system is a one-way tube that includes the mouth, pharynx, esophagus, stomach, small intestine, and large intestine. Other structures—including the salivary glands, pancreas, and liver—add secretions to the digestive system.

Digestion starts in the mouth. The teeth tear and crush food. This begins the process of mechanical digestion. Mechanical digestion is the physical breakdown of large pieces of food into smaller pieces. Salivary glands in the mouth secrete saliva, which contains the enzyme amylase. Amylase breaks down starches into sugars. This begins the process of chemical digestion. Chemical digestion is the breakdown of large food molecules into smaller molecules.

The chewed clump of food that is swallowed is called a bolus. It passes through the pharynx and into the esophagus. The esophagus is a tube that connects the throat with the stomach. Muscle contractions, called peristalsis, squeeze the food through the esophagus.

Food from the esophagus empties into the stomach. The stomach is a large muscular sac. Both chemical and mechanical digestion take place in the stomach. Glands in the lining of the stomach produce an acid and the enzyme pepsin. The acid and pepsin work together to begin the chemical digestion of protein. Stomach muscles also contract to churn and mix the stomach contents. This mechanical digestion produces a liquid mixture called chyme.

From the stomach, chyme passes into the small intestine. Most of the chemical digestion and absorption of food occurs in the small intestine. Enzymes from the pancreas help digest starch, protein, and fat. A liquid called bile from the liver dissolves and breaks up fat droplets. The lining of the small intestine also produces several enzymes that help break down carbohydrates and proteins. Nutrients are absorbed by cells lining the surface of the small intestine.

The surface area is greatly increased by tiny fingerlike projections called villi (singular: villus). By the time chyme reaches the end of the small intestine, virtually all the nutrients have been absorbed.

Chyme next enters the large intestine. The primary function of the large intestine is to remove water from the undigested material. After most of the water has been removed, the remaining waste passes out of the body.

Digestive system disorders include peptic ulcers, diarrhea, and constipation. Peptic ulcers are caused by bacteria. Diarrhea occurs when too little water is removed from waste in the large intestine. Constipation occurs when too much water is removed.

38–3 The Excretory System

During normal metabolism, cells produce wastes such as carbon dioxide and urea. Excretion is the process by which the body eliminates these wastes. The main organs of excretion are the kidneys. The kidneys play an important role in homeostasis. They remove waste products from blood, maintain blood pH, and control water content of blood.

The two kidneys are located in the lower back. Blood containing wastes enters the kidneys. The kidneys remove urea, excess water, and other substances from the blood. Some of the substances are later returned to the blood. The wastes are excreted. The purified blood leaves the kidneys and returns to circulation. The basic unit of function of a kidney is the nephron. Each nephron is a small independent processing unit.

Blood goes through two separate processes in a nephron: filtration and reabsorption. Filtration removes wastes from the blood. It occurs in a structure of the nephron known as the glomerulus. The glomerulus is enclosed within another structure called Bowman's capsule. Reabsorption returns some of the filtered materials back to the blood. These materials include food molecules and water.

The fluid that remains is called urine. Urine contains urea, excess salts, and other substances. Some of the water is removed from the urine in a structure called the loop of Henle. A tube called the ureter leaves each kidney and carries urine to the urinary bladder. The urinary bladder is a saclike organ that stores urine until it can be released from the body. Urine passes from the body through a tube called the urethra.

The kidneys are controlled by hormones and by the composition of the blood. If the blood becomes too concentrated, the kidneys return more water to the blood. If the blood becomes too diluted, the kidneys return less water to the blood.

A person can survive with only one kidney. If both kidneys fail, the person must receive a kidney transplant or undergo dialysis in order to survive. Dialysis purifies the blood by passing it through a filtering machine.

Chapter 38 Digestive and Excretory Systems

Section 38–1 Food and Nutrition (pages 971–977)

🔑 **Key Concepts**

- What are the nutrients your body needs?
- Why is water such an important nutrient?

Food and Energy (page 971)

1. Cells convert the chemical energy in glucose and other molecules into
   _____.

2. The energy stored in food is measured in units called _____.

3. Is the following sentence true or false? Your body can extract energy from almost any
   type of food. _____

4. Besides supplying fuel, what are other important functions of food? _____
   _____
   _____
   _____
   _____

5. What is the study of nutrition? _____
   _____
   _____
   _____

Nutrients (pages 972–975)

6. Substances in food that supply the energy and raw materials your body uses for
   growth, repair, and maintenance are called _____.

7. List the six nutrients that the body needs.

   a. _____   d. _____

   b. _____   e. _____

   c. _____   f. _____

8. Circle the letter of each sentence that is true about water as a nutrient.

   a. Water is the most important of all nutrients.

   b. Every cell in the human body needs water.

   c. Many of the body's processes take place in water.

   d. Water makes up the bulk of bodily fluids, including blood.

9. How is water lost from the body? _____

_____

10. If enough water is not taken in to replace what is lost, _____
can result.

11. Complete the concept map.

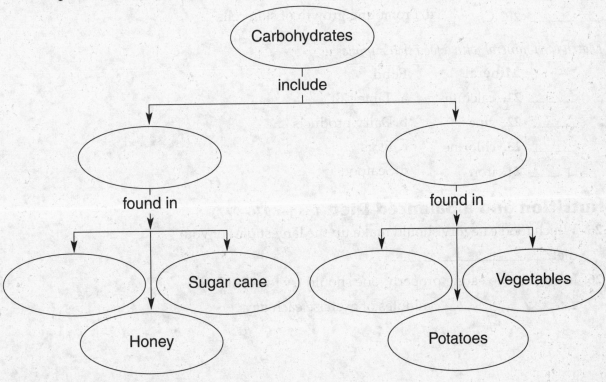

12. Why do you need fiber in your diet? _____

_____

13. Circle the letter of each choice that is a function of fat.

   a. Protecting body organs   **c.** Storing energy

   b. Insulating the body   **d.** Transporting oxygen

14. List four increased health risks associated with a diet high in fat.

   a. _____   **c.** _____

   b. _____   **d.** _____

15. Circle the letter of each choice that is a function of protein.

   a. Supplying raw materials for growth and repair

   b. Making up enzymes

   c. Helping the body absorb certain vitamins

   d. Producing cell membranes

16. The eight amino acids that the body is unable to produce are called

   _____ amino acids.

Match each vitamin with its function.

	Vitamin	Function
_____	**17.** A	**a.** Preventing cellular damage
_____	**18.** D	**b.** Promoting bone growth
_____	**19.** E	**c.** Repairing tissues and healing wounds
_____	**20.** C	**d.** Promoting growth of skin cells

Match each mineral with a food that supplies it.

	Mineral	Food
_____	**21.** calcium	**a.** Table salt
_____	**22.** zinc	**b.** Dairy products
_____	**23.** chlorine	**c.** Eggs
_____	**24.** iron	**d.** Seafood

Nutrition and a Balanced Diet (pages 976–977)

25. Which food category should make up the largest part of your diet? _____

26. In addition to eating properly, one should try to get at least _____ minutes of exercise each day.

Section 38–2 The Process of Digestion
(pages 978–984)

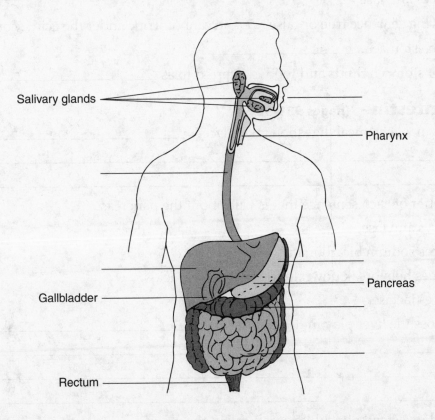 **Key Concepts**
- What are the organs of the digestive system?
- What is the function of the digestive system?

Introduction (page 978)

1. What is the function of the organs of the digestive system? _____

_____

_____

_____

The Mouth (pages 978–979)

2. The physical breakdown of large pieces of food into smaller pieces is referred to as

   _____ digestion.

3. The breakdown of large food molecules into smaller molecules that can be absorbed

   into the bloodstream is called _____ digestion.

4. Label the drawing of the digestive system with the following structures: mouth, esophagus, stomach, liver, small intestine, and large intestine.

Salivary glands

Pharynx

Gallbladder

Pancreas

Rectum

5. What is the role of teeth in digestion? _____

_____

_____

_____

The Esophagus (page 980)

Match each term with its definition.

	Term	Definition
_____	**6.** bolus	**a.** Contractions of smooth muscle that aid in swallowing
_____	**7.** esophagus	**b.** Clump of chewed food
_____	**8.** peristalsis	**c.** Food tube connecting the mouth and stomach

9. Is the following sentence true or false? The pyloric valve prevents the contents of the stomach from moving back up into the esophagus. _____

The Stomach (pages 980–981)

10. Circle the letter of each sentence that is true about the stomach.

    a. It produces hydrochloric acid.

    b. It produces trypsin.

    c. It helps in the mechanical digestion of food.

    d. It produces amylase.

11. Is the following sentence true or false? Pepsin cannot work under the acidic conditions present in the stomach. _____

12. A mixture of stomach fluids and food is referred to as _____.

The Small Intestine (pages 981–982)

13. Where does most chemical digestion take place? _____

_____

_____

14. Circle the letter of each sentence that is true about the pancreas.

    a. It produces amylase.

    b. It produces sodium bicarbonate.

    c. Its enzymes help break down lipids and nucleic acids.

    d. It produces lactase.

15. What role does the liver play in digestion? _____

_____

_____

_____

16. Bile is stored in a small pouchlike organ called the _____.

Use the table to answer the questions.

Digestive Enzymes			
Enzyme	**Site of Action**	**Site of Production**	**Nutrient Digested**
Amylase	Mouth	Salivary glands	Carbohydrate
Pepsin	Stomach	Lining of stomach	Protein
Lipase	Small intestine	Pancreas	Fat
Amylase	Small intestine	Pancreas	Carbohydrate
Trypsin	Small intestine	Pancreas	Protein
Lactase	Small intestine	Lining of small intestine	Carbohydrate
Maltase	Small intestine	Lining of small intestine	Carbohydrate
Sucrase	Small intestine	Lining of small intestine	Carbohydrate
Peptidase	Small intestine	Lining of small intestine	Protein

17. Where are the majority of digestive enzymes active? _____
_____

18. Which organ or gland produces the greatest number of different digestive enzymes?
_____

19. Which digestive enzyme has more than one site of action and production? _____
_____

20. Which digestive enzymes are active at a site different from the site where they are
produced? _____

21. Which nutrient is digested by more enyzmes than any other nutrient? _____
_____

Absorption in the Small Intestine (pages 982–983)

22. Name the two parts of the small intestine where nutrients are absorbed.

   a. _____

   b. _____

23. Projections that cover the folds of the small intestine are called _____.

24. Is the following sentence true or false? Molecules of undigested fat and some fatty
acids are absorbed by lymph vessels called lacteals. _____

25. Is the following sentence true or false? The appendix plays an important role in human
digestion. _____

The Large Intestine (page 984)

26. What is the primary job of the large intestine? _____
_____
_____

Digestive System Disorders (page 984)

27. A hole in the stomach wall is known as a(an) _____.

28. When something happens that interferes with the removal of water by the large intestine, a condition known as _____ results.

Reading Skill Practice

When you read about a complex process, representing the process with a flowchart can help you better understand and remember it. Make a flowchart to show how food travels through the digestive system and is broken down into simpler molecules that the body can use. For more information on flowcharts, see Appendix A of your textbook. Do your work on a separate sheet of paper.

Section 38–3 The Excretory System (pages 985–989)

⊂▬ Key Concepts
- What are the functions of the kidneys?
- How is blood filtered?

Functions of the Excretory System (page 985)

1. The process by which metabolic wastes are eliminated is called _____.

2. List four organs that are used for excretion.

   a. _____   c. _____

   b. _____   d. _____

3. List three ways that the kidneys help maintain homeostasis.

   a. _____

   b. _____

   c. _____

The Kidneys (pages 986–988)

4. Circle the letter of each sentence that is true about the kidneys.

   a. They are the main organs of the excretory system.

   b. They are located on either side of the spinal column.

   c. They remove excess water and waste products from the urine.

   d. They receive blood through the renal vein.

Match each term with its definition.

Term	Definition
_____ 5. ureter	a. Saclike organ where urine is stored
_____ 6. urinary bladder	b. Functional unit of the kidney
_____ 7. renal medulla	c. Outer part of the kidney
_____ 8. renal cortex	d. Tube that carries urine from the kidney to the urinary bladder
_____ 9. nephron	e. Inner part of the kidney

10. Is the following sentence true or false? Nephrons are located in the renal medulla.

    _____

11. What ends up in the collecting duct? _____

    _____

12. List the two processes involved in blood purification.

    a. _____   b. _____

13. The small network of capillaries in the upper end of the nephron is referred to as the

    _____.

14. The glomerulus is enclosed by a cup-shaped structure called the _____.

15. Complete the Venn diagram.

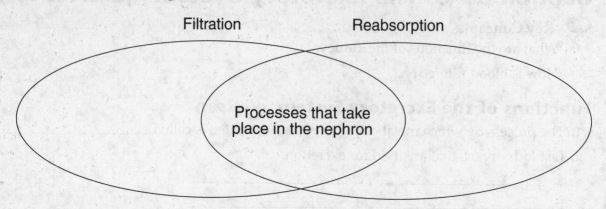

Filtration   Reabsorption

Processes that take place in the nephron

16. The materials that are filtered from the blood are collectively called the

_____.

17. List six materials that are filtered from blood.

a. _____   c. _____   e. _____

b. _____   d. _____   f. _____

18. Which substances are removed from the filtrate and reabsorbed by the capillaries?

_____

_____

19. What happens during the process of secretion? _____

_____

_____

20. Circle the letter of each sentence that is true about urine.

a. It is the material that remains after reabsorption.

b. It contains only urea and water.

c. It is concentrated in the loop of Henle.

d. It is released from the body through the urethra.

Control of Kidney Function (page 988)

21. How are the activities of the kidneys controlled? _____

_____

_____

22. Is the following sentence true or false? As the amount of water in the blood increases, the rate of water reabsorption in the kidneys increases. _____

Homeostasis by Machine (pages 988–989)

23. Is the following sentence true or false? Humans cannot survive with only one kidney.

_____

24. The removal of wastes from blood using a machine is called _____.

Vocabulary Review

Completion   *Fill in the blanks with terms from Chapter 38.*

1. The main source of energy for the body comes from _____.

2. Nutrients that are formed from fatty acids and glycerol are _____.

3. _____ are needed for growth and repair of structures such as skin and muscle.

4. Saliva contains the enzyme _____ that breaks the chemical bonds in starches.

5. The contractions that push food through the esophagus into the stomach are called _____.

6. Organic molecules that help regulate body processes are called _____.

7. The tube that connects the throat with the stomach is the _____.

8. The organ that produces bile is the _____.

9. The mixture of partly digested food that leaves the stomach is called _____.

10. The lining of the small intestine is covered with fingerlike projections called _____.

11. The primary organ of excretion is the _____.

12. The functional units of the kidney are called _____.

13. The process of filtration takes place in a structure called the _____.

14. The saclike organ that stores urine is the _____.

15. Urine leaves the body through a tube called the _____.

16. The cuplike structure that encases the glomerulus is called _____.

17. Urea is primarily concentrated in the _____.

Chapter 38 Digestive and Excretory Systems   **Section Review 38-1**

Reviewing Key Concepts

Matching *On the line provided, match the letter of the nutrient with the description of its function in the human body.*

   a. water
   b. carbohydrates
   c. fats
   d. proteins
   e. vitamins
   f. minerals

_____ **1.** provide the body with building materials for growth and repair

_____ **2.** needed to build cell membranes, produce certain hormones, and store energy

_____ **3.** major source of energy for the body

_____ **4.** most important of all nutrients, makes up the bulk of most bodily fluids

_____ **5.** inorganic nutrients

_____ **6.** organic molecules needed by the body to help regulate body processes

Short Answer *On the lines provided, answer the following questions.*

7. Why do all the cells in your body need water?

_____

_____

8. What problems may result from dehydration of the body?

_____

_____

Reviewing Key Skills

9. Applying Concepts Why can your body store fat-soluble vitamins but not water-soluble vitamins?

_____

_____

10. Applying Concepts If you eat according to the food pyramid, what food group should make up the largest percentage of your diet?

_____

_____

_____

Chapter 38 Digestive and Excretory Systems   Section Review 38-2

Reviewing Key Concepts

Labeling Diagrams *On the lines provided, label the organs of the digestive system that correspond to the numbers on the diagram. Use the following terms:* pancreas, gallbladder, large intestine, rectum, salivary glands, small intestine, stomach, mouth, esophagus, liver, *and* pharynx.

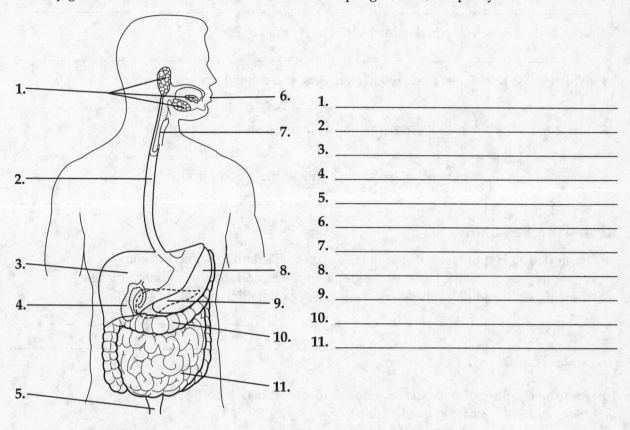

1. _____
2. _____
3. _____
4. _____
5. _____
6. _____
7. _____
8. _____
9. _____
10. _____
11. _____

Short Answer *On the lines provided, answer the following questions.*

12. What is chemical digestion?

_____

13. What is mechanical digestion, and where does it take place?

_____

Reviewing Key Skills

14. **Comparing and Contrasting** How is digestion different in the small and the large intestine?

_____

_____

15. **Posing Questions** Hydrochloric acid and pepsin break down proteins in the stomach. The tissues of the stomach are made of proteins. What question might these facts make you ask?

_____

Chapter 38 Digestive and Excretory Systems   Section Review 38-3

Reviewing Key Concepts

Short Answer *On the lines provided, answer the following questions.*

1. Which organ of the excretory system filters urea, toxins, and wastes from blood?

   _____

2. Your body releases carbon dioxide from which organ of excretion?

   _____

3. Which organ uses sweat to excrete water, salts, and a small amount of urea?

   _____

4. List three ways in which kidneys maintain homeostasis in the body.

   _____

5. What are two ways in which the activity of the kidneys is controlled?

   _____

Reviewing Key Skills

6. **Formulating Hypotheses** Water, urea, glucose, salts, amino acids, and some vitamins pass out of the blood, through membranes, and into the kidneys. Plasma proteins, cells, and platelets do not. Suggest an explanation for this observation.

   _____

   _____

Interpreting Graphics *For questions 7 through 10, use the diagram of a nephron to answer the following questions.*

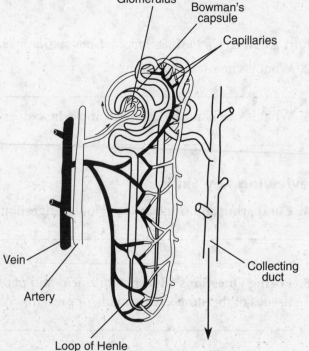

Glomerulus

Bowman's capsule

Capillaries

Vein

Artery

Collecting duct

Loop of Henle

7. Where does the process of filtration take place?

   _____

8. What substances are filtered out of the blood in the glomerulus?

   _____

   _____

9. What happens to the filtrate as it flows through the loop of Henle?

   _____

   _____

10. What is the material called that empties into the collecting duct?

    _____

    _____

Name_____ Class_____ Date _____

Matching *On the line provided, write the letter of the description that matches each term or structure.*

_____ 1. Calorie

_____ 2. proteins

_____ 3. vitamins

_____ 4. amylase

_____ 5. peristalsis

_____ 6. peptic ulcer

_____ 7. chyme

_____ 8. nephron

_____ 9. Bowman's capsule

_____ 10. loop of Henle

a. hole in the stomach wall caused by bacteria

b. functional unit of the kidney

c. mixture of partly digested food and stomach fluids

d. section of a nephron that conserves water and minimizes the volume of urine

e. enzyme contained in saliva

f. organic molecules that are needed by the body to help regulate body processes

g. unit equal to 1000 calories of heat energy, or 1 kilocalorie

h. contractions that squeeze food through the esophagus into the stomach

i. cup-shaped structure found in the upper end of a nephron

j. nutrients that provide the body with the building materials it needs for growth and repair

Labeling Diagrams *On the lines provided, label the parts of the digestive system that correspond with the numbers in the diagram.*

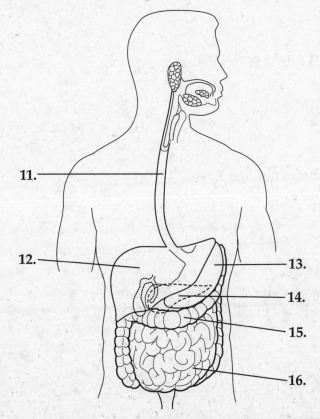

11. _____

12. _____

13. _____

14. _____

15. _____

16. _____

Multiple Choice *On the line provided, write the letter of the answer that best completes the sentence or answers the question.*

_____ **17.** Sugars and starches are the two kinds of
   a. fats.
   b. proteins.
   c. carbohydrates.
   d. minerals.

_____ **18.** What nutrients are made up of fatty acids and glycerol?
   a. carbohydrates
   b. proteins
   c. fats
   d. minerals

_____ **19.** Inorganic nutrients that the body usually needs in small amounts are called
   a. minerals.
   b. proteins.
   c. vitamins.
   d. fats.

_____ **20.** The small intestine is covered with projections called
   a. villi.
   b. nephrons.
   c. chyme.
   d. peristalsis.

_____ **21.** The main organs of the excretory system are the
   a. lungs.
   b. kidneys.
   c. small intestines.
   d. large intestines.

_____ **22.** Each kidney is connected to the urinary bladder by a(an)
   a. urethra.
   b. renal artery.
   c. villus.
   d. ureter.

_____ **23.** The saclike organ where liquid wastes are stored before excretion is the
   a. urethra.
   b. urinary bladder.
   c. ureter.
   d. loop of Henle.

_____ **24.** As blood enters a nephron, it flows through a network of capillaries known as a
   a. loop of Henle.
   b. Bowman's capsule.
   c. villus.
   d. glomerulus.

_____ **25.** The process by which the kidneys remove water, urea, glucose, salts and amino acids from the blood is called
   a. excretion.
   b. reabsorption.
   c. filtration.
   d. absorption.

Chapter 38 Digestive and Excretory Systems   Enrichment

Ulcers

An ulcer is a pit or hole in a skin surface or mucus membrane. Ulcers result from erosion of tissues. There are two types of digestive system ulcers: stress ulcers and peptic ulcers. Peptic ulcers are quite common. It is estimated that between 1 and 20 percent of the population in developed countries have peptic ulcers. Stress ulcers are much less common.

Peptic ulcers usually occur in the duodenum. They can also occur in the stomach. When the defenses of the mucosal layer are not equal to the assault by acid or digestive enzymes, gastric juices may start to digest the wall of the digestive tract, causing an ulcer. Peptic ulcers are often chronic (prolonged or lingering). Researchers do not fully understand what factors lead to the imbalance that causes ulcers. However, they now think most peptic ulcers are caused by infection of the stomach lining by a bacterium called *Helicobacter pylori*. Peptic ulcers may be worsened by certain drugs, aspirin, smoking, and alcohol.

Stress ulcers differ from peptic ulcers. They usually occur in the stomach and are shallow, bleeding erosions. Stress ulcers may heal rapidly, but sometimes they perforate and cause serious bleeding. Despite their name, stress ulcers are associated with physical rather than psychological stress. Patients with stress ulcers have also had physical injuries, such as burns, trauma, or major surgery.

Peptic ulcer symptoms include pain, usually several hours after a meal. Stress ulcers are less painful than peptic ulcers, unless they become perforated. Both types are usually treated with medication. The use of antibiotics to treat peptic ulcers is usually successful. Stress ulcers may be treated with drug therapy to neutralize stomach acids and help regulate gastric secretions. When drug therapy is not effective, surgery may be necessary.

Evaluation *On the lines provided, answer the following questions.*

1. What is the difference between stress ulcers and peptic ulcers? How are they similar?

_____

_____

_____

_____

_____

2. Can you get ulcers from worrying about an exam? If so, what kind?

_____

_____

_____

_____

_____

Chapter 38 Digestive and Excretory Systems   Graphic Organizer

Concept Map

Using information from the chapter, complete the concept map below. If there is not enough room in the concept map to write your answers, write them on a separate sheet of paper.

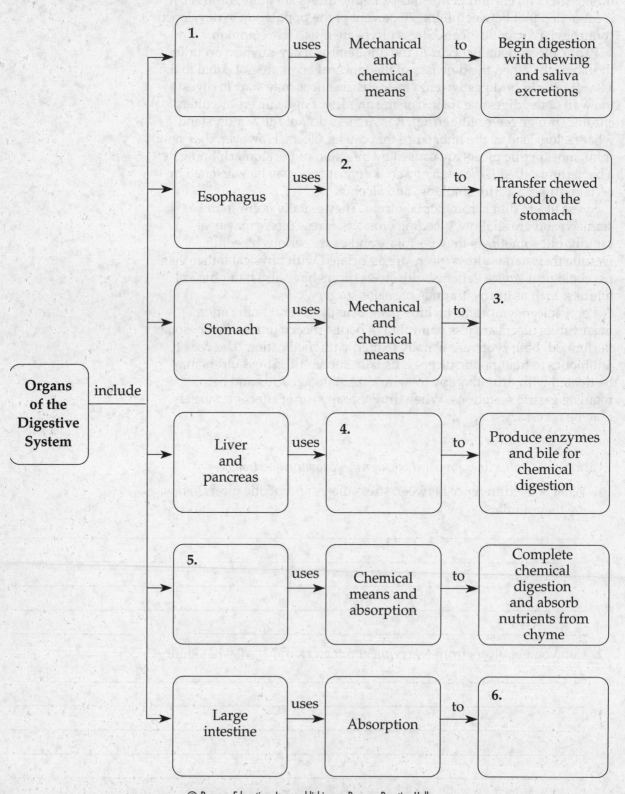

Chapter 38 Digestive and Excretory Systems   Chapter Test A

Multiple Choice
Write the letter that best answers the question or completes the statement on the line provided.

____ 1. The energy available in foods can be measured by
   a. first determining which nutrients the body needs.
   b. burning the foods.
   c. tracing chemical pathways.
   d. all of the above

____ 2. Inorganic molecules that perform vital functions in the body are called
   a. lipids.   c. vitamins.
   b. proteins.   d. minerals.

____ 3. The American Heart Association recommends a diet with a maximum of
   a. 40 percent of Calories from fat, of which only 20 percent should be from unsaturated fats.
   b. 30 percent of Calories from saturated fat, in addition to 10 percent from unsaturated fats.
   c. 50 percent of Calories from saturated fats.
   d. 30 percent of Calories from fat, of which only 10 percent should be from saturated fats.

____ 4. What is the minimum amount of water you should drink every day?
   a. 0.5 liter   c. 2 liters
   b. 1 liter   d. 3 liters

____ 5. Water is lost from the body by each of the following EXCEPT
   a. sweating.   c. respiration.
   b. urinating.   d. digestion.

____ 6. Which of the following statements is incorrect?
   a. Sweating is more likely to occur on hot days than on cool days.
   b. Sweating is likely to occur after strenuous exercise.
   c. Evaporation of sweat warms the body.
   d. Excessive sweating can lead to dehydration.

____ 7. According to the new food pyramid, the majority of food in your diet should be from the
   a. Fruit Group.
   b. Grains Group.
   c. Vegetable Group.
   d. Milk Group.

_____ 8. What is one of the roles of the pancreas in nutrition?
   a. absorbs nutrients   c. dissolves food
   b. churns food   d. neutralizes acids

_____ 9. Where does the process of chemical digestion begin?
   a. stomach   c. small intestine
   b. esophagus   d. mouth

_____10. Through which structure do wastes pass into the rectum?
   a. duodenum   c. small intestine
   b. large intestine   d. villus

_____11. Water is extracted from digested food in the body primarily
        by the
   a. bladder.   c. large intestine.
   b. gallbladder.   d. pancreas.

_____12. The function of the excretory system is to help maintain
        homeostasis by
   a. breaking down nutrients.
   b. removing wastes.
   c. absorbing nutrients.
   d. preventing infection.

_____13. Which of the following is NOT part of a nephron?
   a. urethra   c. glomerulus
   b. renal vein   d. Bowman's capsule

_____14. What percentage of the filtrate's water that enters Bowman's
        capsule is reabsorbed into the blood?
   a. 100 percent   c. 50 percent
   b. almost 99 percent   d. less than 25 percent

_____15. What materials are removed from the blood through dialysis?
   a. urea and excess salts   c. amylase and pepsin
   b. chyme   d. none of the above

Completion

Complete each statement on the line provided.

16. Calcium, iron, and magnesium are all examples of the group of nutrients called
   _____ .

17. Most of the blood, lymph, and other bodily fluids consist of _____ .

18. The teeth are extremely important in _____ digestion.

19. Gastric glands produce mucus, hydrochloric acid, and the enzyme
   _____ .

20. To a large extent, the activity of the kidneys is controlled by the composition of
   _____ .

Name_____ Class_____ Date _____

Short Answer

In complete sentences, write the answers to the questions on the lines provided.

21. Name two functions of fats.

_____
_____
_____
_____

22. How does a calorie differ from a Calorie?

_____
_____
_____
_____
_____

23. What is the Food Pyramid?

_____
_____
_____
_____
_____

24. What is the function of the ureter?

_____
_____
_____
_____
_____
_____

25. What is the function of the urinary bladder?

_____
_____
_____
_____
_____
_____

Using Science Skills

Use the diagram below to answer the following questions on the lines provided.

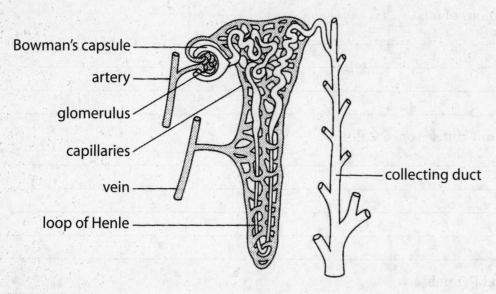

Bowman's capsule

artery

glomerulus

capillaries

vein

loop of Henle

collecting duct

Figure 1

26. **Interpreting Graphics** What is the function of the loop of Henle?

_____

27. **Interpreting Graphics** In Figure 1, in which structure are useful substances reabsorbed into the blood?

_____

28. **Drawing Conclusions** What is the purpose of the collecting duct?

_____

_____

_____

_____

29. **Comparing and Contrasting** What two processes take place in the structures illustrated in Figure 1?

_____

_____

30. **Inferring** In what organ are the structures illustrated in Figure 1 located?

_____

_____

Essay

Write the answer to each question in the space provided.

31. How does the body lose water?

32. Discuss the functions of the following structures of the excretory system: kidneys, ureter, urinary bladder, and urethra.

33. What organs and major accessory structures make up the digestive system?

34. How do the kidneys respond to an increased intake of water? Of salt?

35. Describe the process of dialysis.

Multiple Choice

Write the letter that best answers the question or completes the statement on the line provided.

____ 1. The energy to perform actions, as well as the materials from which body cells and tissues are made, comes from

    a. cellulose.

    b. oxygen.

    c. food.

____ 2. A calorie is the amount of energy needed to

    a. raise the temperature of the body by 1° Celsius.

    b. raise the temperature of 1 g of fat by 1° Celsius.

    c. raise the temperature of 1 g of water by 1° Celsius.

____ 3. Substances that are needed by the body for growth, repair, and maintenance are called

    a. enzymes.

    b. nutrients.

    c. ATP.

____ 4. The raw materials that the body needs for growth and repair come from

    a. proteins.

    b. unsaturated fats.

    c. carbohydrates.

____ 5. Proteins are made of polymers called

    a. lipids.

    b. unsaturated fats.

    c. amino acids.

____ 6. Which of the following structures is made up mostly of water?

    a. blood

    b. lymph

    c. both a and b

____ 7. How many food groups make up the new Food Pyramid?

    a. four

    b. five

    c. six

____ 8. What passage carries food between the pharynx and the stomach?

    a. small intestine

    b. epiglottis

    c. esophagus

_____ 9. What enzyme found in saliva breaks chemical bonds between
the sugar monomers in starches?
   a. amylase
   b. chyme
   c. pepsin

_____ 10. The stomach breaks down food into a soft, partially digested
mixture called
   a. pepsin.
   b. chyme.
   c. bolus.

_____ 11. In what structure do filtration and reabsorption occur?
   a. kidney
   b. renal vein
   c. urinary bladder

_____ 12. The main organs of the excretory system are the
   a. kidneys.
   b. lungs.
   c. intestines.

_____ 13. In the kidneys, both useful substances and wastes are
removed from the blood by
   a. reabsorption.
   b. filtration.
   c. dialysis.

_____ 14. The activity of the kidneys is controlled by hormones and by the
   a. volume of nutrients.
   b. volume of filtrate.
   c. composition of the blood.

_____ 15. Dialysis performs the function of the
   a. liver.
   b. ureter.
   c. kidneys.

Completion

Complete each statement on the line provided.

16. The science of _____ is the study of food and its effects on the body.

17. Contractions, known as _____ , squeeze food through the length of the esophagus into the stomach.

18. If a part of the stomach wall digests itself, a(an) _____ develops.

19. The functional units of the kidneys are the _____ .

20. The kidneys play an important role in maintaining _____ in the body.

Name_____ Class_____ Date _____

Short Answer

In complete sentences, write the answers to the questions on the lines provided.

21. List the six nutrients needed by the body.

_____

_____

_____

_____

22. How is chyme produced?

_____

_____

_____

_____

_____

23. What is the function of the digestive system?

_____

_____

_____

_____

_____

24. How do kidneys maintain homeostasis?

_____

_____

_____

_____

_____

25. What are a person's two options for survival if both of his or her kidneys are unable to function?

_____

_____

_____

_____

Using Science Skills

Use the diagram below to answer the following questions on the lines provided.

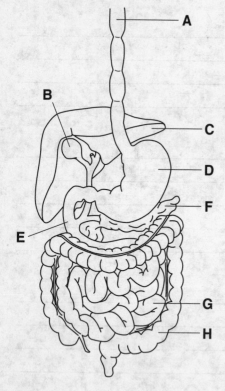

Figure 1

26. **Interpreting Graphics** Which structure shown in Figure 1 is the esophagus?

_____

27. **Interpreting Graphics** Which structure shown in Figure 1 is the stomach?

_____

28. **Interpreting Graphics** Which structure shown in Figure 1 produces bile? What is the name of this structure?

_____

29. **Interpreting Graphics** Hormones that regulate blood sugar are produced in which structure shown in Figure 1? What is the name of this structure?

_____

30. **Interpreting Graphics** Which structure shown in Figure 1 contains villi, which aid in absorbing nutrients? What is the name of this structure?

_____

LESSON PLAN 39–1 (pages 997–1002)

The Endocrine System

Time
2 periods
1 block

Section Objectives

- **39.1.1 State** the function of the endocrine system.
- **39.1.2 Describe** hormones and glands.
- **39.1.3 Explain** how the endocrine system maintains homeostasis.

Vocabulary hormone • target cell • exocrine gland • endocrine gland • prostaglandin

Local Standards

1 FOCUS

Reading Strategy
Have students study the figures and read the captions to preview the material in the section.

Targeted Resources
❑ Transparencies: **584** Section 39–1 Interest Grabber
❑ Transparencies: **585** Section 39–1 Outline

2 INSTRUCT

Build Science Skills: Using Analogies
Help students understand the endocrine system by comparing it with familiar human relationships in which one person directs the actions of others, such as a coach and team. **L1**

Use Visuals: Figure 39–2
Students locate each of the endocrine glands in Figure 39–2 and identify the hormones and roles of the glands. **L1**

Build Science Skills: Comparing and Contrasting
Work with the class to make a table comparing and contrasting steroid and nonsteroid hormone action. **L1 L2**

Demonstration
Students take part in a simple demonstration of positive and negative feedback and gain a better understanding of how feedback inhibition helps maintain homeostasis. **L1 L2**

Targeted Resources
❑ Reading and Study Workbook: Section 39–1
❑ Adapted Reading and Study Workbook: Section 39–1
❑ Teaching Resources: Section Summaries 39–1, Worksheets 39–1
❑ Transparencies: **586** Hormone Action, **587** Figure 39–2 The Endocrine Glands
❑ **NSTA** *sci*$_{LINKS}$ Endocrine system

3 ASSESS

Evaluate Understanding
Have some students compare steroid and nonsteroid hormones, and have other students name examples of each.

Reteach
Guide students in making two Venn diagrams, comparing and contrasting (1) exocrine and endocrine glands and (2) hormones and prostaglandins.

Targeted Resources
❑ Teaching Resources: Section Review 39–1
❑ *i*Text Section 39–1

LESSON PLAN 39–2 (pages 1003–1008)

Human Endocrine Glands

Time
2 periods
1 block

Section Objective

Local Standards

■ **39.2.1 Identify** the functions of the major endocrine glands.

Vocabulary pituitary gland • diabetes mellitus • ovary • testis

1 FOCUS

Vocabulary Preview
Before students read the section, have them preview new Vocabulary by skimming the section and making a list of the boldface Vocabulary words.

Targeted Resources
❏ Transparencies: **588** Section 39–2 Interest Grabber
❏ Transparencies: **589** Section 39–2 Outline
❏ Transparencies: **590** Concept Map

2 INSTRUCT

Use Visuals: Figure 39–6
Relate the close spatial relationship of the pituitary gland and hypothalamus, as shown in Figure 39–6, to the control of the pituitary by the hypothalamus. **L1 L2**

Build Science Skills: Applying Concepts
Students explain how stress could indirectly influence health through its effects on the hypothalamus. **L2**

Make Connections: Health Science
Describe the effects of inadequate dietary iodine on the health of adults and children. **L2**

Use Visuals: Figure 39–9
Students use Figure 39–9 to describe the relationship between the adrenal glands and kidneys. **L1 L2**

Demonstration
Students use glucose test strips and samples of colored water, some with and some without added sugar, to see how diabetes mellitus can be detected by testing urine for glucose. **L1 L2**

Address Misconceptions
Correct the misconception that testosterone is produced only by males and estrogen only by females. **L2**

Targeted Resources
❏ Reading and Study Workbook: Section 39–2
❏ Adapted Reading and Study Workbook: Section 39–2
❏ Teaching Resources: Section Summaries 39–2, Worksheets 39–2
❏ Transparencies: **591** Actions of Insulin and Glucagon
❏ Lab Worksheets: Chapter 39 Exploration
❏ **NSTA** *sci*LINKS Glands

3 ASSESS

Evaluate Understanding
Call on students to identify the hormones produced by each endocrine gland, and call on other students to describe the function of each hormone.

Reteach
Play a quiz game in which students on two teams take turns trying to identify hormones based on descriptions.

Targeted Resources
❏ Teaching Resources: Section Review 39–2
❏ *i*Text Section 39–2

LESSON PLAN 39–3 (pages 1009–1015)

The Reproductive System

Time
2 periods
1 block

Section Objectives

- **39.3.1 Describe** sexual development.
- **39.3.2 Explain** the functions of the male and female reproductive systems.
- **39.3.3 Identify** the four phases of the menstrual cycle.

Vocabulary puberty • scrotum • seminiferous tubule • epididymis • vas deferens • urethra • penis • follicle • ovulation • Fallopian tube • uterus • vagina • menstrual cycle • corpus luteum • menstruation • sexually transmitted disease

Local Standards

1 FOCUS

Vocabulary Preview
Challenge students to predict which of the Vocabulary words refer to the male reproductive system and which refer to the female reproductive system.

Targeted Resources
- ❏ Transparencies: **592** Section 39–3 Interest Grabber
- ❏ Transparencies: **593** Section 39–3 Outline

2 INSTRUCT

Make Connections: Environmental Science
Students predict the effect of estrogenlike compounds in the environment on the development of males. **L2**

Demonstration
Students view and sketch a prepared slide of a sperm cell. **L1 L2**

Make Connections: Mathematics
Students calculate the number of mature eggs a female produces in a lifetime and estimate the number of eggs that never mature. **L2 L3**

Build Science Skills: Using Models
Students create a diagram to model the feedback inhibition mechanisms that regulate the menstrual cycle. **L2**

Address Misconceptions
Correct the misconception that the average length of the menstrual cycle is the normal length by pointing out the variation that normally exists in the menstrual cycle. **L1 L2**

Targeted Resources
- ❏ Reading and Study Workbook: Section 39–3
- ❏ Adapted Reading and Study Workbook: Section 39–3
- ❏ Teaching Resources: Section Summaries 39–3, Worksheets 39–3
- ❏ Transparencies: **594** Menstrual Cycle, **595** Figure 39–12 The Male Reproductive System, **596** Figure 39–14 The Female Reproductive System
- ❏ Lab Manual A: Chapter 39 Lab
- ❏ Lab Manual B: Chapter 39 Lab
- ❏ **NSTA** *sci*LINKS Gametes

3 ASSESS

Evaluate Understanding
Call on students at random to define each of the Vocabulary words, and call on other students to correct any errors.

Reteach
Have students use Figure 39–12 to trace the path of sperm through the male reproductive system and Figure 39–14 to trace the path of an egg through the female reproductive system.

Targeted Resources
- ❏ Teaching Resources: Section Review 39–3
- ❏ 〈*i*Text〉 Section 39–3

LESSON PLAN 39–4 (pages 1016–1024)

Fertilization and Development

Time
3 periods
1 1/2 blocks

Section Objectives

- **39.4.1 Describe** fertilization.
- **39.4.2 Identify** the stages of early development.
- **39.4.3 Describe** the function of the placenta.
- **39.4.4 Outline** the life cycle after birth.

Vocabulary zygote • implantation • differentiation • gastrulation • neurulation • placenta • fetus

Local Standards

1 FOCUS

Reading Strategy
Have students use the headings and subheadings to make an outline before they read the section, and then have them fill in key information as they read.

Targeted Resources
❑ Transparencies: **597** Section 39–4 Interest Grabber
❑ Transparencies: **598** Section 39–4 Outline

2 INSTRUCT

Build Science Skills: Using Models
Students create three-dimensional clay models of the zygote, morula, and blastocyst stages of early development. **L1** **L2**

Make Connections: Health Science
Explain the health problems that result when Rh antibodies from a pregnant woman cross the placenta and enter the blood of an Rh-positive fetus. **L2**

Build Science Skills: Making Judgments
Students research and make judgments about the advantages and disadvantages of stem cell research. **L2** **L3**

Demonstration
Demonstrate how people change as they age by having students try to identify photographs of each other as young children. **L1**

Targeted Resources
❑ Reading and Study Workbook: Section 39–4
❑ Adapted Reading and Study Workbook: Section 39–4
❑ Transparencies: **599** Fertilization and Implantation, **600** Figure 39–22 The Placenta
❑ Teaching Resources: Section Summaries: 39–4, Worksheets 39–4, Enrichment
❑ **NSTA** *sci*$_{LINKS}$ Human growth and development

3 ASSESS

Evaluate Understanding
Call on students at random to name the stages of development of the embryo and fetus, and call on other students to describe the features of the embryo or fetus at each stage.

Reteach
Work with students to develop a time line of important events from fertilization to birth.

Targeted Resources
❑ Teaching Resources: Section Review 39–4, Chapter Vocabulary Review, Graphic Organizer, Chapter 39 Tests: Levels A and B
❑ ⟨**iText**⟩ Section 39–4, Chapter 39 Assessment
❑ **PHSchool.com** Online Chapter 39 Test

Chapter 39   Endocrine and Reproductive Systems

Summary

39–1 The Endocrine System

A gland is an organ that makes and releases a secretion. **Exocrine glands** release their secretions through ducts directly to the organs that use them. **Endocrine glands** release hormones into the bloodstream. **The endocrine system is made up of endocrine glands.**

Hormones are chemicals made in one part of the body that affect cells elsewhere in the body. Hormones bind to target cells. **Target cells** are specific chemical receptors on cells.

There are two types of hormones: steroid hormones and nonsteroid hormones. Steroid hormones can cross cell membranes of target cells, enter the nucleus, and turn genes on or off. Nonsteroid hormones cannot cross cell membranes. Compounds called secondary messengers carry the messages of nonsteroid hormones inside target cells.

All cells, except for red blood cells, produce hormonelike substances called **prostaglandins.** Prostaglandins usually affect only nearby cells and tissues. They are known as "local hormones."

The endocrine system is controlled by feedback mechanisms that help maintain homeostasis. For example, the level of a hormone in the blood may be the feedback that signals a gland to make more or less of the hormone. Two hormones with opposite effects may work together to maintain homeostasis. This is called complementary hormone action.

39–2 Human Endocrine Glands

There are several endocrine glands scattered throughout the body.
- The **pituitary gland** secretes nine hormones that regulate body functions and control the actions of other endocrine glands.
- Hormones from the **hypothalamus** control the secretions of the pituitary gland.
- Hormones from the **thyroid gland** regulate metabolism.
- Hormones from the thyroid gland and **parathyroid glands** maintain blood calcium levels.
- The **adrenal glands** make hormones that help the body prepare for and deal with stress.
- The **pancreas** is both an exocrine gland and an endocrine gland. Hormones produced in the pancreas help keep levels of glucose in the blood stable.
- **Reproductive glands,** or gonads, make gametes and secrete sex hormones. The female gonads, **ovaries,** produce eggs. The male gonads, **testes,** produce sperm.

39–3 The Reproductive System

Hormones released by the ovaries and testes cause puberty. **Puberty** is a period of rapid growth and sexual maturation. It usually starts between the ages of 9 and 15. At the end of puberty, the male and female reproductive organs are fully developed and become fully functional.

- **The main role of the male reproductive system is to make and deliver sperm.** The testes are the main organs of this system. The testes are held in the **scrotum.** In the testes, sperm are made in tiny tubes called **seminiferous tubules.** The mature sperm move through a tube and leave the body through the urethra. The urethra is the tube in the penis that leads to the outside. Contractions eject sperm from the penis in a process called ejaculation.
- **The main roles of the female reproductive system are to make eggs and prepare the female body to nourish an embryo.** The ovaries are the main organs of this system. Each ovary has thousands of follicles. A **follicle** is a cluster of cells that surround an egg. A mature egg moves through the **Fallopian tube** to the **uterus.** The uterus is connected to the outside of the body by the **vagina.**

Beginning in puberty, the female body goes through a series of events that prepares the body to care for a fertilized egg. This is called the **menstrual cycle.** The endocrine system and reproductive system are both involved in the menstrual cycle. **The menstrual cycle has four phases:**

- During the **follicular phase,** an egg matures in its follicle.
- **Ovulation** occurs when the mature egg is released from the ovary. If sperm are present in the Fallopian tube, the egg may be fertilized.
- During the **luteal phase,** the follicle develops into a structure called the **corpus luteum.** If the egg was fertilized, it implants in the lining of the uterus. If the egg was not fertilized, it moves through the uterus without implanting.
- During **menstruation,** the lining of the uterus falls away and leaves the body through the vagina.

Diseases spread during sexual contact are called **sexually transmitted diseases** (STDs). Bacteria and viruses can cause STDs. Chlamydia, syphilis, gonorrhea, and AIDS are STDs. Abstinence is the only sure way to prevent infection from STDs.

39–4 Fertilization and Development

Fertilization is the joining of a sperm and an egg. A fertilized egg is a **zygote.**

- The zygote divides and undergoes repeated mitosis and develops into a hollow ball of cells called a blastocyst. About a week after fertilization, the blastocyst **implants** in the lining of the uterus.
- Cells of the blastocyst start to specialize through **differentiation.** Some cells migrate to form two cell layers. A third layer is produced by a process of cell migration called **gastrulation.** The three layers eventually develop into the different organs of the embryo.
- Gastrulation is followed by **neurulation,** or the development of the nervous system.

As the embryo develops, membranes form to protect and nourish it. One membrane forms the **placenta.** The mother and embryo exchange gases, food, and waste products across the placenta. **It is the embryo's organ of respiration, nourishment, and excretion.**

After eight weeks of development, the embryo is called a **fetus.** By the end of three months, most organs are fully formed. During this time, the umbilical cord forms. The umbilical cord connects the fetus to the placenta.

During the next six months before birth, the organ systems mature. The fetus grows in size and mass.

Childbirth occurs when hormones cause contractions in the mother's uterus. The contractions push the baby out through the vagina.

Growth and development continue throughout childhood. Adolescence begins with puberty and ends with adulthood. Development continues during adulthood. The first signs of aging often appear in the thirties.

Steroid Hormones

Steroid hormones can cross cell membranes easily. Once inside the cell, the hormone binds to a receptor, forming a hormone-receptor complex. The hormone-receptor complex initiates mRNA transcription. This leads to protein synthesis.

Draw arrows to show the sequence of steps in steroid hormone function.

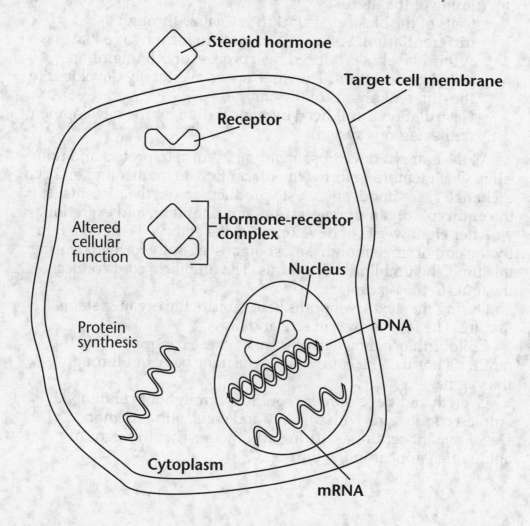

Use the diagram to answer the questions. Circle the correct answers.

1. To what does the hormone-receptor complex bind?

cytoplasm   DNA

2. What are steroid hormones?

lipids   nucleic acids

Nonsteroid Hormones

Nonsteroid hormones bind to receptors on cell membranes. The binding activates an enzyme on the inner surface of the cell membrane. This enzyme activates secondary messengers that carry the message of the hormone inside the cell.

Draw arrows to show the sequence of steps in nonsteroid hormone function.

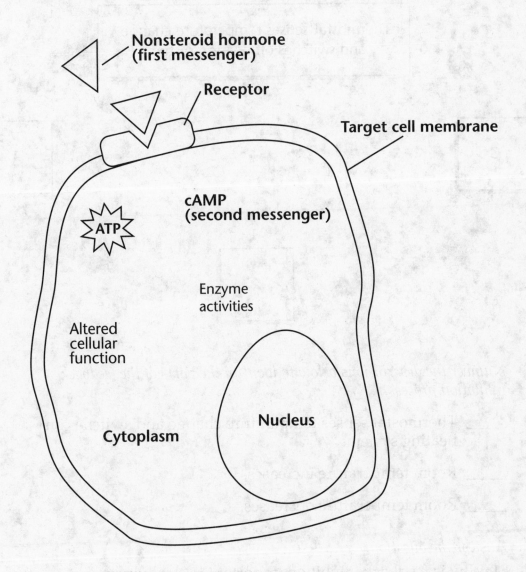

Use the diagram to answer the questions. Circle the correct answer.

1. Which kind of hormone generally cannot cross cell membranes?

    steroid   nonsteroid

2. Which of the following is found inside the cell?

    first messenger   second messenger

Feedback Inhibition

Feedback inhibition occurs when high levels of a substance inhibit the process that produces the substance. This is similar to the way that a thermostat regulates the temperature in a house. The diagram below shows how feedback inhibition works in a thermostat.

```
        ┌──────────────────────────────────┐
        │ Thermostat senses temperature change │
        │    and switches off heating system.   │
        └──────────────────────────────────┘

   ┌───┐                                    ┌───┐
   │ 3 │                                    │ 1 │
   └───┘                                    └───┘

                    ┌───┐
                    │ 2 │
                    └───┘
```

Number the descriptions below to identify the parts of the feedback inhibition process.

_____ Thermostat senses temperature change and switches on heating system.

_____ Room temperature increases.

_____ Room temperature decreases.

Answer the question.

1. Why is feedback inhibition important to the human endocrine system?

_____

_____

Endocrine Gland Functions

The table shows some important endocrine glands in the human body and their functions.

Use the words below to complete the table. The first one has been completed for you.

adrenal glands ovaries	pancreas pituitary	testes thyroid

Gland	Function	Some Hormones Produced
hypothalamus	controls the secretions of the pituitary gland	thyroid-releasing hormone
	regulates body functions and controls actions of other glands	growth hormone, thyroid-stimulating hormone
	regulates the body's metabolism	thyroxine
	helps the body prepare for and deal with stress	corticosteroids, epinephrine, norepinephrine
	maintains the level of glucose in the blood	insulin, glucagon
	produce eggs and female sex hormones	estrogen, progesterone
	produce sperm and male sex hormones	testosterone

The Male Reproductive System

Sperm are produced in the testes and mature in the epididymis. To leave the body, they travel through the vas deferens and the urethra. Glands, including the seminal vesicles, produce seminal fluid that nourishes and protects the sperm.

Use the words below to label the diagram.

epididymis	seminal vesicle	urethra
testis	vas deferens	

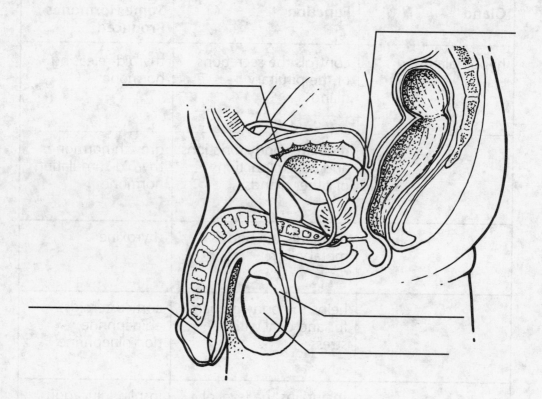

Use the diagram to answer the questions. Circle the correct answer.

1. Through what structure does the urethra pass?

    testis   penis

2. Through which structure do sperm pass?

    seminal vesicle   vas deferens

The Female Reproductive System

Eggs are produced in the ovaries. They travel through the Fallopian tubes to the uterus. The vagina is a canal that leads from the uterus to the outside of the body.

Follow the prompts to identify important structures in the female reproductive system.

- Color the ovaries blue.
- Color the Fallopian tubes yellow.
- Color the uterus red.
- Color the vagina orange.

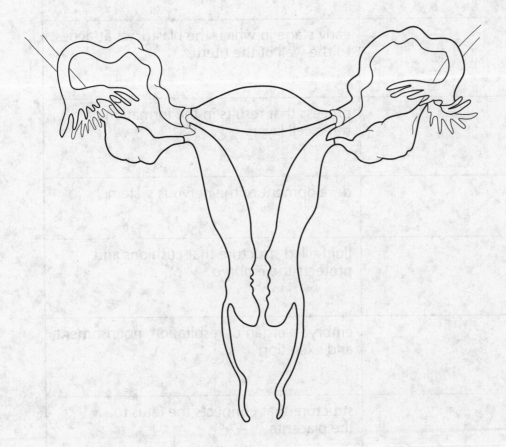

Use the diagram to answer the question. Circle the correct answer.

1. Which structure allows a baby to pass out of the body during birth?

ovary   vagina

Fertilization and Development

Use the words below to identify important events and structures in early human development. The first one has been completed for you.

amniotic sac	implantation	placenta
gastrulation	neurulation	umbilical cord

Event or Structure	What It Is
fertilization	the process of a sperm joining an egg
	early stage in which the blastocyst attaches to the wall of the uterus
	process that results in the formation of three cell layers
	development of the nervous system
	fluid-filled structure that cushions and protects the embryo
	embryo's organ of respiration, nourishment, and excretion
	structure that connects the fetus to the placenta

Use the table to answer the question. Circle the correct answer.

1. Which step occurs shortly after gastrulation?

   implantation   neurulation

Chapter 39   Endocrine and Reproductive Systems

Vocabulary Review

Matching   *In the space provided, write the letter of the definition that best matches each term.*

_____ **1.** endocrine

_____ **2.** exocrine

_____ **3.** gastrulation

_____ **4.** hormone

_____ **5.** implantation

_____ **6.** menstruation

a. type of gland that releases its chemicals directly into the bloodstream

b. chemical made in one part of the body that travels through the bloodstream and affects the activities of cells in other parts of the body

c. attachment of the blastocyst to the uterine wall

d. type of gland that releases its chemicals through ducts

e. discharge of uterine tissue and blood through the vagina

f. the process of cell migration that produces a third layer of cells in the blastocyst

Matching   *In the space provided, write the letter of the definition that best matches each term.*

_____ **7.** ovary

_____ **8.** placenta

_____ **9.** puberty

_____**10.** vas deferens

_____**11.** zygote

a. period of rapid growth and sexual maturation

b. a fertilized egg

c. organ for respiration, nourishment, and excretion

d. female reproductive gland that produces eggs and sex hormones

e. the tube that carries sperm from the epididymis to the urethra

Summary

39–1 The Endocrine System

The endocrine system consists of glands that release secretions into the bloodstream. The secretions are called hormones. Hormones are chemicals released in one part of the body that travel throughout the body and affect cells elsewhere. Hormones bind to specific chemical receptors on cells called target cells. In addition to endocrine glands, there are exocrine glands, such as sweat glands. Exocrine glands release their secretions through ducts directly to tissues and organs.

There are two types of hormones. Steroid hormones can cross cell membranes of target cells, enter the nucleus, and turn genes on or off. Nonsteroid hormones cannot cross cell membranes. Compounds called secondary messengers carry the messages of nonsteroid hormones inside target cells. A wide range of cells also produce hormonelike substances called prostaglandins that affect only nearby cells.

The endocrine system is regulated by feedback mechanisms that help maintain homeostasis. For example, the level of a hormone in the blood may be the feedback that signals a gland to produce more or less of the hormone. Two hormones with opposite effects may work together to maintain homeostasis. This is called complementary hormone action.

39–2 Human Endocrine Glands

Human endocrine glands include the pituitary gland, hypothalamus, thyroid gland, parathyroid glands, adrenal glands, pancreas, and reproductive glands.

The nine pituitary hormones either directly regulate body functions or control the actions of other endocrine glands.

Hormones from the hypothalamus control the pituitary gland. The thyroid gland regulates metabolism. Hormones produced in the parathyroid gland help regulate calcium levels in the blood. The adrenal gland produces hormones that help the body deal with stress. The pancreas secretes insulin and glucagon. Insulin and glucagon keep the level of sugar in the blood stable. If the pancreas fails to produce, or properly use, insulin, diabetes mellitus occurs. Reproductive glands, or gonads, produce gametes. Gonads also secrete sex hormones that produce male and female physical characteristics.

39–3 The Reproductive System

Sex hormones produced by the gonads of an embryo cause the embryo to develop into either a female or a male. Sex hormones also cause puberty to occur. Puberty is a period of rapid growth and sexual maturation that usually begins between ages 9 and 15. At the end of puberty, the male and female reproductive organs are fully developed and able to function.

The main function of the male reproductive system is to produce and deliver sperm. The main organs of the male reproductive system are the testes, which are held in a sac called the scrotum. In the testes, sperm are produced in tiny tubes called seminiferous tubules. Sperm then mature in a structure known as the epididymis. They leave the epididymis through a tube called the vas deferens, which merges with the urethra. The urethra is the tube in the penis that leads to the outside. Sperm are ejected from the penis by contractions. This is called ejaculation.

The main function of the female reproductive system is to produce eggs and prepare the female body to nourish an embryo. The main organs of the female reproductive system are the ovaries. Each ovary contains thousands of follicles. A follicle is a cluster of cells surrounding a single egg. The follicle helps the egg mature. About once a month, an egg matures and is released from the ovary. The egg moves through the Fallopian tube, where it can be fertilized if sperm are present.

After a few days, the egg reaches the uterus. The uterus is connected to the outside of the body by a canal called the vagina.

One egg develops each month during the menstrual cycle. The cycle is controlled by hormones. It has four phases: follicular phase, ovulation, luteal phase, and menstruation. During the follicular phase, an egg matures in its follicle and the uterus is prepared to receive a fertilized egg. Then, the egg is released from the ovary. This is called ovulation. The luteal phase follows. During the luteal phase, the follicle turns into a structure called the corpus luteum. If the egg has been fertilized, it implants in the lining of the uterus. If the egg has not been fertilized, it passes through the uterus without implanting, and menstruation occurs. During menstruation, the lining of the uterus falls away and leaves the body through the vagina.

Diseases that are spread during sexual contact are called sexually transmitted diseases (STDs). STDs can be caused by bacteria and viruses. Common STDs include chlamydia, syphilis, gonorrhea, and AIDS. Abstinence is the only sure way to avoid being infected with STDs.

39–4 Fertilization and Development

Fertilization is the process of a sperm joining an egg. A fertilized egg is called a zygote. The zygote undergoes repeated mitosis and soon develops into a hollow ball of cells called a blastocyst. About a week after fertilization, the blastocyst embeds itself in the lining of the uterus. This is called implantation.

The cells of the blastocyst begin to specialize in a process called differentiation. Some cells migrate to form three cell layers. This process is called gastrulation. The three layers eventually develop into the different organs of the embryo. Researchers are just beginning to understand what controls the development of specialized cells and organs. Gastrulation is followed by neurulation, or the development of the nervous system. As the embryo develops, membranes also form to protect and nourish it. One of these membranes develops into the placenta. The mother and embryo exchange gases, food, and waste products across the placenta.

After eight weeks of development, the embryo is called a fetus. By the end of three months, most of the major organs are fully formed. During the remaining six months before birth, the organ systems mature, and the fetus grows in size and mass.

Childbirth occurs when hormones stimulate the mother's uterus to contract. The contractions push the baby from the uterus and out through the vagina. Twins are born if more than one egg was fertilized or if one zygote split into two embryos during early development.

Growth and development continue throughout infancy and childhood. Adolescence begins with puberty and ends with adulthood. Development continues during adulthood. The first signs of aging usually appear in the thirties.

Section 39–1 The Endocrine System (pages 997–1002)

👄 **Key Concepts**
- What is the function of the endocrine system?
- How does the endocrine system maintain homeostasis?

Introduction (page 997)

1. What makes up the endocrine system? _____

_____

_____

2. What do the products of the endocrine system do? _____

_____

_____

Hormones (page 997)

3. Chemicals released in one part of the body that travel through the bloodstream and affect the activities of cells in other parts of the body are called _____.

4. How do hormones affect the activities of other cells? _____

_____

5. Cells that have receptors for a particular hormone are referred to as _____.

6. Is the following sentence true or false? Cells without receptors are not affected by hormones. _____

7. Is the following sentence true or false? Generally, the body's responses to hormones are quicker and shorter lasting than the responses to nerve impulses. _____

Glands (page 998)

8. An organ that produces and releases a substance, or secretion, is called a(an)

_____.

9. What is an exocrine gland? _____

_____

10. Glands that release sweat, tears, and digestive juices are considered _____ glands.

11. What is the function of the parathyroid glands? _____
_____
_____

Match the endocrine gland with the hormone it produces.

	Endocrine Gland	Hormone It Produces
_____	**12.** Pineal	**a.** Glucagon
_____	**13.** Thyroid	**b.** Melatonin
_____	**14.** Pancreas	**c.** Epinephrine
_____	**15.** Thymus	**d.** Thyroxine
_____	**16.** Adrenal	**e.** Thymosin
_____	**17.** Ovary	**f.** Testosterone
_____	**18.** Testis	**g.** Estrogen

19. The hormone that regulates metabolism is _____.

Hormone Action (page 999)

20. List the two general groups into which hormones may be classified.

    a. _____

    b. _____

21. Circle the letter of each sentence that is true about steroid hormones.

    a. They are lipids.

    b. They cannot cross cell membranes.

    c. They help regulate gene expression.

    d. They can enter the nucleus.

22. Is the following sentence true or false? Steroid hormones are produced from cholesterol. _____

23. Circle the letter of each sentence that is true about nonsteroid hormones.

    a. They are proteins, small peptides, or modified amino acids.

    b. They can cross cell membranes.

    c. They rely on secondary messengers.

    d. They cannot enter the nucleus.

24. Is the following sentence true or false? Secondary messengers may include calcium ions, cAMP, nucleotides, and fatty acids. _____

Prostaglandins (page 1000)

25. Hormonelike substances produced by other kinds of cells and tissues are called _____.

26. Why are prostaglandins known as "local hormones"? _____
_____

27. Is the following sentence true or false? Some prostaglandins cause smooth muscles to
contract. _____

Control of the Endocrine System (pages 1000–1001)

28. When does feedback inhibition occur? _____
_____

29. Fill in the missing labels in the diagram to show how the thyroid gland is regulated by
feedback controls.

30. Circle the letter of each event that occurs when core body temperature begins to drop.

   a. The hypothalamus produces less TRH.

   b. More TSH is released.

   c. Less thyroxine is released.

   d. Metabolic activity increases.

31. Is the following sentence true or false? As you lose water, the concentration of
dissolved materials in the blood falls. _____

Complementary Hormone Action (page 1002)

32. What is complementary hormone action? _____
_____

33. Is the following sentence true or false? Calcitonin increases the concentration of
calcium in the blood. _____

34. If calcium levels drop too low, the parathyroid glands release _____.

35. How does PTH increase calcium levels? _____
_____
_____

36. Why is the regulation of calcium levels so important? _____
_____
_____

Section 39–2 Human Endocrine Glands (pages 1003–1008)

🔑 **Key Concept**
- What are the functions of the major endocrine glands?

Introduction (page 1003)

1. List seven major glands of the endocrine system.

   a. _____   e. _____

   b. _____   f. _____

   c. _____   g. _____

   d. _____

Pituitary Gland (page 1003)

2. Describe the pituitary gland and its location. _____
_____

3. List the two parts of the pituitary gland.

   a. _____   b. _____

4. In general, what is the role of pituitary gland hormones? _____
_____

Hypothalamus (page 1004)

5. Is the following sentence true or false? The hypothalamus controls the secretions of the
   pituitary gland. _____

6. What influences the activity of the hypothalamus? _____
_____
_____

7. In what way is the posterior pituitary an extension of the hypothalamus?
_____
_____

8. Is the following sentence true or false? The hypothalamus has direct control of the
   anterior pituitary. _____

Match each pituitary hormone with its action.

	Hormone	Action
_____	9. ADH	a. Stimulates ovaries and testes
_____	10. FSH	b. Stimulates production of eggs and sperm
_____	11. LH	c. Stimulates release of hormones from adrenal cortex
_____	12. GH	d. Stimulates protein synthesis and growth in cells
_____	13. ACTH	e. Stimulates the kidneys to reabsorb water

14. What are releasing hormones, and what do they do? _____

_____

_____

_____

Thyroid Gland (page 1005)

15. Where is the thyroid gland located? _____

_____

_____

16. Is the following sentence true or false? The thyroid gland regulates reproduction.

_____

17. List the two hormones produced by the thyroid.

a. _____   b. _____

18. What does thyroxine do in the body? _____

_____

19. Production of too much thyroxine leads to a condition called

_____.

20. An enlargement of the thyroid gland is called a(an) _____.

21. Infants who lack enough iodine to produce normal amounts of thyroxine suffer from a condition called _____.

22. How can cretinism usually be prevented? _____

_____

_____

Parathyroid Glands (page 1005)

23. How does parathyroid hormone regulate calcium levels in the blood? _____

_____

_____

Adrenal Glands (page 1006)

24. What is the general role of the adrenal glands? _____

_____

_____

25. The outer part of the adrenal gland is called the _____, and the inner part is called the _____.

26. Is the following sentence true or false? The release of hormones from the adrenal medulla is regulated by the sympathetic nervous system. _____

27. Complete the table about adrenal gland hormones.

HORMONES OF THE ADRENAL GLAND

Part of Adrenal Gland	Hormones It Produces	Role of the Hormones
	Corticosteroids	Regulating minerals, metabolism
Adrenal medulla		

Pancreas (pages 1007–1008)

28. Is the following sentence true or false? The pancreas is both an endocrine gland and an exocrine gland. _____

29. What is the role of insulin and glucagon? _____
_____
_____

30. When the pancreas fails to produce or properly use insulin, a condition known as _____ occurs.

31. _____ is an autoimmune disorder that usually develops in people before the age of 15.

32. People with what type of diabetes produce low to normal amounts of insulin? _____

Reproductive Glands (page 1008)

33. List the two important functions served by the gonads.

a. _____ b. _____

34. The female gonads are the _____, and the male gonads are the

_____.

Reading Skill Practice

Taking notes can help you identify and remember the most important information in a section. Take notes on Section 39–2 by writing the main headings and under each heading listing the most important points. Do your work on a separate sheet of paper.

Section 39–3 The Reproductive System (pages 1009–1015)

🔑 **Key Concepts**
- What are the main functions of the male and female reproductive systems?
- What are the four phases of the menstrual cycle?

Sexual Development (page 1009)

1. Circle the letter of each sentence that is true about sexual development before birth.

   a. Testes and ovaries begin to develop during the first six weeks.

   b. Male and female reproductive organs develop from the same tissues in the embryo.

   c. The testes produce testosterone, and the ovaries produce estrogen.

   d. Hormones determine whether the embryo will develop into a male or a female.

2. What is puberty? _____

   _____

   _____

3. How does the hypothalamus begin puberty? _____

   _____

   _____

   _____

The Male Reproductive System (pages 1010–1011)

4. Is the following sentence true or false? The release of FSH and LH stimulates cells in the testes to produce testosterone. _____

5. Circle the letter of each term that refers to a structure of the male reproductive system.

   a. testes

   b. Fallopian tube

   c. vas deferens

   d. urethra

6. The testes are contained in a sac called the _____.

7. Why do the testes remain outside the body cavity? _____

   _____

   _____

   _____

8. Is the following sentence true or false? Sperm are produced in the vas deferens.

   _____

9. The structure in which sperm fully mature and are stored is the _____.

10. The tube that leads to the outside of the body through the penis is the

    _____.

11. Label the drawing of a sperm with the following structures: head, nucleus, midpiece, and tail.

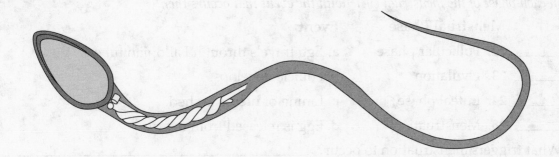

12. A nutrient-rich fluid called seminal fluid, when combined with sperm, forms
_____.

The Female Reproductive System (pages 1011–1012)

13. Circle the letter of each choice that is a structure of the female reproductive system.

   a. ovary   **c.** uterus

   b. epididymis   **d.** vagina

14. Is the following sentence true or false? The ovaries usually produce only one mature ovum each month. _____

15. Clusters of cells surrounding a single egg are called primary _____.

16. The hormone that stimulates a follicle to grow and mature each month is
_____.

17. Is the following sentence true or false? Fertilization takes place in the uterus.
_____

The Menstrual Cycle (pages 1013–1014)

18. Circle the letter of each sentence that is true about the menstrual cycle.

   a. It lasts an average of 3 to 7 days.

   b. It is controlled by hormones.

   c. It prepares the uterus to receive an egg.

   d. It has four phases.

19. Is the following sentence true or false? The level of estrogen falls at the start of the follicular phase of the menstrual cycle. _____

20. During the luteal phase, the follicle turns yellow and is now known as the
_____.

21. Is the following sentence true or false? The chances that an egg will be fertilized are the greatest during the first two days of the luteal phase. _____

Match each phase of the menstrual cycle with the event that occurs then.

	Menstrual Phase	**Event**
_____	**22.** Follicular phase	**a.** Egg travels through Fallopian tube.
_____	**23.** Ovulation	**b.** Follicle develops.
_____	**24.** Luteal phase	**c.** Lining of uterus is shed.
_____	**25.** Menstruation	**d.** Egg is released from ovary.

26. What triggers menstruation to occur? _____

_____

27. Is the following sentence true or false? A new cycle begins with the last day of menstruation. _____

Sexually Trasmitted Diseases (page 1015)

28. Diseases spread from one person to another during sexual contact are known as

_____.

29. Is the following sentence true or false? Viral infections can be treated with antibiotics.

_____.

30. The most common STD is _____.

Reading Skill Practice

When you read a section, taking notes can help you organize and remember the information. As you read or review Section 39–3, take notes by writing each heading and listing the main points under each heading. Do your work on a separate sheet of paper.

Section 39–4 Fertilization and Development
(pages 1016–1024)

Key Concepts
- What is fertilization?
- What are the stages of early development?
- What is the function of the placenta?

Fertilization (pages 1016–1017)

1. The process of a sperm joining an egg is called _____.

2. Is the following sentence true or false? A fertilized egg is known as a zygote. _____

Early Development (pages 1017–1020)

Match each term with its definition.

	Term	Definition
_____	3. Morula	a. Organ that nourishes the embryo
_____	4. Blastocyst	b. Name of embryo when it is a solid ball of about 64 cells
_____	5. Implantation	c. Name of morula when it is a hollow ball of cells
_____	6. Gastrulation	d. Membrane that surrounds and protects the embryo
_____	7. Amnion	e. Process in which the blastocyst attaches to the wall of the uterus
_____	8. Placenta	f. Process of cell migration that produces three cell layers

9. Is the following sentence true or false? The first few cell divisions take place in the

Fallopian tube. _____

10. After eight weeks of development, the embryo is called a(an) _____.

11. Is the following sentence true or false? Most of the major organs and tissues are fully

formed by the end of three months of development. _____

Control of Development (page 1020)

12. Is the following sentence true or false? The fates of many cells in the early embryo are

not fixed. _____

Later Development (page 1021)

13. What changes occur during the last three months of fetal development? _____

_____

_____

_____

Childbirth (pages 1022–1023)

14. Is the following sentence true or false? The process of childbirth begins when the

hormone calcitonin is released from the posterior pituitary gland. _____

15. The series of rhythmic contractions of the uterine wall that force the baby out through the vagina is known as _____.

16. What stimulates the production of milk in the breast tissues of the mother? _____
_____
_____

Multiple Births (page 1023)

17. If two eggs are released and fertilized by two different sperm, _____ twins result.

18. If a single zygote splits apart to produce two embryos, _____ twins result.

Early Years (pages 1023–1024)

19. Is the following sentence true or false? A baby's birth weight generally triples within 12 months of birth. _____

20. Is the following sentence true or false? Infancy refers to the first year of life. _____

21. Circle the letter of each development that occurs during infancy.
a. Crawling
c. Appearance of first teeth
b. Walking
d. First use of language

22. Childhood lasts from infancy until the onset of _____.

23. Is the following sentence true or false? Reasoning skills are not developed until adolescence. _____

24. Adolescence begins with puberty and ends with _____.

25. What produces the growth spurt that starts at puberty? _____
_____
_____

Adulthood (page 1024)

26. Is the following sentence true or false? Adults reach their highest levels of physical strength and development between the ages of 25 and 35. _____

27. When do the first signs of physiological aging appear in most individuals?
_____

Vocabulary Review

Labeling Diagrams   *Fill in each blank with the correct name of the structure from the list.*

penis   urethra   epididymis
scrotum   testis   vas deferens

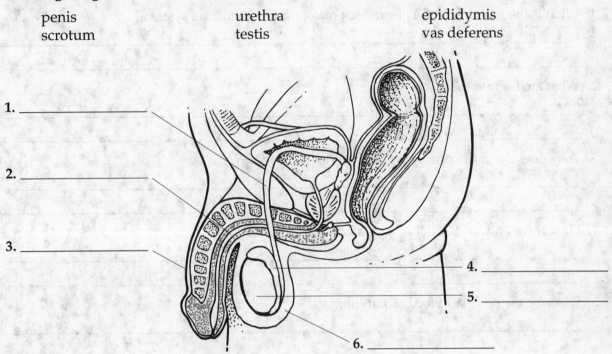

1. _____

2. _____

3. _____

4. _____

5. _____

6. _____

Completion   *Fill in the blanks with terms from Chapter 39.*

7. Secretions of endocrine glands are called _____.

8. Cells that have receptors for a particular hormone are known as _____ cells.

9. The nine hormones produced by the _____ gland regulate body functions or control other endocrine glands.

10. Female gonads are referred to as _____.

11. The reproductive system matures during a period of rapid growth and development called _____.

12. In the ovary, eggs mature in a group of cells known as a(an) _____.

13. An egg is released from the ovary in the process of _____.

14. The _____ is a canal that leads from the uterus to the outside of the body.

15. After an egg is fertilized, it is called a(an) _____.

16. During _____, cells migrate to form three cell layers that later develop into the different organs of the embryo.

17. The mother and embryo exchange gases, food, and waste products across the

    _____.

18. After eight weeks of development, the embryo is called a(an) _____.

Chapter 39 Endocrine and Reproductive Systems   Section Review 39-1

Reviewing Key Concepts

Short Answer *On the lines provided, answer the following questions.*

1. What is the function of the glands that make up the endocrine system?

   _____

   _____

2. What are hormones?

   _____

   _____

3. Why does the endocrine system have to be controlled?

   _____

   _____

4. How is the endocrine system regulated?

   _____

   _____

5. Describe the process of feedback inhibition.

   _____

   _____

Reviewing Key Skills

6. **Applying Concepts** Feedback inhibition takes place both in our bodies and in the world around us. Use your own experience to give one example of feedback inhibition.

   _____

   _____

7. **Comparing and Contrasting** What is the difference between endocrine and exocrine glands?

   _____

   _____

Classifying *On the lines provided, write S if the statement describes the action of a steroid hormone and N if it describes the action of a nonsteroid hormone.*

_____ 8. passes directly across a cell's membrane

_____ 9. uses secondary messengers to carry a message inside the cell

10. **Inferring** If it took the body several hours to respond to a particular stimulus, which system was most likely involved in the response, the nervous system or the endocrine system? Explain your answer.

   _____

   _____

   _____

Chapter 39 Endocrine and Reproductive Systems   Section Review 39-2

Reviewing Key Concepts

Matching *On the line provided, match the endocrine gland with its function.*

_____ 1. pituitary gland

_____ 2. hypothalamus

_____ 3. thyroid gland

_____ 4. parathyroid glands

_____ 5. adrenal glands

_____ 6. pancreas

_____ 7. ovaries

_____ 8. testes

a. produce eggs and sex hormones

b. regulate the level of calcium in the blood

c. controls the secretions of the pituitary gland

d. helps keep the level of glucose in the blood stable

e. secretes nine hormones, some of which directly regulate many bodily functions

f. produce sperm and sex hormones

g. regulates the body's metabolism

h. help the body prepare for and deal with stress

Reviewing Key Skills

9. **Inferring** How is the posterior pituitary gland related to both the central nervous system and the endocrine system?

_____

_____

_____

_____

_____

10. **Comparing and Contrasting** How do Type I and II diabetes mellitus differ?

_____

_____

_____

_____

_____

Chapter 39 Endocrine and Reproductive Systems   **Section Review 39-3**

Reviewing Key Concepts

Short Answer *On the lines provided, answer the following questions.*

1. What is the function of the male reproductive system?

_____

2. What is the function of the female reproductive system?

_____

3. What are the four main phases of the menstrual cycle?

_____

Matching *On the line provided, write the letter of the structure in the male or female reproductive system that is being described.*

_____ 4. organ that produces sperm   a. penis

_____ 5. structure where sperm fully mature and are stored   b. ovary

_____ 6. tube that carries sperm from the epididymis to the urethra c. testis

_____ 7. tube through which urine and sperm are released from the body d. vas deferens

_____ 8. external male reproductive organ that contains the urethra e. epididymis

_____ 9. organ that produces eggs   f. Fallopian tube

_____ 10. site where eggs are fertilized   g. vagina

_____ 11. external sac containing the testes   h. urethra

_____ 12. canal that leads to the outside of a woman's body   i. uterus

_____ 13. organ in which a fertilized egg can develop   j. scrotum

Reviewing Key Skills

Interpreting Graphics *Use the diagram to answer the following questions.*

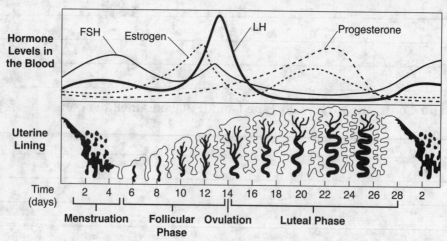

14. What occurs when the hormone LH peaks?

_____

15. What days on the chart show the menstruation phase?

_____

Reviewing Key Concepts

Identifying Processes *On the lines below, use numbers to order the sequence of events in fertilization (from 1 through 6).*

_____ 1. A sac in the sperm head ruptures and releases powerful enzymes that break down the protective layer of the egg.

_____ 2. Sperm swim through the uterus into the Fallopian tubes.

_____ 3. Semen is ejaculated through the penis into the vagina.

_____ 4. The sperm nucleus enters the egg.

_____ 5. The cell membrane of the egg changes, preventing other sperm from entering the cell.

_____ 6. A sperm attaches to a binding site on an egg.

Short Answer *On the lines provided, answer the following question.*

7. What is the purpose of the placenta?

_____

_____

_____

Reviewing Key Skills

8. **Inferring** How does a pregnant woman endanger her embryo or fetus by smoking tobacco?

_____

_____

_____

_____

9. **Inferring** Since calcium is important to bone formation, why would doctors encourage teens to eat foods containing calcium?

_____

_____

_____

_____

10. **Comparing and Contrasting** Describe the effect of aging on the body at age 35 and at age 65.

_____

_____

_____

_____

Chapter 39 Endocrine and Reproductive Systems   Chapter Vocabulary Review

Defining Terms *On the lines provided, define each of the following terms.*

1. endocrine gland _____

   _____

2. prostaglandin _____

   _____

3. pituitary gland_____

   _____

4. diabetes mellitus _____

   _____

5. puberty _____

   _____

6. placenta_____

   _____

Short Answer *On the lines provided, answer the following questions.*

7. Explain the relationship between hormones and target cells.

   _____

   _____

8. Explain how a male produces and releases sperm. Use the terms
   testes, scrotum, seminiferous tubules, epididymis, vas deferens, urethra,
   and *penis* in your explanation.

   _____

   _____

Labeling Diagrams *On the lines provided, label the following diagram.*

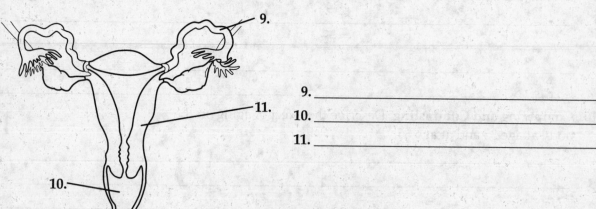

9. _____

10. _____

11. _____

Name_____ Class _____ Date _____

Multiple Choice *On the line provided, write the letter of the answer that best answers the question or completes the sentence.*

_____ 12. Organs that release their secretions through ducts are called
  a. endocrine glands.
  b. exocrine glands.
  c. corpus Luteum.
  d. testes.

_____ 13. Clusters of cells surrounding a single egg are called
  a. target cells.   c. vas deferens.
  b. fallopian tubes.   d. follicles.

_____ 14. What process occurs when an egg is released from the ovary?
  a. implantation
  b. menstruation
  c. gastrulation
  d. ovulation

_____ 15. When a ruptured follicle turns yellow it becomes known as the
  a. prostaglandin.
  b. vas deferens.
  c. corpus luteum.
  d. epididymis.

_____ 16. The stage of the menstrual cycle in which the uterine lining is discharged from the body is called
  a. ovulation.   c. gastrulation.
  b. implantation.   d. menstruation.

_____ 17. A fertilized egg is called a
  a. zygote.
  b. fetus.
  c. follicle.
  d. placenta.

_____ 18. What occurs when the blastocyst attaches itself to the wall of the uterus?
  a. fertilization
  b. implantation
  c. gastrulation
  d. menstruation

_____ 19. What process forms the three cell layers known as the ectoderm, mesoderm, and endoderm?
  a. gastrulation
  b. menstruation
  c. implantation
  d. ovulation

_____ 20. After eight weeks of development, the embryo is called a(an)
  a. fetus.   c. blastocyst.
  b. zygote.   d. ovary.

Chapter 39 Endocrine and Reproductive Systems

Enrichment

In Vitro Fertilization

Some couples have difficulty conceiving a child. Modern medical techniques offer these couples alternative methods of conception, such as in vitro fertilization. In vitro fertilization (IVF) is the fertilization of eggs by sperm in a laboratory rather than in the body. Eggs are collected from the ovaries of the mother, and sperm are collected from the father. The eggs and sperm are then combined in a special medium for fertilization to take place. In some cases, a tiny glass needle may be used to inject a single sperm cell directly into an individual egg. After fertilization, the resultant embryos are transferred to the uterus of the woman who wishes to become pregnant. In addition to helping many infertile couples, the IVF technique has helped medical professionals understand how fertilization and early embryonic development occur.

IVF was first developed in the 1970s as a treatment for problems with Fallopian tubes. The first birth of a baby via IVF was reported in England in 1978. In recent years, intracytoplasmic sperm injection (ICSI), the injection of a sperm cell directly into an egg, has been developed as a therapy for the fertility problems of men.

Typically, in the IVF process, multiple embryos are produced and placed in a woman's uterus to increase the chance of implantation. Because multiple pregnancies are likely, no more than four embryos are used. Unused embryos can be frozen and stored in liquid nitrogen for future implantation. Frozen embryos have become a topic of controversy. There have been unusual legal cases concerning ownership of the embryos after a death or the divorce of the participants.

While at times IVF has been successful and has generated much enthusiasm, the overall success rate is only about 20 percent. Researchers are working to improve the technique and to create other techniques for the treatment of fertility problems.

Evaluation *On the lines provided, answer the following questions.*

1. Describe the process of in vitro fertilization.

_____

_____

_____

_____

_____

2. What do you think is an ethical way to handle frozen embryos? Should embryos be considered property?

_____

_____

_____

_____

Flowchart

In the following flowchart, enter the stages of embryo development listed below in the order they occur during human development.

Chorion becomes the placenta; Embryo becomes a morula; Fertilization; Gastrulation occurs; Zygote begins cell division; Embryo becomes a blastocyst; Implantation occurs; Embryo becomes a fetus

1.

↓

2.

↓

3.

↓

4.

↓

5.

↓

6.

↓

7.

↓

8.

Chapter 39 Endocrine and Reproductive Systems   Chapter Test A

Multiple Choice

Write the letter that best answers the question or completes the statement on the line provided.

_____ 1. The endocrine system
   a. affects only the reproductive system.
   b. releases hormones into the bloodstream.
   c. competes with the nervous system.
   d. is made up primarily of glands with ducts.

_____ 2. Unlike endocrine glands, exocrine glands
   a. have ducts.
   b. release hormones.
   c. release secretions directly into the bloodstream.
   d. are found throughout the body.

_____ 3. A thermostat is a good example of a(an)
   a. hormone-receptor complex.
   b. feedback system.
   c. prostaglandin.
   d. exocrine gland.

_____ 4. Which endocrine gland regulates the level of calcium in the blood?
   a. parathyroid glands
   b. thymus gland
   c. adrenal glands
   d. pineal gland

_____ 5. Which gland produces epinephrine and norepinephrine?
   a. parathyroid
   b. hypothalamus
   c. pituitary
   d. adrenal

_____ 6. Which of the following secondary sex characteristics is caused by testosterone?
   a. deepening of the voice
   b. widening of the hips
   c. development of breasts
   d. all of the above

_____ 7. Which structure produces sperm?
   a. scrotum
   b. epididymis
   c. seminiferous tubules
   d. vas deferens

_____ 8. When during the menstrual cycle does an egg have the best chance of being fertilized?

  a. during the follicular phase

  b. just before menstruation

  c. at the beginning of the luteal phase

  d. on the day of ovulation

_____ 9. Menstruation does not occur if the

  a. uterine lining thickens.

  b. estrogen level falls.

  c. progesterone level falls.

  d. egg is fertilized.

_____10. A zygote is a

  a. two-celled embryo.

  b. solid ball of about 50 cells.

  c. blastocyst.

  d. fertilized egg.

_____11. The chances of fertilization are very good if sperm are present when a(an)

  a. blastocyst is already present.

  b. egg is in a Fallopian tube.

  c. woman is menstruating.

  d. all of the above

_____12. Which of the following are required for fertilization to occur inside the female body?

  a. Sperm must swim into a Fallopian tube.

  b. An egg must be present in the Fallopian tube.

  c. The nucleus of a sperm must enter an egg cell.

  d. all of the above

_____13. What is the result of gastrulation?

  a. a blastocyst   c. the amnion

  b. a zygote   d. germ layers

_____14. Which of the following is a function of the placenta?

  a. mixing the blood of the mother and the fetus

  b. protecting the fetus from any drugs or alcohol in the mother's body

  c. providing nutrients to the fetus

  d. cushioning and protecting the fetus

_____15. Which of the following is characteristic of infancy?

  a. Teeth appear.

  b. Puberty begins.

  c. The first signs of aging appear.

  d. An individual reaches 70 percent of his or her height.

Completion

Complete each statement on the line provided.

16. The _____ system is made up of glands that release their products into the _____ .

17. The shortest phase of the menstrual cycle is _____ .

18. The testes are contained in an external sac called the _____ .

19. During _____ , three germ layers form. They are called _____ , ectoderm, and mesoderm.

20. A problem with the _____ can disrupt an embryo's respiration, nourishment, and excretion.

Short Answer

In complete sentences, write the answers to the questions on the lines provided.

21. Compare endocrine glands and exocrine glands. Give an example of each kind of gland.

_____

_____

_____

_____

_____

_____

22. What are prostaglandins? How are they different from true hormones?

_____

_____

_____

_____

23. Give an example of how the endocrine system maintains homeostasis.

_____

_____

_____

_____

24. List the structures that sperm pass through from the time they are produced until they are expelled from the male body.

_____

_____

_____

25. Many sperm will take the same path toward fertilizing an egg. What prevents more than one sperm from fertilizing an egg?

_____

_____

_____

Using Science Skills

Use the diagram below to answer the following questions on the lines provided.

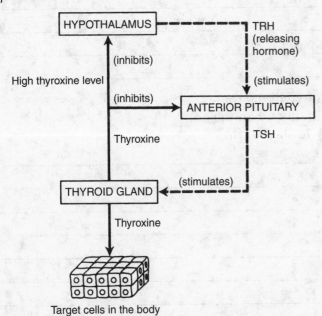

Target cells in the body

Figure 1

26. Interpreting Graphics What does Figure 1 show?

_____

_____

27. Interpreting Graphics Based on Figure 1, what happens as the level of thyroxine increases in the blood?

_____

_____

_____

_____

28. Inferring Based on Figure 1, which hormone directly stimulates target cells in the body?

_____

29. **Predicting** Give an example of how Figure 1 would change to show a person who has hyperthyroidism. What are some symptoms of this condition?

_____

_____

_____

_____

_____

_____

_____

_____

30. **Applying Concepts** Look at Figure 1. How will the three endocrine glands shown behave on a cold day when the body needs a higher level of metabolic activity to stay warm?

_____

_____

_____

_____

_____

_____

_____

_____

Essay

Write the answer to each question in the space provided.

31. Describe complementary hormone action and give an example.

32. Identify the functions of the hormones released by the pituitary gland. What controls the release of these hormones?

33. Describe the action of nonsteroid hormones.

34. What is puberty?

35. What characteristics are produced in males and females by their sex hormones?

Multiple Choice

Write the letter that best answers the question or completes the statement on the line provided.

_____ **1.** The endocrine system is made up of
   a. hormones.
   b. glands.
   c. prostaglandins.

_____ **2.** Which of the following is a gland of the endocrine system?
   a. sweat gland
   b. tear gland
   c. pituitary gland

_____ **3.** Glands that secrete hormones directly into the bloodstream are
   a. exocrine glands.
   b. target cells.
   c. endocrine glands.

_____ **4.** In the action of steroid hormones, the hormone-receptor complex
   a. activates genes.
   b. involves a second messenger.
   c. acts directly on the blood.

_____ **5.** Which endocrine gland secretes sex hormones?
   a. adrenal medulla
   b. testis
   c. hypothalamus
   d. pituitary

_____ **6.** Which gland releases nine hormones and regulates many of the other endocrine glands?
   a. pituitary
   b. thyroid
   c. adrenal

_____ **7.** Which gland produces insulin?
   a. adrenal
   b. hypothalamus
   c. pancreas

_____ **8.** Puberty usually begins between the ages of
   a. 5 and 8.
   b. 9 and 15.
   c. 16 and 19.

____ **9.** The testes and the ovaries do not begin making active
reproductive cells until
a. birth.
b. fertilization.
c. puberty.

____**10.** Which organ system is responsible for making and delivering sperm?
a. female reproductive system
b. male reproductive system
c. nervous system

____**11.** One menstrual cycle usually lasts about a
a. day.
b. week.
c. month.

____**12.** In which organ does implantation occur?
a. penis
b. ovary
c. uterus

____**13.** Which of the following forms during gastrulation?
a. three cell layers
b. blastocyst
c. nervous system

____**14.** The placenta connects the
a. fetus to the mother's uterus.
b. ectoderm to the endoderm.
c. umbilical cord to the mother's vagina.

____**15.** Which stage of the human life cycle occurs first?
a. childhood   c. adolescence
b. adulthood

Completion

Complete each statement on the line provided.

16. _____ are chemicals that travel through the bloodstream and affect the
activities of other cells.

17. Hormonelike substances that generally affect only nearby cells and tissues are called
_____ .

18. _____ is a period of rapid growth and sexual maturation during which
the reproductive system becomes fully functional.

19. In the female body, each egg is surrounded by a(an) _____ , in which
the egg matures.

20. Almost everything that the mother takes into her body passes through the
_____ to the embryo.

Short Answer

In complete sentences, write the answers to the questions on the lines provided.

21. What is the function of the endocrine system?

_____

_____

_____

_____

22. What is the main function of the parathyroid glands?

_____

_____

_____

_____

_____

_____

_____

23. What is each of the four phases of the menstrual cycle called?

_____

_____

_____

_____

_____

_____

_____

24. List the three germ layers that result from gastrulation.

_____

_____

_____

_____

25. Name and describe one of the four stages of the human life cycle.

_____

_____

_____

_____

_____

Name_____ Class_____ Date _____

Using Science Skills

Use the diagram below to answer the following questions on the lines provided.

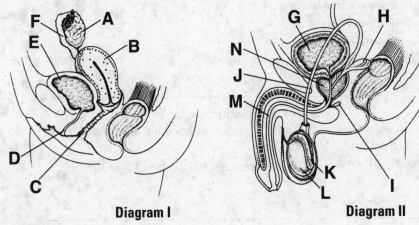

Diagram I   Diagram II

Figure 1

26. **Comparing and Contrasting** Which body systems do Diagrams I and II show?

_____

_____

_____

27. **Interpreting Graphics** Which structure in Figure 1 releases eggs? What is this structure called?

_____

28. **Applying Concepts** Where does fertilization typically occur?

_____

_____

_____

29. **Applying Concepts** Which structure in Figure 1 produces sperm?

_____

_____

30. **Interpreting Graphics** Through which structure do sperm exit the male body? Give both the name and the letter of the structure in Figure 1.

_____

_____

LESSON PLAN 40–1 (pages 1031–1035)

Infectious Disease

Section Objectives

■ **40.1.1 Identify** the causes of disease.

■ **40.1.2 Explain** how infectious diseases are transmitted.

■ **40.1.3 Describe** how antibiotics fight infection.

Vocabulary disease • pathogen • germ theory of disease • Koch's postulates • vector • antibiotic

Local Standards

1 FOCUS

Reading Strategy
Before they read, have students list some of the diseases they have had, and later, as they read, have them identify which pathogen might have caused each disease.

Targeted Resources
❑ Transparencies: **601** Section 40–1 Interest Grabber

❑ Transparencies: **602** Section 40–1 Outline

2 INSTRUCT

Demonstration
Show students death rates, by cause of death, for the United States for the late 1800s and for a recent year to demonstrate how the number of deaths caused by infectious diseases has declined. **L2**

Build Science Skills: Drawing Conclusions
Students research and report on different types of pathogens and draw conclusions about how the different types cause disease. **L2**

Address Misconceptions
Correct the misconception that all infectious diseases are contagious by using the example of tetanus. **L1** **L2**

Build Science Skills: Designing Experiments
Students design an experiment to measure the effects of frequent hand washing on the transmission of infectious diseases such as the common cold. **L2** **L3**

Make Connections: Health Science
Students explain why failing to take antibiotics long enough to kill all the bacteria causing an infection can lead to bacterial resistance to antibiotics. **L2**

Targeted Resources
❑ Reading and Study Workbook: Section 40–1

❑ Adapted Reading and Study Workbook: Section 40–1

❑ Teaching Resources: Section Summaries 40–1, Worksheets 40–1

❑ Transparencies: **603** Koch's Postulates, **604** Pathogens and Disease

❑ BioDetectives DVD: "Influenza: Tracking a Virus"; "Hantavirus: A Tale of Mice and People"

❑ Lab Manual A: Chapter 40 Lab

❑ **NSTA** *scLINKS* Diseases

3 ASSESS

Evaluate Understanding
Call on students at random to name the agents of disease, and call on other students to give an example of each agent.

Reteach
Have students write each of Koch's postulates on an index card, shuffle the cards, and then try to put the cards back in the correct order.

Targeted Resources
❑ Teaching Resources: Section Review 40–1

❑ *i Text* Section 40–1

LESSON PLAN 40–2 (pages 1036–1042)

The Immune System

Time
2 periods
1 block

Section Objectives

- **40.2.1 Identify** the body's nonspecific defenses against invading pathogens.
- **40.2.2 Describe** the function of the immune system.

Vocabulary immunity • inflammatory response
• fever • interferon • immune response • antigen
• humoral immunity • cell-mediated immunity • antibody
• vaccination • active immunity • passive immunity

Local Standards

1 FOCUS

Reading Strategy
Have students preview the section by studying the figures and reading the captions.

Targeted Resources
❑ Transparencies: **605** Section 40–2 Interest Grabber
❑ Transparencies: **606** Section 40–2 Outline

2 INSTRUCT

Build Science Skills: Applying Concepts
Students identify nonspecific defenses that help protect the body from bacteria in food. **L1 L2**

Make Connections: Health Science
Students report on the results of recent research on the use of interferon to prevent disease. **L2 L3**

Demonstration
Students participate in a demonstration of how the immune system responds to specific pathogens. **L1**

Use Visuals: Figure 40–9
Students use the flowchart in Figure 40–9 to trace the steps involved in humoral immunity. **L1 L2**

Use Community Resources
Students obtain a schedule of recommended vaccinations from a local pediatrician or health department and make a poster to convey the information. **L1 L2**

Build Science Skills: Inferring
Students infer why passive immunity lasts for only a few weeks or months. **L2**

Targeted Resources
❑ Reading and Study Workbook: Section 40–2
❑ Adapted Reading and Study Workbook: Section 40–2
❑ Teaching Resources: Section Summaries 40–2, Worksheets 40–2
❑ Transparencies: **607** Primary and Secondary Responses, **608** Figure 40–7 The Inflammatory Response, **609** Figure 40–8 Structure of an Antibody, **610** Figure 40–9 Humoral Immunity, **611** Figure 40–10 Cell-Mediated Immune Response
❑ Lab Worksheets: Chapter 40 Real-World Lab
❑ Lab Manual B: Chapter 40 Lab
❑ **NSTA** *sci*$_{LINKS}$ Immune system

3 ASSESS

Evaluate Understanding
Have students make a concept map entitled "Defenses Against Pathogens."

Reteach
Play a quiz game in which you read definitions of the Vocabulary words and student contestants try to identify the words from the definitions.

Targeted Resources
❑ Teaching Resources: Section Review 40–2
❑ **iText** Section 40–2

LESSON PLAN 40–3 (pages 1043–1047)

Immune System Disorders

Time
2 periods
1 block

Section Objectives

- **40.3.1 State** what happens when the immune system overreacts.
- **40.3.2 Explain** what an autoimmune disease is.
- **40.3.3 Describe** how HIV is transmitted and affects the immune system.

Vocabulary allergy • histamine • asthma

Local Standards

1 FOCUS

Vocabulary Preview
Suggest that students scan the section for the boldface Vocabulary words and write a definition for each word based on the information in the text.

Targeted Resources
❏ Transparencies: **612** Section 40–3 Interest Grabber
❏ Transparencies: **613** Section 40–3 Outline

2 INSTRUCT

Build Science Skills: Using Tables and Graphs
Students design and administer allergy questionnaires and summarize the results in tables and graphs. **L2** **L3**

Make Connections: Health Science
Describe other relatively common autoimmune diseases, such as systemic lupus erythematosus. **L2**

Address Misconceptions
Point out differences between the words *HIV infection* and *AIDS,* which are often misused interchangeably. **L1** **L2**

Build Science Skills: Applying Concepts
Students explain how HIV "tricks" helper T cells into making new copies of HIV and how HIV enters the central nervous system. **L1** **L2**

Use Community Resources
Invite a professional who works with people with AIDS to speak to the class about the medical, emotional, and financial consequences of "living with AIDS." **L1** **L2**

Targeted Resources
❏ Reading and Study Workbook: Section 40–3
❏ Adapted Reading and Study Workbook: Section 40–3
❏ Teaching Resources: Section Summaries 40–3, Worksheets 40–3
❏ Transparencies: **614** Stages of HIV Infection
❏ **PHSchool.com** Infectious diseases and the immune system

3 ASSESS

Evaluate Understanding
Have students write a concise, informative paragraph correctly using each of the Vocabulary words.

Reteach
Make a concept map of the types of disorders covered in the section, and call on students to describe or give an example of each type of disorder.

Targeted Resources
❏ Teaching Resources: Section Review 40–3
❏ **iText** Section 40–3

LESSON PLAN 40–4 (pages 1049–1054)

Time
1 period
1/2 block

The Environment and Your Health

Section Objectives

Local Standards

- **40.4.1 Identify** environmental factors that affect your health.
- **40.4.2 Describe** how you can maintain your health.

Vocabulary risk factor • tumor • carcinogen

1 FOCUS

Reading Strategy
Challenge students to predict what each of the Vocabulary words means before they read the section.

Targeted Resources
- ❏ Transparencies: **615** Section 40–4 Interest Grabber
- ❏ Transparencies: **616** Section 40–4 Outline
- ❏ Transparencies: **617** Concept Map

2 INSTRUCT

Build Science Skills: Applying Concepts
Students identify ways that plants, animals, and other people in their environment might affect their health. **L1** **L2**

Make Connections: Health Science
Point out the dangers of carbon monoxide and the importance of using carbon monoxide detectors. **L2**

Build Science Skills: Drawing Conclusions
Students conclude why infectious diseases, such as smallpox and anthrax, are effective weapons of bioterrorism. **L2**

Analyzing Data
Students analyze and graph data from a table that shows cancer mortality rates by time period, gender, and type of cancer. **L2**

Build Science Skills: Applying Concepts
Students think of at least one specific way they can maintain their health for each of the four general ways presented in the section. **L1**

Targeted Resources
- ❏ Reading and Study Workbook: Section 40–4
- ❏ Adapted Reading and Study Workbook: Section 40–4
- ❏ Teaching Resources: Section Summaries: 40–4, Worksheets 40–4, Enrichment
- ❏ **NSTA** *sci*LINKS Cancer cells

3 ASSESS

Evaluate Understanding
Ask students to make a concept map of environmental factors that affect health.

Reteach
Work with students to make an outline of the section by writing the headings and subheadings as outline topics and subtopics and calling on students to fill in important details.

Targeted Resources
- ❏ Teaching Resources: Section Review 40–4, Chapter Vocabulary Review, Graphic Organizer, Chapter 40 Tests: Levels A and B
- ❏ Lab Assessment: Laboratory Assessment 10
- ❏ *i*Text Section 40–4, Chapter 40 Assessment
- ❏ **PHSchool.com** Online Chapter 40 Test

Chapter 40   The Immune System and Disease

Summary

40–1 Infectious Disease

A **disease** is any change, other than an injury, that disrupts normal body functions. **Some diseases are produced by agents, such as bacteria, viruses, and fungi. Others are caused by materials in the environment, such as cigarette smoke. Still others, such as hemophilia, are inherited.**

Before the 1800s, scientists did not know that microorganisms caused infectious diseases. Disease-causing microorganisms are called **pathogens.** The idea that infectious diseases are caused by pathogens was introduced by Louis Pasteur and Robert Koch. This idea is called the **germ theory of disease.** Koch also developed a series of rules called **Koch's postulates.** These rules help scientists identify which organism causes a specific disease.

Viruses, bacteria, protists, worms, and fungi all can be pathogens. Some pathogens cause disease by destroying cells. Some release toxins into the body. Other pathogens disrupt body functions. Infectious diseases can be spread in several ways.

- **Some infectious diseases are spread from one person to another through coughing, sneezing, or physical contact.** Most are spread through indirect contact, such as when pathogens are carried through the air. These pathogens can be inhaled, or they can be picked up from surfaces.
- **Other infectious diseases are spread through contaminated water or food.**
- **Still others are spread by infected animals.** Animals that carry pathogens from person to person are called **vectors.**

Antibiotics are drugs that kill bacteria without harming the host's cells. Antiviral drugs fight some viral diseases. Rest, a balanced diet, and fluids also help treat disease.

40–2 The Immune System

The function of the immune system is to fight infection through the production of cells that inactivate foreign substances or cells. This system makes cells that recognize, attack, destroy, and "remember" each type of pathogen that enters the body. This process is called **immunity.**

The immune system has nonspecific defenses to stop pathogens from entering the body. These defenses include physical and chemical barriers.

- **First line of defense.** The function of the first line of defense is to keep pathogens out of the body. This role is carried out by skin, mucus, sweat, and tears. **Your body's most important nonspecific defense is the skin.** It forms a barrier that few pathogens can get through. Mucus, saliva, and tears trap pathogens and contain an enzyme that kills bacteria.

- **Second line of defense.** When pathogens do enter the body, other nonspecific defenses go to work. **The inflammatory response is a nonspecific defense reaction to tissue damage caused by injury or infection.** Blood vessels near the wound expand. White blood cells enter the tissues to fight infection. A **fever,** or higher than normal body temperature, can slow pathogen growth. Fever is a chemical response to pathogens.

If a pathogen gets past the nonspecific defenses, specific defenses go to work. This is called the **immune response.** There are two types of immune response.

- In **humoral immunity,** white blood cells, called B cells, make antibodies that attack pathogens in the blood. **Antibodies** are proteins that recognize and bind to specific antigens.

- In **cell-mediated immunity,** white blood cells, called T cells, find and destroy abnormal or infected cells. When a pathogen is destroyed, memory cells are formed. These cells respond if the same pathogen enters the body again.

You can acquire immunity without having a disease. **Vaccination** is the injection of a weakened or mild form of a pathogen to cause immunity. Immunity that results from vaccines is called **active immunity.** Active immunity appears after exposure to an antigen. **Passive immunity** forms when antibodies are introduced into the body. Passive immunity lasts only as long as the antibodies stay in the body.

40–3 Immune System Disorders

Sometimes, disorders occur in the immune system itself. The most common disorder is **allergies.** Allergies occur when antigens enter the body and bind to mast cells. Mast cells are immune cells found throughout the body. The mast cells become activated, and release chemicals called **histamines.** Histamines increase the flow of blood and fluids to the area. This causes allergy symptoms.

When the immune system makes a mistake and attacks the body's own cells, an autoimmune disease results. Autoimmune diseases include Type I diabetes, rheumatoid arthritis, and multiple sclerosis.

Immunodeficiency diseases occur when the immune response breaks down. AIDS is one example of an immunodeficiency disease. AIDS is caused by HIV (human immunodeficiency virus). HIV attaches to receptors on helper T cells. Once inside the cells, HIV copies itself and kills the infected cells. HIV gradually kills off all the helper T cells. As a result, the immune system can no longer fight infections.

AIDS can be transmitted from mother to child during pregnancy, childbirth, and breast-feeding. It can also be transmitted from one person to another through shared needles, contact with infected blood, and sexual intercourse. **The only no-risk behavior with respect to HIV and AIDS is abstinence.**

40–4 The Environment and Your Health

Anything that increases the chance of disease or injury is a **risk factor. Environmental factors that can affect your health include air and water quality, poisonous wastes in landfills, and exposure to solar radiation.**

Bioterrorism is a new health threat. Bioterrorism is the intentional use of biological agents, such as viruses, to disable or kill people.

Cancer is a life-threatening disease in which cells multiply uncontrollably and destroy healthy tissue. Cancer may cause a tumor, a mass of cells that grows out of control. Some tumors are not cancerous.

All forms of cancer result from harmful mutations. Mutations may be inherited. Viruses, chemicals, and radiation can also cause mutations. Sunlight and radon gas are sources of potentially harmful radiation. Radon gas is found in rocks and can leak into buildings. **Carcinogens** are chemicals that cause cancer. Some carcinogens are produced in nature. Others are made by humans. For example, tobacco smoke contains carcinogens. Cigarette smoking is responsible for nearly half of the cancers that occur in the United States.

You can choose behaviors that help keep your immune system functioning properly. **Some healthful behaviors include:**
- **eating a healthful diet**
- **getting plenty of exercise and rest**
- **abstaining from harmful activities**
- **having regular checkups**

Nonspecific Defenses

Nonspecific defenses are immune responses that do not distinguish between one pathogen and another.

Use the words below to complete the table. The first one has been done for you.

cilia	inflammatory response	skin
fever	interferon	

Nonspecific Defense	Role
mucus	traps pathogens in the nose and throat
	increases body temperature to slow the growth of pathogens
	inhibits the synthesis of viral proteins and helps block viral replication
	push pathogens away from the lungs
	provides a barrier that prevents pathogens from entering the body
	produces white blood cells to fight infection

Use the table to answer the question. Circle the correct answer.

1. Which nonspecific defense, considered part of the first line of defense, helps keep pathogens out of the body?

    skin   fever

Humoral Immunity

When an antigen first enters the body, some B cells recognize the antigen. They grow and divide rapidly, producing plasma cells and memory B cells. The plasma cells produce antibodies against the antigen. The memory B cells remain able to produce those antibodies. The next time that antigen enters the body, the body's reaction is much faster.

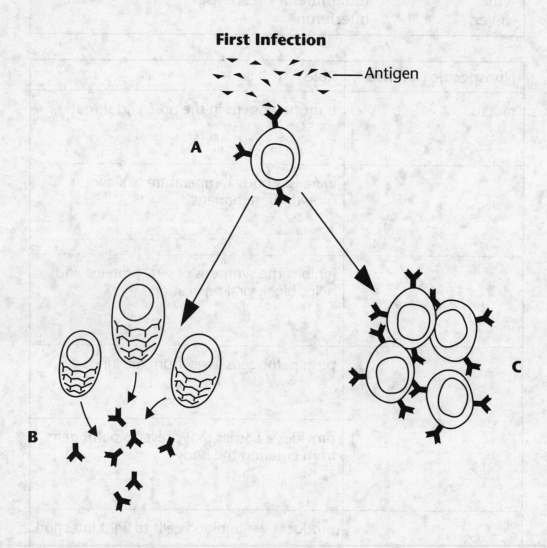

First Infection

Antigen

A

B

C

Identify each step shown in the diagram. Write A, B, or C to match the descriptions with the diagram above.

_____ Antigen binds to B cell.

_____ Some B cells develop into memory B cells.

_____ Some B cells develop into plasma cells. Plasma cells produce antibodies that are released into the bloodstream.

Cell-Mediated Immunity

When a body cell becomes infected with a pathogen, cell-mediated immunity occurs. Different types of T cells are involved in cell-mediated immunity. These include killer T cells, helper T cells, suppressor T cells, and memory T cells.

The table describes the function of four different types of T cells. Use the words below to complete the table. The first one has been done for you.

helper T cell	killer T cell	suppressor T cell

Type of T cell	Function
memory T cell	Causes a secondary response if a pathogen that has already caused a response enters the body again
	Releases substances that shut down killer T cells
	Finds and destroys cells infected with a pathogen
	Produces memory T cells

Answer the questions.

1. Which provides a defense against body cells that have become infected with a pathogen?

   cell-mediated immunity   humoral immunity

2. Why might patients that receive organ transplants need to take medicines that suppress the cell-mediated immune response?

   _____

   _____

   _____

Environmental Health Factors

Factors in your environment, such as air quality, water quality, wastes, and solar radiation, can affect your health.

Use the words below to complete the table. The first one has been completed for you.

carbon monoxide	ozone	radiation	water contaminants

Environmental Factor	Source	Effect on Health
particulates	dust mites, pollen, mold, dander, lead, asbestos	trigger allergic reactions; lead can poison the liver, kidneys, and nervous system; asbestos can cause lung cancer
	automobile exhaust, cigarette smoke, heaters	prevents hemoglobin from carrying oxygen
	vehicle exhaust and factory emissions	can aggravate respiratory conditions
	untreated sewage, chemicals	can cause digestive diseases, hepatitis, cholera; interfere with organ and tissue development; chemicals can cause cancer
	sunlight, X-rays, nuclear radiation, radon	can cause cancer

Answer the question. Circle the correct answer.

1. What is the term for a chemical compound that can cause cancer?

carcinogen   tumor

Vocabulary Review

Matching   *In the space provided, write the letter of the definition that best matches each term.*

_____ **1.** antibiotic

_____ **2.** antibody

_____ **3.** asthma

_____ **4.** disease

_____ **5.** histamine

a. chronic respiratory disease in which air passageways in the lungs are reduced in size

b. compound that kills bacteria without harming the cells of the animal host

c. change other than injury that disrupts normal body functions

d. protein that recognizes and binds to antigens

e. chemical that increases the flow of blood and fluids to the surrounding area

Matching   *In the space provided, write the letter of the definition that best matches each term.*

_____ **6.** inflammatory

_____ **7.** interferon

_____ **8.** pathogen

_____ **9.** tumor

_____**10.** vector

a. mass of growing tissue that is a result of uncontrolled cell division

b. disease-causing agent

c. type of response that is a nonspecific defense reaction to tissue damage caused by injury or infection

d. protein that helps cells resist viral infections

e. animal that carries disease-causing organisms from person to person

Summary

40–1 Infectious Disease

A disease is any change, other than an injury, that disrupts the normal functions of the body. Diseases are produced by agents such as bacteria, materials in the environment such as cigarette smoke, or inherited conditions. Disease-causing agents are called pathogens. Diseases caused by pathogens are called infectious diseases.

In the 1800s, scientists concluded that infectious diseases are caused by microorganisms, or germs. This idea is now known as the germ theory of disease. A scientist named Robert Koch developed rules to identify the microorganism that causes a specific disease. These rules, known as Koch's postulates, are still used.

Pathogens cause disease by destroying cells, releasing toxins, or disrupting body functions. Types of pathogens include viruses, bacteria, protists, worms, and fungi. Infectious diseases can be transmitted in several ways. Many are spread from one person to another through coughing, sneezing, or physical contact. Some are spread through contaminated water or food. Others are spread by infected animals. Vectors are animals that carry pathogens from person to person.

Antibiotics are drugs that kill bacteria without harming the cells of the host. Antiviral drugs fight certain viral diseases. The best treatment for most infections includes rest, a balanced diet, and fluids.

40–2 The Immune System

The immune system is the body's main defense against pathogens. It produces cells that recognize, attack, destroy, and "remember" each type of pathogen that enters the body. This process is called immunity. The immune system has both nonspecific and specific defenses.

The skin is the most important nonspecific defense. It forms a barrier that few pathogens can get through. Mucus, saliva, and tears trap pathogens and contain an enzyme that kills bacteria. If pathogens manage to enter the body, other nonspecific defenses go to work. The inflammatory response occurs when tissue is damaged by injury or infection. Blood vessels near the site expand, and white blood cells enter the tissues to fight infection. The immune system also releases chemicals that cause a fever. The higher body temperature slows the growth of many pathogens. In addition, cells infected with a virus may produce proteins called interferons, which interfere with the growth of the virus.

If a pathogen is able to get past the nonspecific defenses, the immune system reacts with specific defenses against that particular pathogen. This is called the immune response. A substance that triggers the immune response is known as an antigen. Pathogens may serve as antigens.

There are two types of immune response: humoral immunity and cell-mediated immunity. In humoral immunity, white blood cells, called B cells, produce antibodies that travel through the bloodstream and attack pathogens in the blood. Antibodies are proteins that recognize and bind to specific antigens. In cell-mediated immunity, white blood cells, called T cells, track down and destroy abnormal or infected cells. T cells also attack the cells of transplanted organs. This is called rejection. It can be prevented with drugs. After a pathogen is destroyed, certain B cells or T cells, called memory cells, remain in the body. Memory cells can quickly respond to the same pathogen if it enters the body again. This greatly reduces the chance that the disease develops again.

Besides having a disease, immunity can be acquired in other ways. Vaccination is the injection of a weakened or mild form of a pathogen to produce immunity. This type of immunity is called active immunity. Active immunity appears after exposure to an antigen. Another type of immunity is called passive immunity. It is produced when antibodies enter the body. Antibodies may be injected to fight an infection. Antibodies also pass from mother to fetus. Passive immunity lasts only as long as the antibodies remain in the body.

40–3 Immune System Disorders

There are three types of immune system disorders: allergies, autoimmune diseases, and immunodeficiency diseases. Allergies are overreactions of the immune system to antigens such as pollen. Antigens that cause allergic reactions are called allergens. In response to allergens, the body produces chemicals called histamines, which cause symptoms such as sneezing and watery eyes. Some allergic reactions lead to asthma. Asthma is a chronic respiratory disease in which the air passages become narrower than normal. This may cause coughing and difficulty breathing.

Autoimmune diseases occur when the immune system attacks the body's own cells. For example, in Type I diabetes, the immune system attacks cells of the pancreas that make insulin. Other examples of autoimmune diseases are rheumatoid arthritis, myasthenia gravis, and multiple sclerosis (MS).

Immunodeficiency diseases occur when the normal immune response breaks down. The most common immunodeficiency disease is AIDS. It is caused by the human immunodeficiency virus (HIV). HIV can be transmitted through the exchange of body fluids such as blood. The only no-risk behavior with respect to HIV and AIDS is abstinence. At present, there is no cure or vaccine for AIDS.

40–4 The Environment and Your Health

Anything that increases the chance of disease or injury is a risk factor. Risk factors in the environment include poor air quality and solar radiation. Air quality refers to the number and types of dangerous gases and particles in the air. Water, like air, can carry dangerous substances. For example, human or animal wastes can pollute water with bacteria. Bioterrorism is a new health threat. Bioterrorism is the intentional use of biological agents, such as viruses, to disable or kill people.

Cancer is a life-threatening disease in which cells multiply uncontrollably and destroy healthy tissue. Cancer may cause a tumor. A tumor is a mass of cells growing out of control. Some tumors are not cancerous. All forms of cancer are ultimately caused by harmful mutations. Mutations may be inherited or caused by viruses, chemicals, or radiation. Chemicals that cause cancer are called carcinogens. Sources of potentially harmful radiation include sunlight and radon gas, which is found in rocks and can leak into buildings. Protecting the body from radiation and carcinogens can help prevent cancer. Other ways of maintaining health include eating a healthful diet, getting plenty of exercise and rest, abstaining from harmful activities, and having regular checkups.

Section 40–1 Infectious Disease (pages 1031–1035)

🔑 Key Concepts
- What causes disease?
- How are infectious diseases transmitted?

Introduction (page 1031)

1. Any change, other than an injury, that disrupts the normal functions of the body, is a(an) _____.

2. What are three ways diseases can come about? _____
_____
_____

3. Disease-causing agents are called _____.

The Germ Theory of Disease (pages 1031–1032)

4. State the germ theory of disease. _____
_____

5. Circle the letter of each scientist whose work led to the germ theory of disease.

   a. Koch   b. Steere   c. Pasteur   d. Burgdorfer

6. Is the following sentence true or false? Lyme disease is caused by bacteria.

   _____

7. Circle the letter of the type of organism that spreads Lyme disease.

   a. mosquito   b. deer tick   c. deer fly   d. horse fly

Koch's Postulates (page 1032)

8. What are scientists trying to identify when they use Koch's postulates? _____
_____
_____

9. Number the steps in the flowchart below so they show how to apply Koch's postulates.

| Pathogen identified | Pathogen injected into healthy lab mouse | Pathogen grown in pure culture | Healthy mouse becomes sick | Pathogen identified |

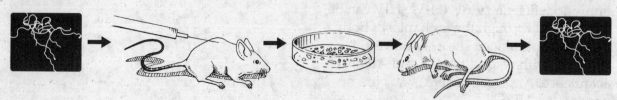

_____   _____   _____   _____   _____

Agents of Disease (pages 1033–1034)

10. Is the following sentence true or false? Most of the bacteria and yeast that are found in the body are harmful and cause disease. _____

11. List two ways that bacteria can produce illness.

    a. _____ b. _____

Match each type of pathogen with a disease caused by that type.

Type of Pathogen	Disease
_____ 12. Virus	a. Athlete's foot
_____ 13. Bacterium	b. Anthrax
_____ 14. Protist	c. Tapeworm
_____ 15. Worm	d. Influenza
_____ 16. Fungus	e. Malaria

How Diseases Are Spread (page 1034)

17. List three ways that infectious diseases are spread.

    a. _____

    b. _____

    c. _____

18. Animals that carry pathogens from person to person are called _____.

19. Is the following sentence true or false? Thorough hand washing does not help prevent the spread of many pathogens. _____

Fighting Infectious Diseases (page 1035)

20. Compounds that kill bacteria without harming the cells of humans or animals are called _____.

21. Circle the letter of each sentence that is true about antibiotics.

    a. They work by interfering with the cellular processes of microorganisms.

    b. Many of them are produced by living organisms.

    c. They were first discovered in the 1940s.

    d. They are effective against viruses.

22. How do antiviral drugs fight viral diseases? _____

    _____

    _____

Section 40–2 The Immune System
(pages 1036–1042)

👌 **Key Concepts**
- What is the function of the immune system?
- What are the body's nonspecific defenses against invading pathogens?

Introduction (page 1036)

1. The body's main defense against pathogens is the _____.

Match the type of defense with its role in the body.

Defense	Role
_____ 2. Nonspecific	a. Destroying harmful pathogens that enter the body
_____ 3. Specific	b. Preventing pathogens from entering the body

Nonspecific Defenses (pages 1036–1038)

4. What is the job of the body's first line of defense? _____

_____

_____

5. List the four components of the body's first line of defense.

a. _____   c. _____

b. _____   d. _____

6. Is the following sentence true or false? The body's most important nonspecific defense is the skin. _____

7. How does mucus help protect the body from disease? _____

_____

8. Body secretions contain an enzyme, called _____, that kills bacteria.

9. When does the body's second line of defense come into play? _____

_____

_____

10. Is the following sentence true or false? The inflammatory response is a nonspecific reaction to tissue damage caused by injury or infection. _____

11. White blood cells called _____ engulf and destroy bacteria.

12. Why does an increase in the number of white blood cells indicate that the body is dealing with a serious infection? _____

_____

_____

13. An elevated body temperature is called a(an) _____.

14. Circle the letter of each sentence that is true about elevated body temperature.

   a. It kills many pathogens.

   b. It speeds up the action of white blood cells.

   c. It decreases heart rate.

   d. It slows down chemical reactions.

15. Is the following sentence true or false? Interferon is a protein that helps fight bacterial infections. _____

Specific Defenses (pages 1038–1040)

16. What is the immune response? _____

   _____

   _____

17. A substance that triggers the immune response is known as a(an) _____.

18. What are some examples of antigens? _____

   _____

   _____

19. List the two different immune responses.

   a. _____   b. _____

20. Circle the letter of each sentence that is true about humoral immunity.

   a. It is a response to pathogens in body fluids.

   b. It depends on lymphocytes.

   c. It involves antibodies.

   d. It involves plasma cells.

21. A protein that helps destroy pathogens is called a(an) _____.

22. Is the following sentence true or false? Antibodies can fight viruses but not bacteria.

   _____

23. Label the antigen-binding sites in the drawing below.

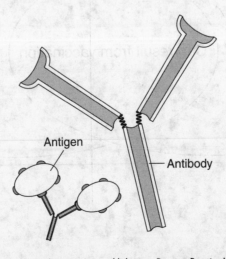

Antigen

Antibody

24. Is the following sentence true or false? Plasma cells are specialized B cells.
_____

25. What happens once the body has been exposed to a pathogen? _____
_____
_____
_____

26. Circle the letter of each sentence that is true about cell-mediated immunity.
a. It is a defense against the body's own cells.
b. It involves killer T cells.
c. It involves antibodies.
d. It causes pathogen cells to rupture and die.

27. Is the following sentence true or false? Cell-mediated immunity is particularly important for diseases caused by prokaryotic pathogens. _____

Acquired Immunity (pages 1041–1042)

28. What is vaccination? _____
_____
_____

29. How do vaccines work? _____
_____
_____

30. Complete the Venn diagram by labeling the two types of immunity.

_____   _____

Is due to antigens
Lasts for life

Can result from vaccination

Is due to antibiotics
Lasts for a short time

Section 40–3 Immune System Disorders
(pages 1043–1047)

Key Concepts
- What is an autoimmune disease?
- How can AIDS be prevented?

Allergies (page 1043)

1. An overreaction of the immune system caused by antigens is called a(an)

_____.

2. Circle the letter of each choice that is a result of allergens binding to mast cells.

   a. The mast cells release chemicals known as histamines.

   b. There is increased flow of blood and fluids to the surrounding area.

   c. Sneezing, runny nose, watery eyes, and other symptoms occur.

   d. Antihistamines are released by the mast cells.

Asthma (page 1044)

3. A chronic respiratory disease in which air passages become narrower than normal is

called _____.

Autoimmune Diseases (page 1044)

4. What produces an autoimmune disease? _____

_____

_____

5. Complete the table about autoimmune diseases.

AUTOIMMUNE DISEASES

Autoimmune Disease	Organ or Tissue That Is Attacked
Rheumatoid arthritis	
Type I diabetes	
Myasthenia gravis	
Multiple sclerosis	

AIDS, an Immunodeficiency Disease (pages 1045–1047)

6. Is the following sentence true or false? AIDS is a type of disease in which the immune

system is weakened by infection. _____

7. What does AIDS stand for? _____

8. List some of the diseases that may be symptoms of AIDS.

   a. _____

   b. _____

9. Circle the letter of the choice that refers to the cells that are attacked by HIV.

   a. Helper T cells   c. Red blood cells

   b. Killer T cells   d. Helper B cells

10. Is the following sentence true or false? The body does not produce antibodies against HIV. _____

11. Circle the letter of each choice that is true about the spread of HIV.

    a. It is usually spread by casual contact.

    b. It is spread only by sexual contact.

    c. It can be spread by sharing needles.

    d. It is spread only by contact with infected blood or other body fluids.

12. Is the following sentence true or false? Any sexual contact carries some risk of contracting HIV. _____

Reading Skill Practice

When you read about new or difficult concepts, making a concept map can help you better understand and remember the ideas. Make a concept map that shows how immune system disorders are classified, based on the material in Section 40–3. For more information about concept maps, see Appendix A of your text. Do your work on a separate sheet of paper.

Section 40–4 The Environment and Your Health
(pages 1049–1054)

🔑 **Key Concepts**
- What environmental factors affect your health?
- How can you maintain your health?

Introduction (page 1049)

1. A _____ is anything that increases the chance of disease or injury.

2. Is the following sentence true or false? Both heredity and environmental factors can affect your health. _____

Air Quality (pages 1049–1050)

3. Circle the letter of each factor that is part of air quality.

   a. number and concentrations of gases

   b. amount of sunlight

   c. nature and amount of tiny particles

4. Why can overexposure to carbon monoxide be fatal? _____

   _____

   _____

5. _____ is a highly reactive form of oxygen that is produced by vehicle exhaust and factory emissions.

6. Allergic reactions can be triggered by _____.

Water Quality (pages 1050–1051)

7. What has probably been the single most important factor in nearly doubling human life expectancy over the last century or so? _____

8. Circle the letter of each of the following that can be a water pollutant.

   a. human and animal wastes

   b. carbon monoxide

   c. chemicals

   d. dust mites

Bioterrorism (page 1051)

9. The intentional use of biological agents to disable or kill individuals is called

   _____ .

10. Why could the release of smallpox virus cause serious problems? _____

    _____

    _____

Name_____ Class_____ Date _____

Cancer (pages 1052–1053)

11. Circle the letter of each sentence that is true about cancer.

   a. It is generally a life-threatening disease.

   b. It is characterized by cells multiplying uncontrollably and destroying healthy tissue.

   c. It is caused by foreign cells invading the body.

   d. It is easy to treat and to understand.

12. When do cancers begin? _____

_____

_____

13. A mass of growing tissue is known as a(an) _____.

14. Is the following sentence true or false? All tumors are cancerous. _____

Match the type of tumor with its description.

Tumor Type	Description
_____ **15.** Benign	**a.** Does not spread to surrounding healthy tissue or to other parts of the body
_____ **16.** Malignant	**b.** Can invade and destroy surrounding healthy tissue

17. List three ways that cancer cells cause illness as they spread.

   a. _____

   b. _____

   c. _____

18. Complete the concept map.

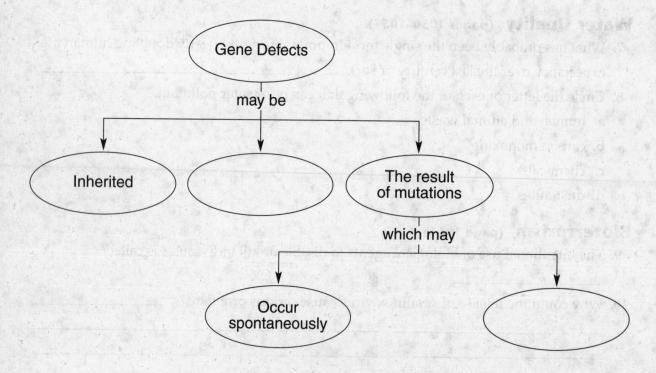

19. Chemical compounds that are known to cause cancer are called

_____.

20. Why is it important to detect cancer early? _____

_____

Maintaining Health (page 1054)

21. Give three reasons it is important to eat a healthful diet. _____

_____

_____

_____

22. For most people, adequate rest means getting about _____ hours of sleep each
night.

23. _____ can cause a variety of respiratory conditions as
well as cancers of the lung, mouth, and throat.

24. Is the following sentence true or false? Discovering a disease early does not make it
easier to treat._____

Reading Skill Practice

When you read a section with difficult material, writing a summary can help you
identify and remember the main ideas and supporting details. Write a concise
paragraph summing up the material under each heading in Section 40–4. Each of
your paragraphs should be much shorter than the text under that heading in your
book. Include each of the highlighted, boldface vocabulary terms in your summary.
Do your work on a separate sheet of paper.

Vocabulary Review

Matching   *In the space provided, write the letter of the definition that best matches each term.*

_____ **1.** disease

_____ **2.** pathogen

_____ **3.** antibiotic

_____ **4.** immunity

_____ **5.** inflammatory response

_____ **6.** antigen

_____ **7.** vaccination

_____ **8.** allergy

_____ **9.** histamine

_____ **10.** asthma

_____ **11.** risk factor

_____ **12.** vector

a. process in which the immune system produces cells that destroy pathogens or make them harmless

b. substance that triggers the immune response

c. overreaction of the immune system to antigens such as pollen

d. any change, other than an injury, that disrupts the normal functions of the body

e. chemical the body produces in response to allergens

f. drug that kills bacteria without harming the cells of the host

g. disease-causing agent

h. injection of a weakened or mild form of a pathogen to produce immunity

i. animal that carries pathogens from person to person

j. anything that increases the chance of disease or injury

k. response in which blood vessels expand and white blood cells enter infected tissues to fight infection

l. chronic respiratory disease in which the air passages become narrower than normal

Multiple Choice   *In the space provided, write the letter of the answer that best completes each sentence.*

_____ **13.** Koch's postulates are rules for
   a. identifying the microorganism that causes a specific disease.
   b. keeping the environment safe for human health.
   c. determining which vector spreads a disease.
   d. protecting the skin from sunlight.

_____ **14.** Nonspecific defenses include
   a. fever.
   b. interferon.
   c. the skin.
   d. all of the above.

_____ **15.** The type of immunity that results when antibodies are passed from mother to fetus is called
   a. active immunity.
   b. passive immunity.
   c. permanent immunity.
   d. inherited immunity.

_____ **16.** The type of immunity in which T cells attack abnormal or infected cells is known as
   a. humoral immunity.
   b. passive immunity.
   c. cell-mediated immunity.
   d. T cell immunity.

_____ **17.** An example of an autoimmune disease is
   a. Type I diabetes.
   b. AIDS.
   c. asthma.
   d. allergy to pollen.

Chapter 40 The Immune System and Disease   **Section Review 40-1**

Reviewing Key Concepts

Short Answer *On the lines provided, answer the following:*

1. What is a disease?

_____

_____

2. What are three general causes of disease?

_____

_____

3. Name the four ways in which infectious diseases are spread.

_____

_____

Reviewing Key Skills

4. **Applying Concepts** The organism that causes meningitis has been identified as a bacterium named *Neisseria meningitis*. Does this identification support the germ theory of disease? Explain your answer.

_____

_____

_____

5. **Inferring** Koch's postulates state that a pathogen must be isolated and grown in a laboratory in pure culture. Why is this step essential to identifying the pathogen that causes a specific disease?

_____

_____

_____

Classifying *On the line provided, write the type of pathogen—bacterium, virus, fungi, protist—that causes each disease.*

6. Influenza _____

7. Anthrax _____

8. Malaria _____

9. Athlete's foot _____

10. **Applying Concepts** Would an antibiotic help you get rid of the common cold? Explain your answer.

_____

_____

Name_____ Class_____ Date _____

Reviewing Key Concepts

Short Answer *On the lines provided, answer the following questions.*

1. How does skin act as a nonspecific defense against pathogens?

   _____

   _____

2. How does the inflammatory response protect your body from pathogens?

   _____

   _____

3. What is permanent immunity? _____

   _____

Matching *On the line provided, write the letter of the type of immunity that matches the description.*

a. cell-mediated immunity   b. active immunity   c. humoral immunity   d. passive immunity

_____ 4. Pathogens marked by antibodies are destroyed by phagocytes.

_____ 5. Killer T cells bind to infected cells, disrupting their cell membranes and destroying them.

_____ 6. A vaccine is injected that enables the body to mount an immune response against the pathogen.

_____ 7. Antibodies from another animal are injected into the bloodstream and remain for several weeks.

Reviewing Key Skills

Interpreting Graphics *Use the diagram to answer the following question.*

8. What happens to the antibody concentration after the second exposure? Why does this change occur?

   _____

   _____

   _____

   _____

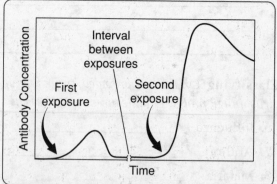

Primary and Secondary Immune Responses

9. **Applying Concepts** After having chicken pox, a person carries millions of memory B cells. Why is it unlikely for this person to develop the disease again?

   _____

   _____

Chapter 40 The Immune System and Disease   **Section Review 40-3**

Reviewing Key Concepts

Short Answer *On the lines provided, answer the following questions.*

1. What causes an autoimmune disease?

_____

_____

_____

2. What factors can trigger asthma attacks?

_____

_____

_____

Matching *On the line provided, write the letter of the disease or disorder that best matches the description.*

_____ 3. smooth muscle contractions reduce the size of air passageways in the lungs

_____ 4. mast cells release histamines

_____ 5. an autoimmune reaction attacks the insulin-producing cells of the pancreas

_____ 6. antibodies attack neuromuscular junctions

_____ 7. there is destruction of the functions of neurons

_____ 8. most of the helper T cells are destroyed

a. allergy
b. AIDS
c. multiple sclerosis
d. asthma
e. myasthenia gravis
f. Type I diabetes

Reviewing Key Skills

9. **Applying Concepts** The prefix *anti-* means *against*. Most allergy medications contain an *anti*histamine. Explain what happens during an allergic reaction and how antihistamines help ease the symptoms.

_____

_____

_____

_____

_____

10. **Applying Concepts** How does HIV weaken the immune system?

_____

_____

_____

_____

_____

Reviewing Key Concepts

Short Answer *On the lines provided, answer the following questions.*

1. What is bioterrorism?

   _____

   _____

2. What can you do to help prevent cancer?

   _____

   _____

   _____

   _____

Reviewing Key Skills

3. **Applying Concepts** Why has improving the quality of drinking
   water probably been the single most important factor in nearly doubling human life expectancy over the last century or so?

   _____

   _____

   _____

4. **Inferring** What environmental risk factors might be found inside a home?

   _____

   _____

   _____

5. **Comparing and Contrasting** As an environmental risk factor, how
   is radon similar to asbestos? How is it different?

   _____

   _____

   _____

6. **Inferring** People with some genetic disorders have abnormal
   hemoglobin. Why might these people be more susceptible to the
   effects of carbon monoxide than people with normal hemoglobin?

   _____

   _____

   _____

7. **Applying Concepts** Why has the worldwide elimination of smallpox made humans more susceptible to use of the smallpox virus in
   bioterrorism?

   _____

   _____

   _____

Chapter 40 The Immune System and Disease   Chapter Vocabulary Review

Crossword Puzzle *Use the clues below and on the following page to complete the puzzle.*

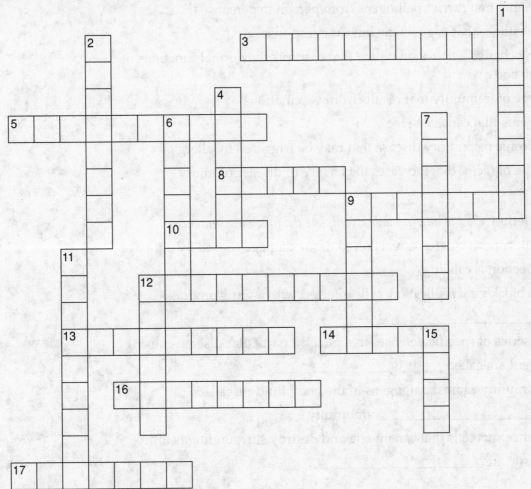

Across

3. injection of a weakened or mild form of a pathogen to produce immunity

5. Koch's rules

8. mass of cells growing out of control

9. immune disorder characterized by the production of histamines

10. another word for microorganisms

12. drug that fights bacterial infections

13. chemical produced by mast cells that causes sneezing and watery eyes

14. higher-than-normal body temperature

16. ability of the body to resist a specific pathogen

17. type of immunity that results from a woman passing antibodies to her fetus

Down

1. protein that recognizes and binds to antigens
2. type of pathogen that causes anthrax and diphtheria
4. animal that carries pathogens from person to person
6. substance that triggers the immune response
7. any change, other than injury, that disrupts the normal functions of the body
9. type of immunity that results from vaccination
11. agents that cause disease
12. chronic respiratory disease that may be triggered by allergies
15. type of factor that increases the chance of disease or injury

Completion *On the lines provided, complete the following sentences.*

18. A nonspecific defense reaction to tissue damage caused by injury or infection is called _____ .

19. To block viral replication, cells infected with a virus produce

    _____ .

20. A series of specific defenses that attack a particular disease-causing agent are called _____ .

21. Immunity against pathogens in the body fluids is called _____ immunity.

22. Cancerous cells that can invade and destroy surrounding healthy tissue are _____ .

Chapter 40 The Immune System and Disease Enrichment

With Every Breath You Take

In the last few decades, there has been a growing awareness of the connection between cigarette smoking and lung cancer. Smoking is not the only cause of lung cancer, but the majority of people who contract lung cancer are smokers.

What is lung cancer? Normally, the division of a lung cell to form new cells is carefully controlled by the body. Occasionally, something goes wrong as a lung cell divides, resulting in two new cells that do not respond to the body's signal to stop dividing. The new cells continue to divide uncontrollably. Eventually, a tumor—a mass of rapidly dividing, abnormal cells—may develop.

Lung cancer follows a series of diagnosable steps. First, there is inflammation, with a loss of the ciliated cells that clear the lungs. Then, the normal columnar cells that line the airways become flatter. Eventually, metaplasmic, or abnormal, cells appear. Metaplasmic cells are found in over 90 percent of smokers. However, these cells will disappear if a smoker quits for 5 years or more.

The next stage of lung cancer is called *cancer in situ*. In this stage, a small (several centimeters long) tumor develops in the lining of the lung. At this stage, the cancer has not spread or invaded surrounding tissues. Cancer in situ may eventually turn into an invasive, or malignant, tumor. If it does, the tumor will spread to the other lung, the lymph nodes, and other parts of the body. Once the cancer has spread to other parts of the body, there is little chance for a cure.

Although lung cancer has been linked to cigarette smoking, there are other causes of lung cancer. People who work in jobs where they are exposed to carcinogens (cancer-causing substances) have an increased risk of developing lung cancer. Medical technicians who work near forms of radiation such as X-rays are also at risk. Other carcinogens include arsenic, chromium, iron oxide, asbestos, and petroleum products. Because of the increased awareness of the dangers of workplace carcinogens, many mining, petroleum, and chemical industries have had to reduce their employees' exposure to harmful chemicals.

Lung cancer is not the only health hazard associated with the use of tobacco. Studies indicate that smokers have higher rates of mouth, throat, and esophagus cancer. Smokers are at greater risk if they started to smoke at an early age. Other factors that increase risk include inhaling deeply, taking more puffs per cigarette, and keeping the cigarette in the mouth between puffs.

Lately, social pressure has helped to create laws that require many public gathering places to be smoke free. Increased awareness of the dangers of second-hand smoke has made people more concerned about protecting their health.

Evaluation *Answer the following questions on a separate sheet of paper.*

1. What are some other causes of lung cancer besides smoking?

2. Which person is at greater risk of contracting lung cancer:

    a. A 40-year old man who has been smoking for 20 years.

    b. A 40-year old man who has been smoking for 5 years.

    Explain your answer.

Chapter 40 The Immune System and Disease   **Graphic Organizer**

Concept Map

*Using information from the chapter, complete the concept map below. If there is
not enough room in the concept map to write your answers, write them on a
separate sheet of paper.*

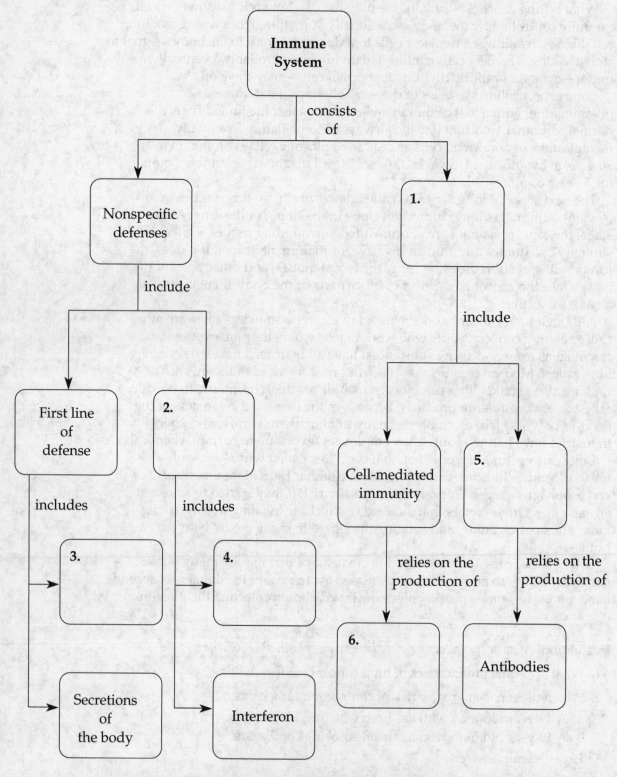

Chapter 40 The Immune System and Disease   **Chapter Test A**

Multiple Choice

Write the letter that best answers the question or completes the statement on the line provided.

_____ 1. Diseases are caused by
    a. pathogens.   c. fungi.
    b. cigarette smoke.   d. all of the above

_____ 2. An example of an infectious disease that is spread by viruses in the air is
    a. athlete's foot.   c. flu.
    b. tuberculosis.   d. tetanus.

_____ 3. How can you prevent the spread of Lyme disease?
    a. Wash your hands frequently.
    b. Avoid sexual contact.
    c. Avoid areas where ticks may be present.
    d. Cover your mouth with a tissue when you cough.

_____ 4. Antibiotics fight infections by
    a. preventing viruses from replicating.
    b. killing bacteria.
    c. killing infected cells.
    d. growing green mold that inhibits bacterial growth.

_____ 5. The inflammatory response can cause
    a. permanent immunity.
    b. pain, swelling, and fever.
    c. antibodies to bind to antigens.
    d. killer T cells to attack infected cells.

_____ 6. If the skin is cut or broken, an infection can result from microorganisms
    a already inside the body.   c. in the blood.
    b. on the skin.   d. in the mucus.

_____ 7. Unlike in passive immunity, in active immunity antibodies are produced by
    a. the mother of an infant.
    b. your own body.
    c. other animals.
    d. an autoimmune disease.

_____ 8. Humoral immunity is carried out by
    a. killer T cells.   c. antibodies.
    b. lymphocytes.   d. macrophages.

_____ 9. Asthma is an example of

   a. the immune system's attacking its own body cells.

   b. the immune system's overreacting to an antigen.

   c. an autoimmune disease.

   d. cancer.

_____10. The sneezing, runny nose, and itchy eyes associated with allergies are caused when

   a. smooth muscles reduce the size of air passageways in the lungs.

   b. the immune system attacks the body's own cells.

   c. mast cells release histamines.

   d. infected cells produce interferon.

_____11. Autoimmune diseases result when the immune system

   a. fails to distinguish self from nonself.

   b. overreacts to certain antigens.

   c. is weakened by asthma.

   d. all of the above

_____12. All of the following are ways that HIV can be spread EXCEPT

   a. sharing needles for intravenous drug use.

   b. tending to another person's bleeding wound when you have a cut on your hand.

   c. using another person's hairbrush.

   d. engaging in sexual activity.

_____13. HIV spreads through the body by

   a. replicating inside the cells of the immune system.

   b. preventing the body from producing antigens.

   c. causing the body to have asthma attacks.

   d. strengthening the immune system.

_____14. Cancer cells affect other cells in the body by

   a. taking in nutrients needed by other cells.

   b. increasing nerve connections.

   c. forming benign tumors throughout the body.

   d. all of the above

_____15. Transplanted organs may be rejected in the type of immune response called

   a. cell-mediated immunity.

   b. inflammatory response.

   c. humoral immunity.

   d. antibody response.

Completion

Complete each statement on the line provided.

16. Smallpox, botulism, and malaria are all examples of _____ diseases.

17. Insecticides are used to kill mosquitoes, which are _____ for West Nile virus and the protists that cause malaria.

18. _____ are effective at treating bacterial infections but not at treating colds.

19. Any opening in the skin is a potential entrance for _____ .

20. A person who has _____ is likely to suffer from a number of other rare infections because a virus attacks the immune system.

Short Answer

In complete sentences, write the answers to the questions on the lines provided.

21. What role does interferon play in the immune system? Is it effective against all pathogens?

_____
_____
_____
_____

22. Describe the mechanism that causes allergies.

_____
_____
_____
_____

23. What causes autoimmune diseases?

_____
_____
_____
_____

24. What effects does HIV have on the immune system?

_____
_____
_____
_____

25. Describe the relationship between antigens and antibodies.

_____

_____

_____

_____

Using Science Skills

Use the diagram below to answer the following questions on the lines provided.

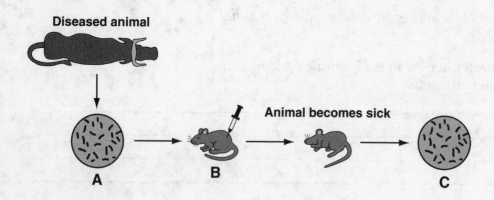

Figure 1

26. Inferring What is the purpose of the culture labeled A in Figure 1?

_____

_____

_____

27. Interpreting Graphics What is happening in step B of Figure 1?

_____

_____

_____

28. Inferring What is the purpose of the culture labeled C in Figure 1?

_____

_____

_____

_____

_____

29. **Predicting** Look at Figure 1. Predict what will happen if the microorganisms grown in the petri dish labeled C are injected into a healthy mouse. Support your answer using the figure.

_____

_____

_____

_____

30. **Drawing Conclusions** Assume that the cultures in A and C in Figure 1 are identical. What can you conclude from this experiment based on this information?

_____

_____

_____

_____

Essay

Write the answer to each question in the space provided.

31. Identify three main causes of disease. Give an example of a disease caused by each factor you identify.

32. Describe active and passive immunity and explain how an individual develops each type.

33. Describe the inflammatory response in terms of a wound.

34. What are three main causes of cancer? Explain how each factor causes cancer.

35. Compare and contrast cell-mediated immunity and humoral immunity.

Chapter 40 The Immune System and Disease

Multiple Choice

Write the letter that best answers the question or completes the statement on the line provided.

____ 1. The germ theory of disease states that infectious diseases are caused by
   a. toxins.
   b. microorganisms.
   c. heredity.

____ 2. An infectious disease is one that is caused by
   a. heredity.
   b. materials in the environment.
   c. pathogens.

____ 3. How are infectious diseases spread?
   a. through coughing, sneezing, or physical contact
   b. by infected animals
   c. both a and b

____ 4. Compounds that kill bacterial cells without harming the cells of humans or other animals are called
   a. antiviral drugs.
   b. insecticides.
   c. antibiotics.

____ 5. The body's nonspecific defenses against invading pathogens include
   a. antibiotics.
   b. mucus, sweat, and tears.
   c. antibodies.

____ 6. The body's most important nonspecific defense is
   a. the skin.
   b. cell-mediated immunity.
   c. the inflammatory response.

____ 7. An immune response is triggered by a(an)
   a. antibiotic.
   b. antibody.
   c. antigen.

____ 8. The symptoms of allergies include
   a. fever and rare types of cancer.
   b. sneezing and watery eyes.
   c. unusual infections of the lungs, mouth, throat, and skin.

____ 9. An example of an autoimmune disease is
   a. asthma.
   b. allergies.
   c. multiple sclerosis.

____10. Doctors first suspected that AIDS was weakening the immune
       system of infected patients when their patients developed
   a. asthma.
   b. allergies.
   c. rare infections.

____11. HIV weakens the immune system by killing
   a. antibodies.
   b. B cells.
   c. helper T cells.

____12. HIV is spread by
   a. sharing utensils.
   b. hugging.
   c. contact with infected blood.

____13. Cancer can be caused by
   a. bacteria.
   b. asthma.
   c. radiation.

____14. A benign tumor is one that
   a. is cancerous.
   b. is malignant.
   c. does not spread to other parts of the body.

____15. Regular exercise helps maintain health by
   a. maintaining cardiovascular fitness.
   b. increasing blood pressure.
   c. helping the body to conserve energy.

Completion

Complete each statement on the line provided.

16. A(An) _____ is any disease-causing organism.

17. Antibiotics are used to treat infectious diseases caused by _____ .

18. Killer T cells attack pathogens in _____ immunity.

19. A weakened or mild form of a pathogen injected to produce immunity is a
   _____ .

20. _____ immunity involves antibodies in the bloodstream.

Short Answer

In complete sentences, write the answers to the questions on the lines provided.

21. What are three general causes of disease?

_____

_____

_____

_____

22. Describe one way that antibiotics fight infection.

_____

_____

_____

_____

23. How does the skin act as a nonspecific defense against pathogens?

_____

_____

_____

_____

24. What are allergies?

_____

_____

_____

_____

25. What is the difference between a benign tumor and a malignant tumor?

_____

_____

_____

_____

Name______________________________ Class__________________ Date ______________

Using Science Skills

Use the diagram to answer the following questions on the lines provided.

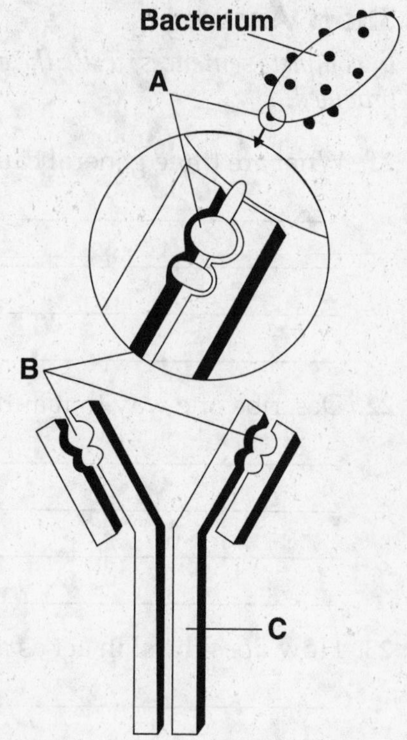

Figure 1

26. Interpreting Graphics What does Figure 1 represent?

____

____

____

____

27. Interpreting Graphics What does letter B represent?

____

____

____

____

28. Interpreting Graphics Which structure or structures trigger the production of antibodies?

____

____

29. Interpreting Graphics What kind of immunity is represented in Figure 1?

____

____

____

30. Interpreting Graphics What role do antigen-binding sites play in an infection?

____

____

____

____

____

____

Unit 10 The Human Body   **Unit Test A**

Multiple Choice

Write the letter that best answers the question or completes the statement on the line provided.

____ 1. The human organ system that pumps blood through the body is the
  a. nervous system.
  b. circulatory system.
  c. endocrine system.
  d. immune system.

____ 2. Neurons that carry messages from the brain to glands are called
  a. sensory neurons.
  b. interneurons.
  c. motor neurons.
  d. secretor neurons.

____ 3. The function of cerebrospinal fluid is to
  a. transmit messages between neurons.
  b. carry messages from the cerebrum to the spinal cord.
  c. prevent the exchange of wastes between blood and nervous tissue.
  d. protect the brain and spinal cord.

____ 4. If a bone is modeled by a lever, what does the fulcrum represent?
  a. tendon   c. muscle
  b. joint   d. ligament

____ 5. What is the difference between a weak and a strong muscle contraction?
  a. number of muscle cells contracting
  b. distance the actin filaments move
  c. distance between the Z lines
  d. height of the cross-bridges between filaments

____ 6. The chamber of the heart that receives blood from the body is the
  a. left atrium.
  b. left ventricle.
  c. right atrium.
  d. right ventricle.

_____ 7. Cells in the breathing center monitor the blood level of
     a. carbon monoxide
     b. hemoglobin
     c. oxygen
     d. carbon dioxide.

_____ 8. Which of the following is NOT needed for blood clotting?
     a. vitamin A
     b. vitamin K
     c. calcium
     d. thrombin

_____ 9. The enzyme amylase is found in the
     a. mouth.
     b. gall bladder.
     c. stomach.
     d. liver.

_____10. The volume of urine is minimized in the
     a. glomerulus.
     b. urethra.
     c. ureter.
     d. loop of Henle.

_____11. Where does chemical digestion takes place?
     a. mouth, stomach, and large intestine
     b. mouth, pancreas, and small intestine
     c. mouth, stomach, and small intestine
     d. stomach, small intestine, large intestine

_____12. An example of complementary hormone action is the
complementary action of insulin and
     a. diabetes mellitus.
     b. carbohydrates.
     c. glucagon.
     d. glucose.

_____13. The ectoderm germ layer develops into
     a. the skin and the nervous system.
     b. many of the body's internal tissues and organs.
     c. the lining of the digestive system and many of the
        digestive organs.
     d. all of the above

____14. All forms of cancer are ultimately caused by
     a. blocked nerves.
     b. harmful mutations.
     c. pathogens.
     d. radiation.

____15. The researcher most directly responsible for the development
of vaccines was
     a. Louis Pasteur.
     b. Robert Koch.
     c. Allen Steere.
     d. Edward Jenner.

Completion

Complete each statement on the line provided.

16. Any stimulus that is stronger than the _____ will
produce a nervous impulse.

17. Beneath the periosteum is a thick layer of _____ bone.

18. The _____ connects the trachea and bronchioles.

19. The most important nutrient is _____.

20. Humoral immunity involves lymphocytes called
_____.

Short Answer

*In complete sentences, write the answers to the questions on the lines
provided.*

21. What structures are found in the dermis?

   _____
   _____
   _____

22. What is the role of the pancreas in digestion?

   _____
   _____
   _____

23. Define and give an example of a carcinogen.

   _____
   _____
   _____

24. What role do platelets play in blood clotting?

_____

_____

_____

25. What is the significance of villi in the small intestine?

_____

_____

_____

Using Science Skills

Use the diagram to answer the following questions on the lines provided.

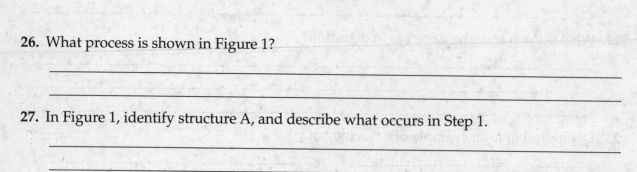

Figure 1

26. What process is shown in Figure 1?

_____

_____

27. In Figure 1, identify structure A, and describe what occurs in Step 1.

_____

_____

28. What is the name of structure B in Figure 1, and what role does it play in the process?

_____

_____

29. Identify structure C in Figure 1, and describe what occurs in Step 3.

_____

_____

30. How is the process shown in Figure 1 different from humoral immunity? How is it similar?

_____

_____

Essay

Write the answer to each question in the space provided.

31. Compare and contrast the endocrine and nervous systems as communication systems.

32. List the levels of organization of the body, from smallest and simplest to largest and most complex, and give an example of each level.

33. Describe how bones develop from seven months before birth until adulthood.

34. Explain how the endocrine system regulates metabolism.

35. Identify and describe the functions of the body's nonspecific defenses.

Unit 10 The Human Body | Unit Test B

Multiple Choice

Write the letter that best answers the question or completes the statement on the line provided.

_____ 1. A group of tissues that work together to perform a complex function is a(an)

   a. cell.

   b. organ.

   c. organ system.

_____ 2. An insulating membrane that surrounds the axon in some neurons is called a

   a. dendrite.

   b. node.

   c. myelin sheath.

_____ 3. Maintaining a relatively constant internal body temperature is an example of

   a. complementary hormone action.

   b. homeostasis.

   c. threshold effect.

_____ 4. Ossification is the process in which bone replaces

   a. cartilage.

   b. periosteum.

   c. bone marrow.

_____ 5. Which type of muscle is under conscious control?

   a. cardiac muscle

   b. smooth muscle

   c. skeletal muscle

_____ 6. Melanin helps protect skin from

   a. pathogens.

   b. radiation.

   c. keratin.

_____ 7. Which chamber of the heart receives oxygen-rich blood from the lungs?

   a. right atrium

   b. left atrium

   c. right ventricle

_____ **8.** The protein in blood that binds to oxygen is
      a. albumin.
      b. fibrin.
      c. hemoglobin.

_____ **9.** Bronchioles subdivide until they reach the
      a. alveoli.
      b. bronchus.
      c. trachea.

_____**10.** The body needs fatty acids to
      a. produce cell membranes.
      b. make proteins.
      c. absorb certain minerals.

_____**11.** Urea is removed from the blood by the
      a. urinary bladder.
      b. pancreas.
      c. kidneys.

_____**12.** Steroid hormones are
      a. proteins.
      b. carbohydrates.
      c. lipids.

_____**13.** All tumors are
      a. cancerous.
      b. masses of growing tissue.
      c. able to invade surrounding tissues.

_____**14.** Antibiotics fight infections caused by
      a. viruses.
      b. worms.
      c. bacteria.

_____**15.** Passive immunity occurs after a person
      a. recovers from a disease.
      b. receives a vaccination.
      c. receives an injection of antibodies.

Completion

Complete each statement on the line provided.

16. A quick, automatic response to a stimulus is known as a(n)
_____.

17. The tough layer of connective tissue that surrounds bone is called
the _____.

18. The smallest of the blood vessels are the _____.

19. The liver produces a fluid called _____ that
dissolves fats in the small intestine.

20. Multiple sclerosis is an example of a(n) _____
disease.

Short Answer

*In complete sentences, write the answers to the questions on the lines
provided.*

21. How are stimulant and depressant drugs different?

_____

_____

_____

22. What are the functions of ligaments and tendons?

_____

_____

_____

23. What is atherosclerosis and how is it related to cardiovascular
disease?

_____

_____

_____

24. What role does the mouth play in digestion?

_____

_____

_____

25. What are three ways infectious diseases can be spread?

_____

_____

_____

Name_____ Class_____ Date _____

Using Science Skills

Use the diagram to answer the following questions on the lines provided.

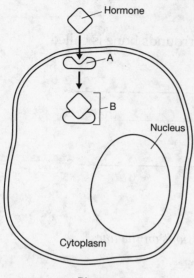

Figure 1

Diagram I   Diagram II

26. In Figure 1, which diagram, I or II, shows the action of a steroid hormone? Of a nonsteroid hormone?

_____

_____

27. In Figure 1, Diagram I, what are the structures labeled A and B, and what are their functions?

_____

_____

28. How does the hormone shown in Diagram I of Figure 1 affect the function of the target cell?

_____

_____

29. In Figure 1, Diagram II, what are the structures labeled A and B, and what role do they play in hormone action?

_____

_____

30. Based on Figure 1, what basic difference between the hormone in Diagram I and the hormone in Diagram II explains their different ways of acting?

_____

_____

Final Exam   Level A

Multiple Choice
Write the letter that best answers the question or completes the statement on the line provided.

____ 1. Which of the following is NOT science?
  a. deciding that human cloning will benefit society
  b. observing the courtship behavior of geese
  c. collecting and cataloging plant specimens from the rain forest
  d. inferring that water from a reservoir is safe to drink

____ 2. Secondary succession occurs when
  a. pioneer species move in to populate an area.
  b. species migrate to find abundant food sources.
  c. plants begin to grow in areas where no soil existed.
  d. land cleared for farming is abandoned.

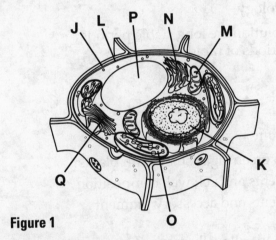

Figure 1

____ 3. The cell illustrated in Figure 1 is a
  a. eukaryotic animal cell.
  b. prokaryotic animal cell.
  c. eukaryotic plant cell.
  d. prokaryotic plant cell.

____ 4. Photosynthesis occurs in
  a. consumers.
  b. autotrophs.
  c. mitochondria.
  d. plant roots.

____ 5. During cellular respiration,
  a. glucose is produced with the sun's energy.
  b. oxygen is exchanged with carbon dioxide.
  c. energy is released when glucose is broken down.
  d. glucose is broken down in the absence of oxygen.

_____ **6.** Mitosis differs from meiosis in that mitosis results in
    a. two genetically identical diploid cells.
    b. four genetically identical haploid cells.
    c. two genetically different diploid cells.
    d. four genetically different haploid cells.

_____ **7.** If a cross between two black guinea pigs produces three black and one white offspring, then
    a. the genes for coat color are linked to different chromosomes.
    b. a mutation occurred.
    c. the alleles for coat color did not assort independently.
    d. the parents were heterozygous for coat color.

_____ **8.** Which of the following is NOT evidence of evolution?
    a. fossil record
    b. homologous body structures
    c. genetic variation within a population
    d. similarities in embryology

_____ **9.** In which pattern of evolution are long stable periods interrupted by brief periods of rapid change?
    a. adaptive radiation
    b. convergent evolution
    c. coevolution
    d. punctuated equilibrium

_____ **10.** What characteristics do green algae share with plants?
    a. photosynthetic pigments and cell wall composition
    b. photosynthetic pigments and accessory pigment composition
    c. accessory pigments and cell wall composition
    d. accessory pigments and cell membrane composition

_____ **11.** An important trend in plant evolution is
    a. reduction of the gametophyte and increased size of the sporophyte.
    b. increased reliance on water for reproduction.
    c. appearance of a life cycle with only a diploid generation.
    d. use of spores for reproduction.

_____ **12.** Which of the following describes the most complex invertebrate?
    a. radial symmetry, cephalization, pseudocoelom
    b. bilateral symmetry, cephalization, true coelom
    c. radial symmetry, no cephalization, true coelom
    d. bilateral symmetry, no cephalization, pseudocoelom

____13. All vertebrates
    a. are chordates.
    b. have bilateral symmetry.
    c. have tails.
    d. all of the above

____14. How does the endocrine system maintain homeostasis in the human body?
    a. helps protect the body from disease
    b. eliminates waste products from the body
    c. coordinates the body's response to changes in the environment
    d. produces hormones that keeps the functions of different organs in balance

____15. Which of the following is NOT a healthful behavior?
    a. wearing sunscreen
    b. exercising regularly
    c. eating a high-fat diet
    d. abstaining from drugs and alcohol

Completion

Complete each statement on the line provided.

16. As resources become less available, the population growth rate _____ .

17. During the process of _____ , RNA polymerase uses DNA to produce a strand of RNA.

18. Eukaryotic heterotrophs that have cell walls made of chitin are classified as _____ .

19. As angiosperm seeds mature, the ovary walls thicken to form a(an) _____ that encloses the developing seeds.

20. A soft-bodied invertebrate that usually has an internal or external shell is a(an) _____ .

Short Answer

In complete sentences, write the answers to the questions on the lines provided.

21. Design an experiment that tests whether plants grow faster with fertilizer. Identify the variables in the experiment.

_____

_____

_____

_____

22. Describe the role of plants in the water cycle.

_____

_____

_____

23. Give two reasons why cells divide.

_____

_____

_____

24. Why is genetic diversity important to plant and animal breeders?

_____

_____

_____

25. How do scientists currently hypothesize that human evolution occurred?

_____

_____

_____

Using Science Skills

Use the diagram below to answer the following questions on the lines provided.

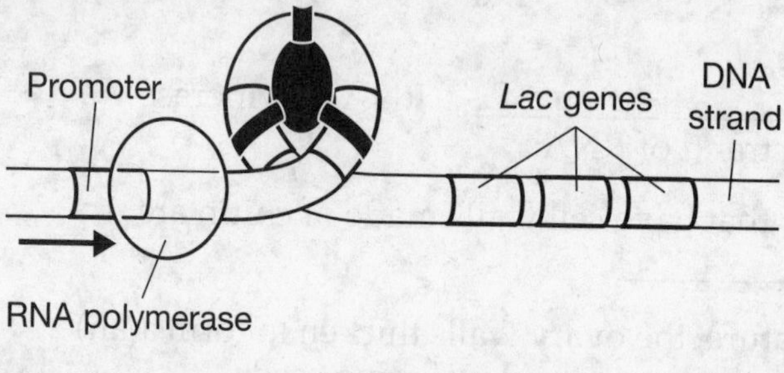

Figure 2

26. Interpreting Graphics In the operon in Figure 2, what is the function of the promoter?

_____

_____

_____

27. Interpreting Graphics In the operon in Figure 2, why can't the *lac* genes be transcribed when the repressor is bound to the operator?

_____

_____

_____

28. Applying Concepts How does the shape of the repressor protein affect its function?

_____

_____

_____

29. Inferring In the operon illustrated in Figure 2, when are the *lac* genes turned on?

_____

_____

_____

30. Applying Concepts Why do *E. coli* cells have a *lac* operon? How is it useful to the cell?

_____

_____

_____

Essay

Write the answer to each question in the space provided.

31. How would a climate change affect the biotic and abiotic factors in an ecosystem?

32. What would happen to life on Earth if plants suddenly became extinct? Explain.

33. Explain how to construct a bacterial cell that produces human insulin.

34. Explain how changes in DNA relate to the evolution of species.

35. Using the stomach as an example, describe the levels of organization in multicellular organisms.

Final Exam   Level B

Multiple Choice

Write the letter that best answers the question or completes the statement on the line provided.

____ 1. An enzyme speeds up a reaction by
   a. raising the activation energy.
   b. lowering the activation energy.
   c. absorbing energy.

____ 2. In an ecosystem, energy flows from
   a. consumers to producers.
   b. carnivores to heterotrophs.
   c. the sun to autotrophs.

____ 3. A cedar waxwing eats the berries from a bush. The following spring, new berry bushes sprout from the seeds deposited in the bird droppings far from the parent plant. This is an example of
   a. predation.
   b. pollination.
   c. dispersal.

____ 4. According to the cell theory, cells are
   a. the basic units of all living things.
   b. made up of organs and tissues.
   c. observed only with microscopes.

____ 5. Mitosis differs from meiosis in that mitosis results in
   a. two genetically identical diploid cells.
   b. four genetically identical haploid cells.
   c. four genetically different haploid cells.

____ 6. What is the inheritance pattern illustrated by the genetic cross in the Punnett square in Figure 1?
   a. simple dominance
   b. incomplete dominance
   c. multiple alleles

____ 7. Unlike DNA, RNA
   a. has a ribose sugar.
   b. has thymine.
   c. is double-stranded.

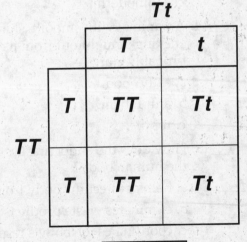

Figure 1

T = tall
t = short

_____ 8. Which of the following procedures would you use to separate fragments of DNA?

    a. polymerase chain reaction

    b. DNA fingerprinting

    c. gel electrophoresis

_____ 9. In order for a new species to evolve,

    a. new mutations must be induced.

    b. abiotic factors in the environment must change.

    c. reproductive isolation must occur.

_____10. In a drop of pond water under a light microscope, you observe a unicellular organism completely covered with cilia. This organism is probably a(an)

    a. bacteria.

    b. animal-like protist.

    c. fungi.

_____11. Which of the following plant adaptations does NOT allow a plant to reproduce in areas without water?

    a. sporangia

    b. pollination

    c. seeds

_____12. Phototropism is the response of plants to

    a. touch.

    b. gravity.

    c. light.

_____13. An invertebrate with a segmented body, tough exoskeleton, and jointed appendages is a(an)

    a. arthropod.

    b. mollusk.

    c. echinoderm.

_____14. An animal with smooth, shiny skin; a tail; and four legs sticking straight out from its body just ran past. This animal is probably a(an)

    a. arthropod.

    b. amphibian.

    c. reptile.

_____15. How does the endocrine system help maintain homeostasis in the human body?

    a. helps protect the body from disease

    b. eliminates waste products from the body

    c. coordinates the body's response to changes within the body

Completion

Complete each statement on the line provided.

16. Examples of _____ factors in an ecosystem are climate, wind, and soil type.

17. In the cell cycle, DNA replication occurs during _____ .

18. Over time, _____ , or the survival of the fittest, results in changes in the inherited characteristics of a population.

19. Invertebrates with _____ symmetry have body parts that extend from the center of the body.

20. Vertebrates that are _____ can generate and retain heat inside their bodies.

Short Answer

In complete sentences, write the answers to the questions on the lines provided.

21. Do you agree or disagree that plants are not living things because they are not mobile? Explain.

_____

_____

_____

_____

22. Explain how the decreasing genetic diversity of a species could lead to extinction.

_____

_____

_____

23. Summarize the process of photosynthesis, using the reactants and the products.

_____

_____

_____

24. What are the two main sources of genetic variation?

_____

_____

_____

25. Why is behavior important for survival and reproduction?

_____

_____

_____

Name______________________ Class______________ Date__________

Using Science Skills

Use the diagram below to answer the following questions on the lines provided.

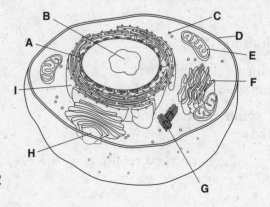

Figure 2

Diagram I **Diagram II**

26. Interpreting Graphics Which of the cells in Figure 2 is a plant cell? How do you know?

27. Interpreting Graphics Are these cells eukaryotic cells or prokaryotic cells? Explain.

28. Applying Concepts What is the function of the mitochondrion?

29. Applying Concepts How does the nucleus control most cell processes?

30. Inferring If a plant cell were placed in a hypertonic solution, what would happen to it? Explain.

Chapter 35 Nervous System

Answers for the Adapted Reading and Study Workbook worksheets (pp. 9–17) can be found in the Adapted Reading and Study Workbook, Annotated Teacher's Edition.

Answers for the Adapted Reading and Study Workbook worksheets (pp. 20–31) can be found in the Adapted Reading and Study Workbook, Annotated Teacher's Edition.

Section Review 35-1

1. Cells **2.** Tissues **3.** Organs **4.** Organ systems **5.** external **6.** nervous system **7.** integumentary system **8.** skeletal system **9.** muscular system **10.** circulatory system **11.** respiratory system **12.** endocrine system **13.** digestive system **14.** excretory system **15.** Possible answer: An example of feedback inhibition in the body is sweating. When the temperature of the body is too high, the body responds by producing sweat and cools down when the sweat is evaporated. When the body cools down enough, sweating stops.

Section Review 35-2

1. The role that the nervous system plays is to control and coordinate functions throughout the body and respond to internal and external stimuli. **2.** The sources of stimulation for a nerve impulse are another neuron or the environment. **3.** 5 **4.** 3 **5.** 6 **6.** 2 **7.** 4 **8.** 1 **9.** axon terminals **10.** nodes **11.** myelin sheath **12.** cell body **13.** axon **14.** nucleus **15.** dendrites

Section Review 35-3

1. The central nervous system relays messages, processes information, and analyzes information. **2.** The sensory division of the peripheral nervous system transmits impulses from sense organs to the central nervous system. **3.** The motor division transmits impulses from the central nervous system to the muscles or glands. **4.** Possible answer: A switchboard operator of a large company receives calls from outside the company and then directs the calls to the proper person. **5.** The somatic nervous system regulates activities that are under conscious control such as walking, whereas the autonomic system controls activities that are involuntary such as the beating of the heart. **6.** autonomic **7.** somatic **8.** somatic **9.** autonomic **10.** A person's somatic nervous system will react with a reflex. The pain impulses from the hand reach the spinal cord, and a group of neurons immediately react by activating motor neurons. This stimulates muscles in the hand to pull back from the pot.

Section Review 35-4

1. c **2.** e **3.** a **4.** d **5.** b **6.** The skin would respond to a change in temperature. **7.** The eyes would respond to a flashing light. **8.** The inner ears would respond to being rocked on a ship. **9.** The tiny hairs are mechanoreceptors because they are sensitive to the pressure of the fluid in the cochlea. Being sensitive to pressure classifies the hairs as mechanoreceptors. **10.** Rods and cones are both light-sensitive photoreceptor cells in the retina of the eye. Rods are extremely sensitive to light, but do not distinguish different colors. Cones are less sensitive than rods, but they do respond to light of different colors, producing color vision. **11.** Retina **12.** Vitreous humor **13.** Cornea **14.** Pupil **15.** Iris

Section Review 35-5

1. stimulant **2.** stimulant **3.** stimulant **4.** depressant **5.** depressant **6.** depressant **7.** Cocaine affects the body by causing a sudden release of dopamine, a neurotransmitter, in the brain. **8.** Opiates are painkilling drugs produced by the opium poppy. Opiates mimic endorphins and provide the body with higher levels of endorphins. **9.** Alcohol is a depressant. It slows down the rate at which the central nervous system functions. **10.** Psychological dependence on a drug produces a mental craving for the drug, whereas a physical dependence occurs when the body cannot function without a constant supply of the drug. **11.** stimulant **12.** stimulant **13.** depressant **14.** opiate **15.** opiate

Chapter Vocabulary Review

1. epithelial tissue, connective tissue, nervous tissue, muscle tissue. **2.** homeostasis **3.** feedback inhibition **4.** dendrites **5.** resting potential **6.** threshold **7.** synapse **8.** meninges; cerebrospinal fluid **9.** reflex arc **10.** sensory receptors **11.** pupil **12.** rods; cones **13.** stimulants, depressants **14.** addiction **15.** fetal alcohol syndrome **16.** thalamus **17.** cerebellum **18.** medulla oblongata **19.** pons **20.** hypothalamus **21.** cerebrum **22.** d **23.** a **24.** b **25.** a

Enrichment

1. Nearsightedness would best be corrected with a concave lens in front of the eye, allowing the image to focus on the retina rather than in front of it. **2.** Farsightedness would best be treated by placing a convex lens in front of the eye, allowing the image to focus on the retina rather than behind it.

Graphic Organizer

1. Pain receptors **2.** Mechanoreceptors **3.** Chemoreceptors **4.** Skin, body core, and hypothalamus **5.** Skin, skeletal muscles, inner ears **6.** Eyes

7. Sensation of pain **8.** Sensations of hot and cold **9.** Detection of light that enables vision

Chapter 35—Test A

Multiple Choice **1.** D **2.** B **3.** D **4.** C **5.** A **6.** B **7.** D **8.** C **9.** A **10.** A **11.** C **12.** B **13.** A **14.** A **15.** B **Completion** **16.** potential **17.** nerves **18.** direction **19.** Homeostasis **20.** nodes **Short Answer** **21.** A tissue is a group of similar cells that perform a single function. An organ is a group of tissues that work together to perform a complex function. **22.** Fetal alcohol syndrome is caused by the consumption of alcohol by a pregnant woman. The effect of fetal alcohol syndrome is a range of birth defects, such as heart defects, malformed faces, delayed growth, and poor motor development. **23.** Sensory receptors react to the tap on the knee and stimulate the sensory neuron. The sensory neuron relays the signal to an interneuron within the spinal cord. A signal is then sent to the motor neuron, which in turn stimulates the muscle to extend the knee. **24.** Both rods and cones are photoreceptors in the retina. Rods are sensitive to light, but do not distinguish colors. Cones are less sensitive to light than rods, but cones respond to light of different colors. **25.** The spinal cord is the main communications link between the brain and the rest of the body, transmitting information, just as a telephone line carries many calls at once. **Using Science Skills** **26.** vesicles **27.** synaptic cleft **28.** The impulse travels from the axon to the adjacent neuron. **29.** The neurotransmitters may be broken down by enzymes, or taken up and recycled by the axon terminal. **30.** muscle cell or gland cell **Essay** **31.** The sympathetic nervous system and the parasympathetic nervous system have opposite effects on the same organ system. When the sympathetic system speeds up an activity, the parasympathetic system slows down the same activity. **32.** The cerebrum controls voluntary activities, intelligence, learning, and judgment. The cerebellum controls the action of muscles. The brain stem regulates the flow of information between the brain and the rest of the body. The brain stem controls blood pressure, heart rate, breathing, and swallowing. The thalamus receives messages from the sense organs and sends them to the cerebrum. The hypothalamus recognizes sensations of hunger, thirst, fatigue, anger, and body temperatures. **33.** The five general categories are pain receptors, thermoreceptors, mechanoreceptors, chemoreceptors, and photoreceptors. Pain receptors are located throughout the body except in the brain. Thermoreceptors are located in the skin, body core, and hypothalamus. Mechanoreceptors are found in the skin, skeletal muscles, and inner ears. Chemoreceptors are found

in the nose and taste buds. Photoreceptors are found in the eyes. **34.** Stimulants increase the release of neurotransmitters at some synapses in the brain, which then leads to a feeling of energy and well-being. However, when the effects of the stimulants wear off, the brain's supply of neurotransmitters has been depleted. The user quickly falls into fatigue and depression, which can impair his or her ability to drive and lead to accidents. **35.** The difference in electrical charge across the cell membrane of a resting neuron is the resting potential. Once an impulse begins, positive ions rush across the cell membrane, reversing the charge difference. The inside of the membrane gains a positive charge, and the outside of the membrane gains a negative charge. This rapid reversal of charges is called the action potential. As the impulse passes, the positively charged ions flow out of the cell, and the resting potential of the membrane is reestablished.

Chapter 35—Test B

Multiple Choice **1.** C **2.** B **3.** C **4.** C **5.** A **6.** A **7.** A **8.** A **9.** A **10.** C **11.** C **12.** A **13.** B **14.** A **15.** C **Completion** **16.** peripheral **17.** feedback **18.** mechanoreceptors **19.** interneurons **20.** alcohol **Short Answer** **21.** Dendrites carry impulses from the environment or from other neurons toward the cell body. Axons carry impulses away from the cell body. **22.** Opiates mimic natural chemicals in the brain known as endorphins, which normally help to overcome sensations of pain. **23.** the cerebrum, the cerebellum, the brain stem, the thalamus, and the hypothalamus **24.** vision, hearing, smell, taste, and touch **25.** the process by which organisms maintain a relatively constant internal environment **Using Science Skills** **26.** spinal cord **27.** structure A, the cerebrum **28.** hypothalamus **29.** structure B **30.** medulla oblongata and pons

Chapter 36 Skeletal, Muscular, and Integumentary Systems

Answers for the Adapted Reading and Study Workbook worksheets (pp. 57–63) can be found in the Adapted Reading and Study Workbook, Annotated Teacher's Edition.

Answers for the Adapted Reading and Study Workbook worksheets (pp. 66–75) can be found in the Adapted Reading and Study Workbook, Annotated Teacher's Edition.

Section Review 36-1

1. The five functions of the skeletal system are to support the body, protect internal organs, allow movement, store mineral reserves, and provide a site for blood cell formation **2.** Bone is a solid network of living cells and fibers that are surrounded by deposits of calcium salts. **3.** Immovable joint: These joints allow no movement. **4.** Slightly movable joint: these joints permit a small amount of restricted movement. **5.** Freely movable joint: These joints permit movement in one or more directions. **6.** axial **7.** appendicular **8.** axial **9.** Both bone and cartilage support the body. Bone is stronger than cartilage. Unlike bone, cartilage does not contain blood vessels. Cartilage is dense, fibrous, and extremely flexible. **10.** Possible answer: When the knee is twisted or bent in the wrong direction, a ligament in the knee can tear. Since a ligament connects bone to bone at a joint, the bones would then no longer be properly connected, and the knee joint would not be secure.

Section Review 36-2

1. The three types of muscle tissue are smooth, skeletal, and cardiac. **2.** During muscle contraction, myosin attaches to actin, forming a cross-bridge. The myosin changes shape and pulls the actin. The cross-bridge then releases the thin filament, snaps back to its original position, and "grabs" the thin filament again to start another cycle. **3.** The energy for muscle contraction comes from ATP. **4.** smooth muscle **5.** cardiac muscle **6.** smooth muscle **7.** skeletal muscle **8.** Muscles contract when acetylcholine is released and remain contracted until the release of acetylcholine stops. Without an enzyme to breakdown acetylcholine, the muscle, once contracted, would remain contracted. **9.** Skeletal muscle in the calf is attached to the lower leg bones by tendons. These skeletal muscles produce movement by contracting and pulling on the lower leg bones. **10.** The muscles will weaken and become smaller because they are not being used.

Section Review 36-3

1. Yes **2.** Yes **3.** No **4.** Yes **5.** No **6.** Yes **7.** Both sebaceous and sweat glands are major types of glands found in the dermis layer of the skin. Sebaceous glands produce and secrete an oily substance called sebum. Sweat glands produce and secrete perspiration. **8.** The cut must have penetrated to the dermis, where blood vessels are located. A shallow cut would not bleed because the epidermis contains no blood vessels. **9.** When melanin production increases, a person's skin color darkens. As skin is exposed to the sun, it darkens and becomes tan. Tanning is an increase in melanin production. **10.** On a humid day the air is nearly saturated, and sweat will not readily evaporate from the skin. The body is not cooled well if the sweat cannot evaporate. On a day with low humidity, sweat will readily evaporate from the skin, cooling the body very effectively.

Chapter Vocabulary Review

1. Periosteum is the tough layer of connective tissue that surrounds bone. **2.** A ligament is a tough connective tissue that joins bone to bone. **3.** Myosin is the protein that makes up the thick filaments in striated muscle. **4.** Actin is the protein that makes up the thin filaments of striated muscle. **5.** A tendon is the tough connective tissue that joins muscle to bone. **6.** Epidermis is the outer layer of the skin. **7.** Melanin is the dark brown pigment found in the epidermal layer of skin. **8.** Dermis is the inner layer of the skin. **9.** a **10.** c **11.** f **12.** d **13.** b **14.** e **15.** Hair follicles are tubelike pockets of epidermal cells that extend into the dermis. **16.** Ossification is the process in which cartilage is replaced by bone. **17.** compact bone **18.** Haversian canal **19.** periosteum **20.** spongy bone

Enrichment

1. Certain types of food may irritate infections already caused by acne. But food, including chocolate, does not cause pimples. **2.** The causes of acne are not completely understood. Genetic factors and hormonal changes seem to trigger acne; poor skin care, lack of exercise, and lack of sunlight can aggravate it.

Graphic Organizer

1. No **2.** No **3.** Yes **4.** Yes **5.** No **6.** Yes **7.** No **8.** No **9.** Yes **10.** Yes **11.** No **12.** Yes

Chapter 36—Test A

Multiple Choice   1. C **2.** C **3.** B **4.** A **5.** B **6.** A **7.** D **8.** D **9.** B **10.** B **11.** A **12.** A **13.** C **14.** B **15.** D **Completion   16.** spongy bone **17.** movable **18.** sliding-filament model **19.** neuromuscular junction **20.** blood vessels **Short Answer   21.** The two major parts are the axial skeleton and the appendicular skeleton. The axial skeleton consists of the skull, vertebral column, and rib cage. The appendicular skeleton is made of the arms and legs and the bones of the pelvis and shoulder area. **22.** Cartilage is found in parts of the body where flexibility is needed, such as the tip of the nose and the external ear. It is also located where bones are attached to the sternum, which allows the rib cage to move during breathing. **23.** The small sac of synovial fluid is called a bursa; it reduces the friction between the bones of a joint and also acts as a tiny shock absorber. **24.** The left hand would probably be stronger because the person would be using it much more than the right hand, and exercising muscles causes them to get stronger. **25.** Keratin and melanin are both produced in the epidermis. Keratin is a tough, fibrous protein. Melanin is a dark brown pigment. **Using Science Skills 26.** yellow marrow and red marrow **27.** The cell lines the Haversian canal, so it is an osteoclast, which breaks down bone, or an osteoblast, which produces bone. **28.** The Haversian canal contains blood vessels and nerves. **29.** The periosteum contains blood vessels that provide oxygen and nutrients for the bone. **30.** Haversian canals, veins, arteries, osteoclasts, and osteoblasts **Essay 31.** Compact bone is found beneath the periosteum. It is a dense bone, although not solid. Running through compact bone is a network of tubes called Haversian canals that contain blood vessels and nerves. Spongy bone is less dense than compact bone and is found in long bones and in the middle of short, flat bones. It is strong and organized in a latticework structure, which adds strength to the bone without adding mass. **32.** The three types of joints are immovable joints, slightly movable joints, and freely movable joints. The places where the bones in the skull meet are immovable joints. Joints between the two bones of the lower leg and the joints between adjacent vertebrae are examples of slightly movable joints. Freely movable joints include ball-and-socket joints, hinge joints, pivot joints, and saddle joints. **33.** Skeletal muscle tissue is striated, is generally attached to the bones of the skeleton, and is under voluntary control. It is spindle-shaped and contains many nuclei. Cardiac muscle tissue is striated, contains one or two nuclei, and is not under direct control of the central nervous system. Cardiac muscle is found only in the heart. Smooth tissue has spindle-shaped cells that have a single nucleus and are not striated, and it is generally not under control of the central nervous system. **34.** Regular exercise increases muscle size and strength. Exercise also helps body systems to become more efficient, including organs such as the heart and lungs. **35.** Hair is produced at the base of hair follicles from columns of cells that are filled with keratin and then die. Hair follicles, made up of clusters of such cells, are anchored in the dermis. Cells multiply rapidly in the base of the follicle, causing the hair to grow longer.

Chapter 36—Test B

Multiple Choice   1. C **2.** B **3.** C **4.** C **5.** B **6.** A **7.** C **8.** C **9.** A **10.** A **11.** C **12.** C **13.** A **14.** C **15.** A   **Completion   16.** axial **17.** ribs **18.** ossification **19.** melanin **20.** integumentary   **Short Answer   21.** Answers should include any three of the following five functions: supporting the body, protecting internal organs, allowing movement, storing mineral reserves, providing a site for blood cell formation. **22.** Bones are a solid network of living cells and protein fibers that are surrounded by

deposits of calcium salts. **23.** hinge **24.** The three types of muscles are skeletal muscle, smooth muscle, and cardiac muscle. **25.** The integumentary system serves as a barrier against infection and injury, helps to regulate body temperature, removes waste products from the body, and provides protection against ultraviolet radiation from the sun. **Using Science Skills   26.** A **27.** The figure shows that there are no blood vessels in the outer layer of the skin, so a slight scratch will probably not be deep enough to break blood vessels. **28.** dermis **29.** Structure F is an opening similar to that for sweat gland D. **30.** This gland produces oil that keeps the epidermis flexible and waterproof.

Chapter 37 Circulatory and Respiratory Systems

Answers for the Adapted Reading and Study Workbook worksheets (pp. 99–106) can be found in the Adapted Reading and Study Workbook, Annotated Teacher's Edition.

Answers for the Adapted Reading and Study Workbook worksheets (pp. 109–118) can be found in the Adapted Reading and Study Workbook, Annotated Teacher's Edition.

Section Review 37-1

1. The function of the heart is to pump blood throughout the body. **2.** Blood carries oxygen, nutrients, and wastes throughout the body. **3.** All arteries carry blood away from the heart. **4.** All veins carry blood toward the heart. **5.** Capillaries are where nutrients and oxygen are brought to the tissues and carbon dioxide and other wastes are absorbed. **6.** superior vena cava **7.** right atrium **8.** right ventricle **9.** pulmonary arteries **10.** lungs **11.** pulmonary veins **12.** left atrium **13.** left ventricle **14.** aorta **15.** Possible answer: Both heart attacks and strokes may be caused by a blockage in a blood vessel. In either case, without oxygen, cells served by a blocked vessel begin to die. This is why both strokes and heart attacks require immediate emergency care.

Section Review 37-2

1. Red blood cells carry oxygen throughout the body. **2.** The body depends on white blood cells to fight infection. **3.** Platelets prevent blood loss by starting the clotting process. **4.** vessels **5.** lymph **6.** circulatory **7.** During an infection, lymph nodes may become swollen. **8.** Edema, a swelling of the tissues, can occur when lymphatic vessels are blocked. **9.** Hemoglobin carries oxygen throughout the body. A low level of hemoglobin would prevent the red blood cells from carrying adequate oxygen to body cells. **10.** Possible answer: White blood cells are often compared to an army because they fight infection in several ways. There are different types of white blood cells, like the different units of an army. Each has a specific role in and method of fighting infection.

Section Review 37-3

1. nose **2.** pharynx **3.** larynx **4.** trachea **5.** lung **6.** alveolus **7.** Bronchioles are small branching tubes that carry air to tiny sacs called alveoli. **8.** Smoking causes respiratory diseases such as chronic bronchitis, emphysema, and lung cancer. **9.** Emphysema causes the lungs to lose their elasticity. This causes a decrease in the amount of oxygen in the body and a buildup of carbon dioxide in the body. **10.** The respiratory and circulatory systems increase activity to deliver more oxygen during exercise. Breathing faster brings more oxygen into your lungs. By beating faster, your heart sends more red blood cells to your lungs to carry that extra oxygen to the rest of your body.

Chapter Vocabulary Review

1. pulmonary; systemic **2.** arteries; veins; capillaries **3.** atherosclerosis **4.** plasma **5.** hemoglobin **6.** phagocytes **7.** lymph **8.** trachea **9.** larynx **10.** bronchus **11.** alveoli **12.** emphysema **13.** right atrium **14.** right ventricle **15.** aorta **16.** left atrium **17.** left ventricle **18.** a **19.** b **20.** a **21.** c **22.** d **23.** b **24.** a **25.** c

Enrichment

1. An artificial pacemaker uses a battery to stimulate the heart, causing it to beat rhythmically. **2.** Some limitations of an artificial pacemaker include: inability to adapt to the body's changing needs for oxygen, inability to respond to changes in body temperature, and the need for surgery to implant it.

Graphic Organizer

1. Diaphragm contracts **2.** Volume of the chest cavity expands **3.** Pressure decreases in the chest cavity **4.** Air fills the lungs **5.** Diaphragm relaxes **6.** Air rushes out of the lungs

Chapter 37—Test A

Multiple Choice 1. B **2.** A **3.** A **4.** B **5.** C **6.** B **7.** D **8.** B **9.** C **10.** B **11.** C **12.** D **13.** A **14.** C **15.** B **Completion 16.** B **17.** blood pressure **18.** atherosclerosis **19.** water **20.** hemophilia **Short Answer 21.** The ribs are lowered. **22.** Red blood cells transport oxygen. White blood cells perform a variety of protective functions, including guarding against infection, fighting parasites, and attacking bacteria. Platelets help in the clotting pro-

cess. **23.** The air passes from the outside into the body through the nose or mouth, passes through the pharynx and the trachea, and then passes into the bronchi, bronchioles, and alveoli within the lungs. **24.** The chest cavity is largest during inhalation. **25.** Smoking can cause chronic bronchitis, emphysema, and lung cancer. In chronic bronchitis, the bronchi become swollen and clogged with mucus; emphysema is a lack of elasticity in the tissues of the lungs; and lung cancer is a deadly disease that can spread to other parts of the body. **Using Science Skills 26.** The inferior vena cava brings oxygen-poor blood from the lower part of the body to the right atrium of the heart. **27.** These are valves that prevent blood from flowing backward in the heart. **28.** A, the aorta **29.** The valves close. **30.** It carries oxygen-poor blood from the heart to the lungs. **Essay 31.** (a) The muscular walls of the large arteries help them withstand blood pressure. (b) The valves in the veins help to prevent the backward flow of blood in them. (c) The valves in the heart prevent the backward flow of blood in the heart. **32.** The body regulates blood pressure in two ways. First, sensory receptors measure blood pressure. When blood pressure is too low, the sensory receptors send impulses to the medulla oblongata, which stimulates the autonomic nervous system to contract the muscles in blood vessel walls. When blood pressure is too high, the same system helps to decrease blood pressure. Second, the kidneys remove water from the blood, lowering blood volume. The loss of fluid lowers the blood pressure. **33.** Some white blood cells engulf and digest foreign cells. Others slip out of capillary walls and attack invading organisms in the tissues of the body. Some produce antibodies that fight infection. **34.** The lymphatic system is a network of vessels, nodes, and organs that collect fluid leaking from the bloodstream and return it to the circulatory system. Lymph nodes act as filters, trapping bacteria and other microorganisms that cause disease. The organs produce specialized white blood cells, which protect the body from infection. Lymph vessels also aid in nutrient absorption. They absorb fats from the digestive tract and carry fat-soluble vitamins to the blood. **35.** Cellular respiration is the release of energy from the breakdown of food in the presence of oxygen. The second type of respiration is the exchange of oxygen and carbon dioxide between the lungs and the environment.

Chapter 37—Test B

Multiple Choice 1. A **2.** C **3.** C **4.** C **5.** B **6.** B **7.** A **8.** A **9.** A **10.** B **11.** C **12.** B **13.** A **14.** A **15.** B **Completion 16.** blood **17.** capillaries **18.** hemoglobin **19.** bronchi **20.** nervous

Short Answer **21.** The circulatory system consists of the heart, a series of blood vessels, and the blood that flows through them. **22.** Arteries carry blood away from the heart. Capillaries bring nutrients and oxygen to the tissues and absorb carbon dioxide and waste products. Veins carry blood toward the heart. **23.** Blood pressure is the force of the blood on the walls of arteries. **24.** Blood plasma is a straw-colored fluid that makes up 55 percent of the volume of blood. It is 90 percent water and 10 percent dissolved gases, salts, nutrients, enzymes, hormones, waste products, and plasma proteins. **25.** The human respiratory system brings about the exchange of oxygen and carbon dioxide. **Using Science Skills** **26.** C **27.** trachea, windpipe **28.** alveoli **29.** epiglottis **30.** D, bronchus

Chapter 38 Digestive and Excretory Systems

Answers for the Adapted Reading and Study Workbook worksheets (pp. 142–147) can be found in the Adapted Reading and Study Workbook, Annotated Teacher's Edition.

Answers for the Adapted Reading and Study Workbook worksheets (pp. 150–159) can be found in the Adapted Reading and Study Workbook, Annotated Teacher's Edition.

Section Review 38-1

1. d **2.** c **3.** b **4.** a **5.** f **6.** e **7.** All the cells in your body need water because many of the body's processes, including chemical reactions, take place in water. **8.** Dehydration leads to problems with the circulatory, respiratory, and nervous systems. **9.** Fat is stored in the body, so, vitamins that dissolve in fat will stay in the body. However, water is eliminated from the body. So, vitamins that dissolve in water will be lost with the water. **10.** Bread, Cereal, Rice, and Pasta Group; Meat, Poultry, Fish, Dry Beans, Eggs, and Nut Group and Milk, Yogurt, and Cheese Group

Section Review 38-2

1. salivary glands **2.** esophagus **3.** liver **4.** gallbladder **5.** rectum **6.** mouth **7.** pharynx **8.** stomach **9.** pancreas **10.** large intestine **11.** small intestine **12.** Chemical digestion breaks food molecules into smaller, simpler molecules that can be absorbed into the bloodstream. **13.** Mechanical digestion starts in the mouth with your teeth chewing. It is the physical breakdown of large pieces of food into smaller pieces. Mechanical digestion continues in the stomach, where stomach muscles contract to mix food with stomach fluids. **14.** The small intestine uses villi to absorb the products of carbohydrate and protein digestion. In contrast, the large

intestine primarily absorbs water from the leftover undigested material. **15.** Possible answer: Why doesn't the stomach digest itself?

Section Review 38-3

1. The kidneys filter urea, toxins, and wastes from the blood. **2.** lungs **3.** skin **4.** The kidneys regulate the water content of the blood, maintain blood pH, and remove cellular waste from the blood. **5.** The activity of the kidneys is controlled by the action of hormones and by the composition of the blood they filter. **6.** Sample answer: There are holes in the membrane that are larger than particles of water, urea, glucose, salts, amino acids, and some vitamins but smaller than plasma proteins, cells, and platelets. **7.** Accept either Bowman's capsule or the glomerulus. **8.** water, amino acids, glucose, salts, some vitamins, and urea **9.** Most of the water and nutrients are reabsorbed into the blood. **10.** urine

Chapter Vocabulary Review

1. g **2.** j **3.** f **4.** e **5.** h **6.** a **7.** c **8.** b **9.** i **10.** d **11.** esophagus **12.** liver **13.** stomach **14.** pancreas **15.** large intestine **16.** small intestine **17.** c **18.** c **19.** a **20.** a **21.** b **22.** d **23.** b **24.** d **25.** c

Enrichment

1. Both stress ulcers and peptic ulcers are erosions on the surface of the digestive system. However, peptic ulcers are caused by an infection, and stress ulcers are caused by physical stress. Also, peptic ulcers are much more common than stress ulcers. **2.** Peptic ulcers are caused by an infection. Stress ulcers accompany severe physical stress. Neither of these is likely to be the result of worrying about an exam.

Graphic Organizer

1. Mouth **2.** Mechanical means **3.** Break down food into chyme and begin chemical digestion of protein **4.** Chemical means **5.** Small intestine **6.** Remove water from undigested material.

Chapter 38—Test A

Multiple Choice **1.** B **2.** D **3.** D **4.** B **5.** D **6.** C **7.** B **8.** D **9.** D **10.** B **11.** C **12.** B **13.** A **14.** B **15.** A **Completion** **16.** minerals **17.** water **18.** mechanical **19.** pepsin **20.** blood **Short Answer** **21.** Accept any two of the following functions: to protect body organs; insulate the body; store energy; produce cell membranes, myelin sheaths, and certain hormones; help body absorb fat-soluble vitamins. **22.** A calorie is the amount of heat needed to raise the temperature of one gram of water by one Celsius degree. A Calorie is equal to 1000 calories, or 1 kilocalorie (kcal). **23.** a tool made by nutritionists to aid people in selecting a healthful diet **24.** The ureter carries urine from the kidneys to the urinary bladder. **25.** The urinary bladder stores liquid waste, or urine. **Using Science Skills 26.** The loop of Henle is where water is conserved and the volume of urine is minimized. **27.** D, the capillaries **28.** The collecting duct collects impurities filtered from the blood and transports them to the ureter. **29.** filtration and reabsorption **30.** kidney **Essay 31.** The body loses water through sweat. As the water in sweat evaporates, it cools the body. Water in the form of vapor is also lost with every breath exhaled. More water is lost in the urine. **32.** The kidneys remove the wastes of cellular metabolism from the blood and regulate the concentrations of substances found in the body fluids. The ureter transports urine from each kidney to the urinary bladder. The urinary bladder stores the urine until it is excreted by the urethra out of the body. **33.** The digestive system includes the mouth, pharynx, esophagus, stomach, small intestine, and large intestine. Several major accessory structures, including the salivary glands, the pancreas, the gall bladder, and the liver, add secretions to the digestive system. **34.** An increased intake of water causes the concentration of water in the blood to increase. As the amount of water in the blood increases, the rate of water reabsorption in the kidneys decreases. Thus, less water is returned to the blood, and the excess water is excreted as urine. An increased intake of salt causes the level of salt in the blood to rise. The kidneys respond by returning less salt to the blood by reabsorption. The excess salt is excreted in urine. **35.** Dialysis is a process in which a machine is connected to a patient to filter out wastes from the patient's blood. In one type of dialysis, blood is removed from the body through a tube inserted in the arm and pumped through special tubing that acts like nephrons. Tiny pores in the tubing allow salts and small molecules, including nitrogen wastes, to pass through. Wastes diffuse out of the blood into the fluid-filled chamber, allowing purified blood to be returned to the body.

Chapter 38—Test B

Multiple Choice 1. C **2.** C **3.** B **4.** A **5.** C **6.** C **7.** C **8.** C **9.** A **10.** B **11.** A **12.** A **13.** B **14.** C **15.** C **Completion 16.** nutrition **17.** peristalsis **18.** ulcer **19.** nephrons **20.** homeostasis **Short Answer 21.** water, carbohydrates, fats, proteins, vitamins, and minerals **22.** When the chewed-up food reaches the stomach, the stomach muscles contract to churn and mix stomach fluids and food, gradually producing a mixture known as chyme. **23.** The function of the digestive system is to help convert foods into simpler

molecules that can be absorbed and used by the cells of the body. **24.** They maintain homeostasis by regulating the water content of the blood, and therefore, blood volume, by maintaining blood pH, and by removing waste products from the blood. **25.** The person can have a kidney transplant or use a kidney dialysis machine. **Using Science Skills 26.** A **27.** D **28.** C, liver **29.** F, pancreas **30.** G, small intestine

Chapter 39 Endocrine and Reproductive Systems

Answers for the Adapted Reading and Study Workbook worksheets (pp. 184–191) can be found in the Adapted Reading and Study Workbook, Annotated Teacher's Edition.

Answers for the Adapted Reading and Study Workbook worksheets (pp. 194–205) can be found in the Adapted Reading and Study Workbook, Annotated Teacher's Edition.

Section Review 39-1

1. The function of the glands that make up the endocrine system is to release chemicals that will travel through the bloodstream and affect the activities of other cells. **2.** Hormones are the chemical messages released by the endocrine system that affect the activities of other cells. **3.** The powerful hormones produced by the endocrine system must be closely monitored in order to keep the functions of various organs in balance. **4.** The endocrine system is regulated by feedback mechanisms that function to maintain homeostasis. **5.** Feedback inhibition is the process in which a hormone communicates or "feeds back" to stop the gland that is producing the hormone in the first place. **6.** Possible answer: An air conditioner uses a thermostat to measure air temperature. Once the desired air temperature is reached, the thermostat "feeds back" to the air conditioner to stop producing cold air. **7.** Endocrine glands release their secretions directly into the bloodstream, whereas exocrine glands release their secretions through tubelike structures called ducts. **8.** S **9.** N **10.** Most likely it was the endocrine system that responded to the stimulus. A nervous system response would have occurred within a fraction of a second.

Section Review 39-2

1. e **2.** c **3.** g **4.** b **5.** h **6.** d **7.** a **8.** f **9.** The posterior pituitary gland is composed of neurons, called neurosecretory cells, which are part of the central nervous system. These neurons release hormones when stimulated and those hormones become part of the endocrine system. **10.** Type I diabetes is an autoimmune disorder that usually develops in people before age 15 and is caused by little or no secretion of insulin by the pancreas. Type II diabetes most commonly develops in people after the age of 40 and is caused by cells not responding to normal levels of insulin in the body.

Section Review 39-3

1. The function of the male reproductive system is to produce and deliver sperm. **2.** The function of the female reproductive system is to produce eggs and prepare the body to nourish an embryo. **3.** The menstrual cycle has four phases: the follicular phase, ovulation, luteal phase, and menstruation. **4.** c **5.** e **6.** d **7.** h **8.** a **9.** b **10.** f **11.** j **12.** g **13.** i **14.** Ovulation occurs when the hormone LH peaks. **15.** Menstruation occurs on days 1–5.

Section Review 39-4

1. 4 **2.** 2 **3.** 1 **4.** 5 **5.** 6 **6.** 3 **7.** The placenta serves as the embryo's means of respiration, nourishment, and excretion. **8.** Harmful substances in tobacco enter the mother's bloodstream, where they are passed to the embryo through the placenta. **9.** During adolescence there is a growth spurt during which the long bones reach their final length. Growing bones require calcium. **10.** At age 35, the body is at its peak of physical strength and development. At age 65, most systems of the body have become less efficient. In women, menopause has occurred and the menstrual cycle has ceased.

Chapter Vocabulary Review

1. An endocrine gland is an organ that produces and releases hormones directly into the bloodstream. **2.** A prostaglandin is a hormonelike modified fatty acid that is produced by a wide range of cells. Prostaglandins affect only nearby cells and tissue. **3.** The pituitary gland is the endocrine gland found at the base of the skull that regulates many bodily functions and controls the actions of several other endocrine glands **4.** Diabetes mellitus is a condition in which the pancreas produces too little insulin. **5.** Puberty is the period of rapid growth and sexual maturation during which the reproductive system becomes fully functional. **6.** The placenta is an organ through which nutrients, oxygen, carbon dioxide, and wastes are exchanged between embryo and mother. **7.** Hormones are chemicals that travel through the bloodstream and affect the activities of cells. Cells that have receptors for a particular hormone are target cells. **8.** Testes are found in the scrotum. Within each testis, sperm are produced in seminiferous tubules. Sperm mature and are stored in the epididymis. From there, sperm travel through the vas deferens, then the urethra, and leave the body through the penis. **9.** Fallopian tube **10.** vagina **11.** uterus **12.** b **13.** d **14.** d **15.** c **16.** d **17.** a **18.** b **19.** a **20.** a

Enrichment

1. In vitro fertilization starts with removing eggs from the mother and sperm from the father. The sperm and egg are placed in a special medium for fertilization to occur. After fertilization occurs, the resulting embryo is put into the mother's uterus. **2.** Possible answer: Frozen embryos should remain frozen until it is determined that the in vitro fertilization was successful. The embryos should then be disposed of properly. Embryos should be considered joint property of the two partners that produced the egg and sperm that were used in the fertilization process.

Graphic Organizer

1. Fertilization **2.** Zygote begins cell division **3.** Embryo becomes a morula **4.** Embryo becomes a blastocyst **5.** Implantation occurs **6.** Gastrulation occurs **7.** Chorion becomes the placenta **8.** Embryo becomes a fetus.

Chapter 39—Test A

Multiple Choice **1.** B **2.** A **3.** B **4.** A **5.** D **6.** A **7.** C **8.** C **9.** D **10.** D **11.** B **12.** D **13.** D **14.** C **15.** A **Completion** **16.** endocrine, bloodstream **17.** ovulation **18.** scrotum **19.** gastrulation, endoderm **20.** placenta **Short Answer** **21.** Endocrine glands (such as the pituitary, parathyroid, adrenal, or thyroid glands) secrete hormones into the bloodstream, while exocrine glands (such as those that secrete sweat, tears, and digestive juices) pass their secretions through ducts. **22.** Prostaglandins are hormonelike substances that are produced by a wide range of cells. Unlike hormones, they usually affect only nearby cells and tissues. **23.** Students should list a feedback mechanism, such as the feedback inhibition that controls metabolism or the one that controls water balance in the body. **24.** Sperm are produced in the seminiferous tubules. From there, they travel through the epididymis, vas deferens, and urethra. **25.** Once a sperm nucleus has entered the egg, the cell membrane of the egg cell changes, preventing other sperm from entering the cell. **Using Science Skills** **26.** It shows the feedback mechanism that controls the thyroid gland. **27.** High thyroxine levels inhibit the hypothalamus and the anterior pituitary so that less TRH and TSH are released. **28.** thyroxine **29.** Hyperthyroidism is a condition that occurs when the thyroid gland produces too much thyroxine; thus, any change that shows an overproduction of thyroxine is a correct response. Hyperthyroidism is characterized by nervousness, elevated body temperature, increased metabolic rate, increased blood pressure, and weight loss. **30.** The hypothalamus is sensitive to both temperature and the level of thyroxine in the blood. When body temperature decreases, such as on a cold day, the hypothalamus will produce more TRH even if the level of thyroxine does not stimulate it to do so. TRH will stimulate the anterior pituitary to produce more TSH and more thyroxine will be released into the bloodstream, speeding up metabolism and increasing body temperature. **Essay 31.** Complementary hormone action occurs when two hormones with opposite effects act to regulate the body's internal environment. An example is the regulation of blood calcium levels. When calcium levels in the blood are too high, calcitonin is released to help reduce the level. When calcium levels in the blood are too low, parathyroid hormone is released to increase the level. **32.** The hormones released by the pituitary gland regulate many bodily functions. In addition, they control the actions of several endocrine glands. The hypothalamus controls the release of these pituitary glands. **33.** Nonsteroid hormones generally do not enter the target cell. Rather, they bind to receptors on the cell membrane. This action activates enzymes on the inner surface of the cell membrane. This enzyme activates secondary messengers that carry the message of the hormone inside the cell. Once released, these second messengers can activate or inhibit a wide range of other cell activities. **34.** Puberty is a period of rapid growth and sexual maturation during which the reproductive system becomes fully functional. Before this time, neither testes nor ovaries are capable of producing active reproductive cells. At the completion of puberty, however, the male and female gonads are fully developed. **35.** In males, the sex hormones allow for the normal production of sperm as well as bring about an increase of facial hair, increase in body size, and deepening of the voice. In females, the sex hormones bring about the development of the female reproductive system, the widening of the hips, and development of the breasts.

Chapter 39—Test B

Multiple Choice   1. B **2.** C **3.** C **4.** A **5.** B **6.** A **7.** C **8.** B **9.** C **10.** B **11.** C **12.** C **13.** A **14.** A **15.** A   **Completion   16.** Hormones **17.** prostaglandins **18.** Puberty **19.** follicle **20.** placenta **Short Answer   21.** The endocrine system releases hormones, which broadcast messages throughout the body. **22.** The parathyroid glands regulate the amount of calcium in the blood. **23.** The four phases of the menstrual cycle are: follicular phase, ovulation, luteal phase, menstruation. **24.** The germ layers that result from gastrulation are the endoderm, mesoderm, and ectoderm. **25.** Any one of the following: (1) During infancy, a baby learns to walk and talk. (2) During childhood, language and motor coordination are perfected. (3) With puberty begins adolescence and sexual maturity. (4) Signs of aging begin to appear and childbearing ends in adulthood.

Using Science Skills   26. Diagram I is the female reproductive system. Diagram II is the male reproductive system. **27.** The ovary—structure A—releases eggs. **28.** Fertilization usually occurs in a Fallopian tube. **29.** Sperm are formed in the testes. **30.** Sperm exit the male body through the urethra, structure L.

Chapter 40 The Immune System and Disease

Answers for the Adapted Reading and Study Workbook worksheets (pp. 231–235) can be found in the Adapted Reading and Study Workbook, Annotated Teacher's Edition.

Answers for the Adapted Reading and Study Workbook worksheets (pp. 238–248) can be found in the Adapted Reading and Study Workbook, Annotated Teacher's Edition.

Section Review 40-1

1. A disease is any change, other than injury, that disrupts the normal functions of the body. **2.** Diseases are either inherited, caused by materials in the environment, or produced by pathogens. **3.** Infectious diseases are spread by coughing, sneezing, or physical contact; by consuming contaminated food or water; by contact with infected animals; or by sexual contact. **4.** Identifying the bacterium that causes meningitis does support the germ theory of disease, because the theory states that infectious diseases are caused by microorganisms, such as bacteria. **5.** A scientist must isolate a pathogen in order to identify it as a cause of a disease. If the scientist did not isolate the pathogen, there would be no way to tell if that individual pathogen caused the disease. **6.** virus **7.** bacteria **8.** protist **9.** fungus. **10.** No; antibiotics are used for bacterial infections. The common cold is caused by a virus and would not be affected by antibiotics.

Section Review 40-2

1. Skin acts as a nonspecific defense against invading pathogens by providing a layer of dead cells that most pathogens cannot penetrate. **2.** The inflammatory response protects the body by reacting to tissue damage caused by injury or infection. Blood vessels around the wound expand and release white blood cells that engulf and destroy bacteria. **3.** Permanent immunity occurs when millions of memory B cells or memory T cells remain capable of producing an immune response to a pathogen after the body has been exposed to that pathogen. **4.** c **5.** a **6.** b **7.** d **8.** The antibody concentration is much higher for the second exposure because, after the body has been exposed to a pathogen, it remains capable of producing specific antibodies to that pathogen. **9.** Memory

B cells produce a permanent immunity to the chicken pox. If the pathogen for chicken pox were to enter the body again, the memory B cells would be able to quickly produce enough antibodies to destroy the pathogen so that the person would not get sick again.

Section Review 40-3

1. When the immune system makes a mistake and attacks the body's own cells, it causes an autoimmune disease. **2.** Asthma attacks can be triggered by respiratory infections, exercise, emotional stress, certain medications, cold air, pollen, dust, tobacco smoke, pollution, molds, and pet dander. **3.** d **4.** a **5.** f **6.** e **7.** c **8.** b **9.** Histamines are released, and they produce allergy symptoms. Antihistamines work against histamines, reducing or stopping the allergy symptoms. **10.** HIV weakens the immune system by killing off most of the helper T cell population.

Section Review 40-4

1. Bioterrorism is the intentional use of biological agents to disable or kill individuals. **2.** To help prevent cancer, you can protect your DNA from agents, such as tobacco smoke, that cause cancer. In addition, you can exercise regularly and eat a balanced diet with plenty of fruits and vegetables. **3.** Improving the quality of drinking water greatly decreased the exposure of people to sewage-related bacteria. This, in turn, reduced the incidence of infectious diseases spread by contaminated water. **4.** Environmental risk factors that might be found inside a home include carbon monoxide, dust mites, mold spores, animal dander, tobacco smoke, fumes and vapors from household furnishings and products, asbestos, radon, and lead. **5.** Radon is similar to asbestos in that both can cause cancer. They are different in that asbestos occurs as airborne particles and radon as a gas. Also, radon occurs naturally in rocks and seeps into basements, whereas asbestos is usually found in insulation. **6.** Carbon monoxide binds with hemoglobin and prevents it from carrying oxygen. This problem is likely to be worse for a person whose hemoglobin is abnormal and whose blood may therefore already be lacking in enough oxygen. **7.** The worldwide elimination of smallpox resulted in discontinuation of vaccine programs to protect people from smallpox. As a result, most people today have no protection against the smallpox virus.

Chapter Vocabulary Review

1. antibody **2.** bacteria **3.** vaccination **4.** vector **5.** postulates **6.** antigen **7.** disease **8.** tumor **9. (across)** allergy **(down)** active **10.** germ **11.** pathogens **12. (across)** antibiotic **(down)** asthma **13.** histamine **14.** fever **15.** risk **16.** immunity

17. passive **18.** inflammatory response **19.** interferon **20.** immune response **21.** humoral **22.** malignant

Enrichment

1. Other causes of lung cancer besides smoking are exposure to carcinogens at the workplace and exposure to radiation at the workplace. **2.** A 40-year old man who has been smoking for 20 years would be at a greater risk because smokers who start at an early age have an increased risk of developing lung cancer.

Graphic Organizer

1. Specific defenses **2.** Second line of defense **3.** Skin **4.** Inflammatory response **5.** Humoral immunity **6.** Killer T cells

Chapter 40—Test A

Multiple Choice **1.** D **2.** C **3.** C **4.** B **5.** B **6.** B **7.** B **8.** C **9.** B **10.** C **11.** A **12.** C **13.** A **14.** A **15.** A **Completion** **16.** infectious **17.** vectors **18.** Antibiotics **19.** pathogens **20.** AIDS **Short Answer** **21.** Interferon, which interrupts viral replication, is produced by virus-infected cells and helps slow down viral infections; thus, it is not effective at stopping nonviral pathogens. **22.** Allergies result when antigens from allergens bind to mast cells, which release histamines. **23.** When the immune system mistakes its own body's cells for pathogens, an autoimmune disease results. **24.** HIV attacks helper T cells, reducing their number in the blood, weakening the immune system, and making the body susceptible to rare infections that it is usually able to resist. **25.** Antigens are substances that trigger an immune response. Antibodies are immune system proteins that recognize and bind to antigens. **Using Science Skills** **26.** The purpose of this culture is to isolate and grow the pathogen that is responsible for the cow's illness. **27.** A healthy mouse is being injected with the pathogen. **28.** The purpose of this culture is to isolate and grow the pathogen that is responsible for the mouse's illness and to compare it with the pathogen that caused the cow's illness. **29.** A healthy mouse would become as ill as the first mouse and the cow because it would be infected with the same pathogens. **30.** Sample answer: The microorganism isolated in A is the cause of the cow's (as well as the mouse's) disease. **Essay** **31.** Hereditary diseases, such as hemophilia, are caused by heredity, or genes passed from parents to children. Materials in the environment can also cause diseases. For example, cigarette smoke causes cancer, and exposure to the sun can cause skin cancer. Infectious diseases are caused by pathogens, such as bacteria or viruses. **32.** In active immunity, the body produces its own antibodies against a particular antigen. In passive immunity, a person is given antibodies obtained from the blood of either another person or an animal. Active immunity is a type of immunity that may develop as a result of having had a disease, and the disease rarely recurs. Passive immunity, on the other hand, is only temporary and usually does not last for more than several weeks. **33.** The inflammatory response is a nonspecific defense reaction to tissue damage caused by an injury or infection. When a wound occurs, nearby blood vessels expand and white blood cells leak into the infected tissues. Many of these white blood cells are phagocytes, which engulf and destroy pathogens. The infected tissue may swell and feel painful. The area may also be red and feel warm to the touch. **34.** The three main causes of cancer are viruses, radiation, and chemicals. Radiation causes cancer by producing mutations in DNA. If these mutations occur in genes that control cell growth, a normal cell may become a cancer cell. Chemicals, or carcinogens, also produce cancer by causing mutations in DNA. **35.** Both types of immunity are specific defenses. In cell-mediated immunity, killer T cells attack cells infected by pathogens. In humoral immunity, B cells produce antibodies that disable pathogens in the blood and other body fluids.

Chapter 40—Test B

Multiple Choice   1. B 2. C 3. C 4. C 5. B 6. A 7. C
8. B 9. C 10. C 11. C 12. D 13. C 14. C 15. A
Completion   16. pathogen 17. bacteria 18. cell-mediated 19. vaccine 20. Humoral   **Short Answer**
21. Diseases can be inherited, caused by materials in the environment (such as asbestos or tobacco smoke), and produced by pathogens (such as bacteria and viruses). **22.** Antibiotics kill bacteria by interfering with the cellular processes of the bacteria. **23.** As long as the skin is not broken, it forms a barrier against invading pathogens; in addition, oil and sweat glands in the skin produce an acidic environment that kills bacteria on the surface of the skin. **24.** Allergies occur when the immune system overreacts to certain antigens, causing sneezing, runny nose, and watery eyes. **25.** A benign tumor is one that is not cancerous and will not spread throughout the body; a malignant tumor is cancerous and is likely to spread to other parts of the body. **Using Science Skills**   **26.** an antigen (or pathogen) and an antibody **27.** Antigen-binding sites **28.** Structure A—an antigen—triggers the production of antibodies. **29.** humoral immunity
30. Antigen-binding sites allow an antibody to bind to two antigens, destroying the pathogens.

Unit 10—Test A

Multiple Choice 1. B 2. C 3. D 4. B 5. A 6. C
7. D 8. A 9. A 10. D 11. C 12. C 13. A 14. B
15. D **Completion** 16. threshold 17. compact
18. bronchus 19. water 20. B cells   **Short Answer**
21. The dermis contains collagen fibers, blood vessels, nerve endings, glands, sensory receptors, smooth muscles, and hair follicles. **22.** The pancreas produces enzymes that break down carbohydrates, proteins, lipids, and nucleic acids in the small intestine. The pancreas also produces sodium bicarbonate, a base that neutralizes stomach acid so that these enzymes can be effective. **23.** A carcinogen is a chemical compound that is known to cause cancer. Examples include aflatoxin, chloroform, benzene, and chemicals found in tobacco smoke. **24.** When platelets come into contact with the edges of a broken blood vessel, they become sticky and cluster together around the wound. The platelets then release proteins called clotting factors, which start a series of chemical reactions that lead to the formation of a clot. **25.** Nutrients are absorbed across the inside surface of the small intestine. Villi are tiny projections on the surface of the small intestine that greatly increase the intestine's surface area and ability to absorb nutrients.   **Using Science Skills** **26.** A cell-mediated immune response is shown in the diagram.
27. Structure A is a T cell. In Step 1, the T cell binds to the macrophage and is activated to become a helper T cell. **28.** Structure B is a helper T cell. It activates killer T cells and B cells. **29.** Structure C is a killer T cell. In Step 3, the killer T cell binds to the infected cell, disrupting its cell membrane and destroying it. **30.** Cell-mediated immunity, shown in the diagram, involves killer T cells attacking cells infected with pathogens. Humoral immunity, in contrast, involves B cells producing antibodies that disable pathogens in the blood. Both processes are similar in their being specific defenses in the immune response. **Essay** **31.** The endocrine system communicates with hormones, which travel throughout the body via the bloodstream. Hormonal communication is relatively slow but can reach cells everywhere in the body. The nervous system communicates with nerve impulses, which travel through a system of interconnected neurons. Nervous communication is very rapid but limited to parts of the body that are interconnected by nerves.
32. The levels of organization are cells, tissues, organs, and organ systems. Possible examples include: red blood cell (cell); blood (tissue); heart (organ); and cardiovascular system (organ system).
33. The skeleton of an embryo is composed almost entirely of cartilage. Beginning around seven months before birth, ossification begins to take place. Bone

tissue forms as osteoblasts secrete mineral deposits that replace the cartilage in developing bones. The growth of cartilage at the ends, or growth plates, of long bones causes the bones to lengthen. Gradually this new growth of cartilage is also replaced by bone tissue, and the bones become larger and stronger. By adulthood, the cartilage in the growth plates is replaced by bone and the bones become completely ossified. **34.** The thyroid gland controls metabolism. Its hormone, thyroxine, stimulates cells to increase their metabolic activity. When the hypothalamus senses that the level of thyroxine in the blood is low, it secretes thyroid-releasing hormone (TRH). TRH stimulates the pituitary to produce thyroid-stimulating hormone (TSH), which stimulates the thyroid to produce thyroxine. The opposite events occur if the level of thyroxine in the blood is high. **35.** The body's nonspecific defenses are the skin, inflammatory response, fever, and interferons. The skin is a physical barrier that few pathogens can penetrate. Sweat and skin oils also kill many bacteria. The inflammatory response occurs in reaction to tissue damage. It brings many white blood cells to the site to fight infection. Fever raises the body temperature, which slows the growth of many pathogens. Interferons are proteins produced by cells infected with virus. Interferons help block viral replication.

Unit 10—Test B

Multiple Choice   1. B **2.** C **3.** B **4.** A **5.** C **6.** B **7.** B **8.** C **9.** A **10.** A **11.** C **12.** C **13.** B **14.** C **15.** C   **Completion   16.** reflex **17.** periosteum **18.** capillaries **19.** bile **20.** autoimmune   **Short Answer   21.** Stimulant and depressant drugs have opposite effects on the nervous system. Stimulants increase and depressants decrease the actions controlled by the nervous system, such as heart rate. **22.** Ligaments hold bones together in joints. Tendons attach skeletal muscles to bones and make them work like levers around the joints. **23.** Atherosclerosis is a buildup of fat deposits on the inner walls of arteries. It increases the risk of cardiovascular diseases such as heart attack and stroke. **24.** The teeth contribute to mechanical digestion by tearing and grinding food into smaller pieces. The enzyme amylase in saliva begins the chemical digestion of starch. **25.** Infectious diseases can be spread by physical contact, including coughing and sneezing; by contaminated food or water; and by infected animals. **Using Science Skills   26.** Diagram I shows the action of a steroid hormone. Diagram II shows the action of a nonsteroid hormone. **27.** In Diagram I, structure A is the receptor. It is found only in target cells. It binds to the hormone to form structure B, a hormone-receptor complex, which enters the nucleus

of the cell and binds to DNA. **28.** The hormone in diagram I directly affects gene expression by turning on or off whole sets of genes. **29.** In Diagram II, structure A is the receptor. It is found only on the cell membranes of target cells. The receptor binds to the hormone and activates an enzyme on the inner surface of the cell membrane. This enzyme activates structure B, a secondary messenger, which carries the message of the hormone inside the cell. **30.** The steroid hormone in Diagram I is made of lipids, so it can cross cell membranes. The nonsteroid hormone in Diagram II is made of proteins, so it cannot cross cell membranes.

Final Exam—Level A

Multiple Choice   1. A **2.** D **3.** C **4.** B **5.** C **6.** A **7.** D **8.** C **9.** D **10.** A **11.** A **12.** B **13.** D **14.** D **15.** C   **Completion   16.** slows down (stops) **17.** transcription **18.** fungi **19.** fruit **20.** mollusk **Short Answer   21.** Grow two similar plants in the same environmental conditions. Give each the same amount of water. However, add fertilizer to the water of one plant. The controlled variables are temperature, location, soil, type of plant, and water. The manipulated variable is fertilizer. The responding variable is plant growth. **22.** Plant roots absorb precipitation that seeps into the ground. Plant leaves return water to the air through transpiration. **23.** Cells divide because the larger a cell becomes, the more demands the cell places on its DNA. Also, the cell has more trouble moving enough nutrients and wastes across the cell membrane. **24.** Genetic diversity is important to breeders because the more genetic diversity there is, the more genetic traits there are to choose from, and it is more likely that breeders will find the trait they are interested in. **25.** Scientists currently hypothesize that human evolution occurred in a series of complex adaptive radiations that produced a large number of different species. **Using Science Skills   26.** The promoter site is the site on the DNA molecule where RNA polymerase binds to start transcription. **27.** The repressor blocks the movement of RNA polymerase. **28.** When the repressor protein is bound to lactose, its shape changes so that it cannot bind to the operator. When lactose is not present, the shape of the repressor protein allows it to bind to the operator. **29.** The *lac* genes are on when lactose binds to the repressor protein. **30.** The *lac* operon controls when the *lac* genes are turned on. This is useful to the cell so that it doesn't waste resources to make proteins that it doesn't need. **Essay   31.** With a climate change, abiotic factors such as temperature, precipitation, and humidity would change. Biotic factors, or all the living things in the ecosystem, would die out or emi-

grate if they could not adapt to the climate changes. Some living things would adapt to the climate changes and remain in the ecosystem. Other living things might immigrate to the area because the new climatic conditions are optimal for their survival. **32.** Plants are the main land autotrophs that use the energy from sunlight to produce food, or carbohydrates. They also add oxygen to the air as a result of photosynthesis. Plants make up the first trophic level in terrestrial food chains. All consumers rely on plants for energy. Without plants, almost all consumers on land could also become extinct. Consumers in aquatic environments may not be affected because green algae are the main autotrophs in freshwater ecosystems and in the oceans. **33.** The human insulin gene is cut from a sequence of human DNA with restriction enzymes. The fragments are separated by gel electrophoresis, and the human insulin gene is isolated. A bacterial plasmid is cut with the same restriction enzyme. The human DNA fragment and the cut plasmid are mixed together, and the sticky ends of each molecule recombine with each other. The recombinant plasmids are transformed into bacterial cells. Transformed bacteria are separated from bacteria that do not contain a plasmid by growing the bacteria on plates that contain a certain antibiotic. The plasmid carries a gene resistant to an antibiotic; so bacterial cells containing the plasmid will grow in the presence of that antibiotic.
34. Changes in DNA can cause mutations in the sequence of a gene, which in turn changes the action of its protein product. Some mutations are beneficial in that they increase the fitness of individuals that carry them. Individuals with increased fitness are better suited to their environment and better able to survive and reproduce. Over time, most members of a population will carry the mutant allele and exhibit the mutant trait. **35.** Muscle cells make up smooth muscle tissue. Smooth muscle tissue, along with epithelial tissue, nervous tissue, and connective tis-

sue, makes up the stomach. The stomach is an organ that works with other organs in an organ system called the digestive system.

Final Exam—Level B

Multiple Choice **1.** B **2.** C **3.** C **4.** A **5.** A **6.** B **7.** A **8.** C **9.** C **10.** B **11.** A **12.** C **13.** A **14.** B **15.** C **Completion** **16.** abiotic **17.** interphase (S phase) **18.** natural selection **19.** radial **20.** endotherms or warm-blooded **Short Answer** **21.** Plants are living things because they are made up of cells, they reproduce, they contain DNA, they grow and develop, they use energy from the sun and nutrients from the soil, they respond to their environment, they maintain a stable internal environment, and they change over time. **22.** As genetic diversity decreases, there are fewer traits that an organism can "choose" from to adapt to changing conditions. If an organism cannot adapt to changing conditions, it will eventually die off. **23.** Photosynthesis uses the energy of sunlight to convert the reactants, carbon dioxide and water, into the products, sugars and oxygen. **24.** The two main sources of genetic variation are mutations and the shuffling of alleles that occurs from sexual reproduction. **25.** A behavior helps an organism survive and reproduce by helping it get resources and find a healthy mate. **Using Science Skills** **26.** The plant cell is in diagram II. **27.** These cells are eukaryotic cells because they contain genetic material within a nucleus. **28.** The mitochondrion convert chemical energy stored in food into compounds that are easier for the cell to use. **29.** The nucleus codes for proteins. The proteins make up cell structures and regulate cell processes. **30.** A plant cell would shrink because water would move out of the cell. Water would diffuse from the cell because the concentration of water is higher inside the cell than outside the cell.

An Important Process

While walking along a dusty path, you begin to cough. As you continue your walk, a small insect comes flying toward you. You blink and then duck so that it misses you. These actions are just a few examples of homeostasis. Homeostasis is the process by which organisms keep internal conditions relatively constant despite changes in their external environments.

1. List three other examples of homeostasis that occur in organisms.

2. Why is homeostasis important to an organism?

© Pearson Education, Inc.

35–1 Human Body Systems

A. Organization of the Body

  1. Cells

  2. Tissues

  3. Organs

  4. Organ Systems

B. Maintaining Homeostasis

  1. A Nonliving Example

  2. In the Body

© Pearson Education, Inc.

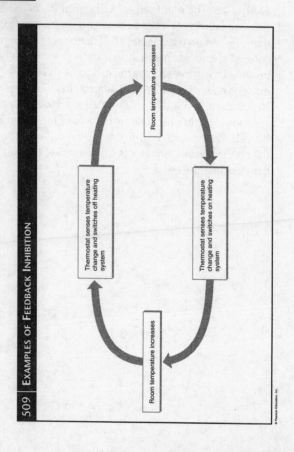

Room temperature decreases

Thermostat senses temperature change and switches off heating system

Thermostat senses temperature change and switches on heating system

Room temperature increases

© Pearson Education, Inc.

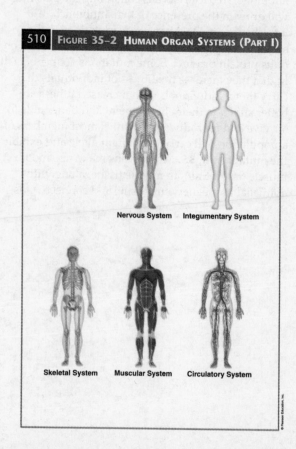

Nervous System   Integumentary System

Skeletal System   Muscular System   Circulatory System

© Pearson Education, Inc.

© Pearson Education, Inc., publishing as Pearson Prentice Hall.

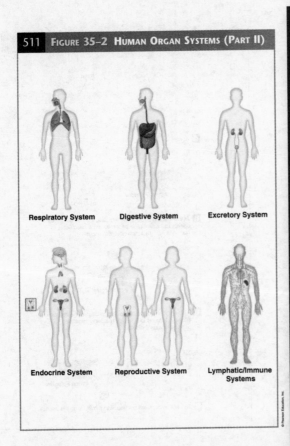

Respiratory System   Digestive System   Excretory System

Endocrine System   Reproductive System   Lymphatic/Immune Systems

You've Got a Lot of Nerve!

The nervous system controls and coordinates functions throughout the body. The nervous system is one of the body's communication systems. Without communication, parts of the body could not work together smoothly.

1. Think about tying the shoelace of a sneaker. Construct a flowchart that shows what happens between your eyes and your brain, and between your brain and your hands, when you tie a bow in the shoelace.

2. How would the communications be different if you tried to tie the shoelace with your eyes closed?

ANSWERS
1. Students' flowcharts should include: The eyes inform the brain about the position of the hands and the shoelace; the brain signals the hands telling them where to tie the shoelace and how to tie it.
2. All information about the position of the shoelace would have to come from the hands as they feel and manipulate the shoelace.

35–2 The Nervous System

A. Neurons

B. The Nerve Impulse

  1. The Resting Neuron

  2. The Moving Impulse

  3. Threshold

C. The Synapse

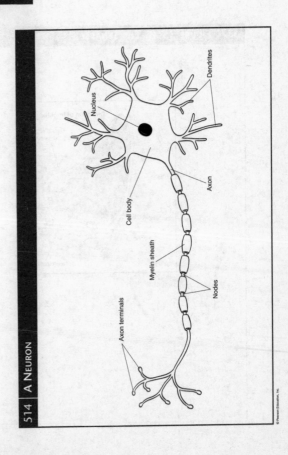

Nucleus · Dendrites · Cell body · Axon · Myelin sheath · Nodes · Axon terminals

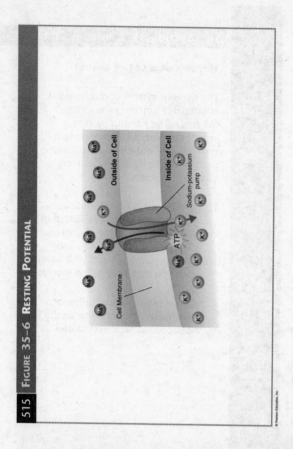

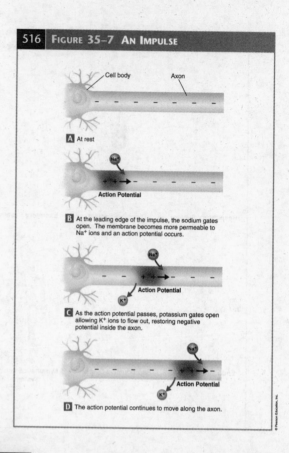

A At rest

B At the leading edge of the impulse, the sodium gates open. The membrane becomes more permeable to Na+ ions and an action potential occurs.

C As the action potential passes, potassium gates open allowing K+ ions to flow out, restoring negative potential inside the axon.

D The action potential continues to move along the axon.

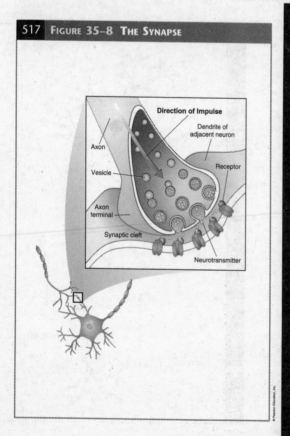

Brainiac

Imagine that you are a computer systems engineer and your job is to design a computer that can perform all the functions of a human brain.

1. Which brainlike functions can already be performed by computers?

2. Which brainlike functions cannot be performed by computers?

3. How successful do you think you (or anyone) could be in designing a computer that can perform all the functions of the human brain? Explain your answer.

ANSWERS
1. Computation and data sorting
2. Original thought and perception of emotions
3. Answers may vary. A likely answer is that a computer cannot be designed to feel emotions.

35-3 Divisions of the Nervous System

A. The Central Nervous System

B. The Brain

   1. The Cerebrum

   2. The Cerebellum

   3. The Brain Stem

   4. The Thalamus and Hypothalamus

C. The Spinal Cord

D. The Peripheral Nervous System

   1. The Somatic Nervous System

   2. The Autonomic Nervous System

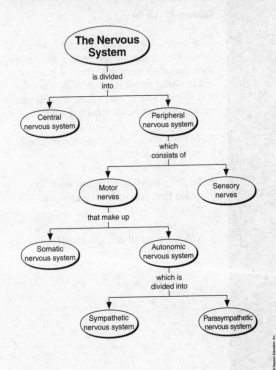

© Pearson Education, Inc.

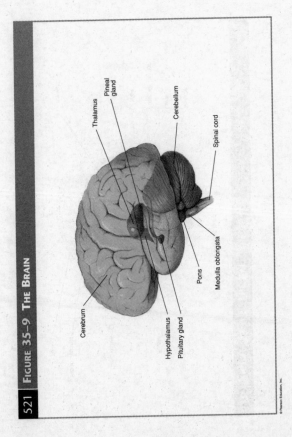

521 | FIGURE 35-9 THE BRAIN

© Pearson Education, Inc.

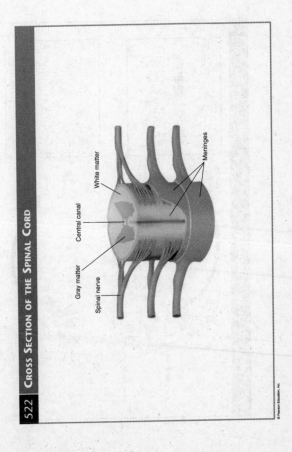

522 | CROSS SECTION OF THE SPINAL CORD

© Pearson Education, Inc.

Taking It All In

Your senses—sight, hearing, smell, touch, taste—are constantly receiving information about your environment. Even if you are not thinking about it, your body is sensing and responding to conditions around you, such as the temperature of the room.

1. List ten things you observe about the room you are in.

2. Next to each observation, write the sense that you used to make that observation.

3. What sense did you use most?

35–4 The Senses

A. Vision

B. Hearing and Balance

   1. Hearing

   2. Balance

C. Smell and Taste

D. Touch and Related Senses

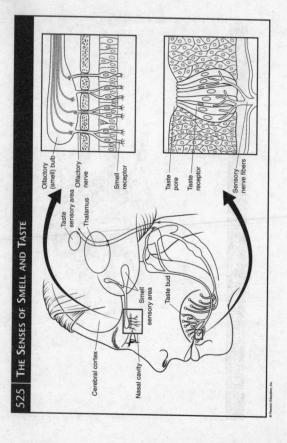

Olfactory (smell) bulb
Olfactory nerve
Smell receptor
Taste sensory area
Thalamus
Taste pore
Taste receptor
Sensory nerve fibers
Smell sensory area
Taste bud
Cerebral cortex
Nasal cavity

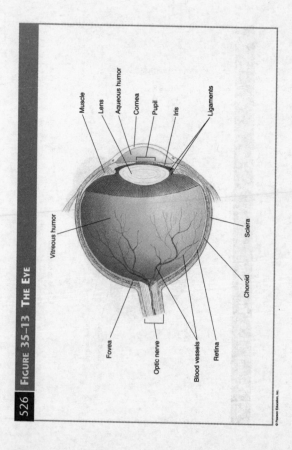

Muscle
Lens
Aqueous humor
Cornea
Pupil
Iris
Ligaments
Vitreous humor
Sclera
Fovea
Optic nerve
Blood vessels
Retina
Choroid

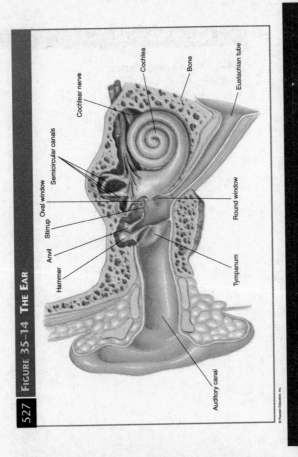

Cochlea
Cochlear nerve
Bone
Eustachian tube
Semicircular canals
Oval window
Stirrup
Anvil
Hammer
Round window
Tympanum
Auditory canal

© Pearson Education, Inc.

Poster Designer

Imagine that you are working with a local community group to help stop drug abuse among teenagers. Your first assignment is to design a drug abuse awareness poster.

1. Complete a brief sketch of your idea on a sheet of paper. What effects of drugs does your poster depict?

2. Why do you think teenagers will pay attention to your poster?

ANSWERS
1. Possible answer: negative effects on the brain, which may include negative effects on the brain, or death. Teenagers
2. Answers will depend on the design of the poster. Teenagers may respond to concern about loss of mental or athletic ability or concern about possible injuries.

© Pearson Education, Inc.

35–5 Drugs and the Nervous System

A. Drugs That Affect the Synapse

1. Stimulants

2. Depressants

3. Cocaine

4. Opiates

5. Marijuana

6. Alcohol

7. Alcohol and Disease

B. Drug Abuse

© Pearson Education, Inc.

Drug Type	Medical Use	Examples	Effects on the Body
Stimulants	Used to increase alertness, relieve fatigue	Amphetamines	Increase heart and respiratory rates; elevate blood pressure; dilate pupils; decrease appetite
Depressants	Used to relieve anxiety, irritability, tension	Barbiturates Tranquilizers	Slow down the actions of the central nervous system; small amounts cause calmness and relaxation; larger amounts cause slurred speech and impaired judgment
Opiates	Used to relieve pain	Morphine Codeine	Act as a depressant; cause drowsiness, restlessness, nausea

© Pearson Education, Inc.

Give Yourself a Hand

If you've ever looked at a construction site, you know that a building is supported by a framework of beams. Your body also has a supporting framework. Instead of steel beams, bones support the human body. The beams that support a building are attached in a way that forms a rigid structure. Unlike these beams, the bones that support the body are connected in a way that allows them to move.

1. On a sheet of paper, draw an outline of a hand and arm.

2. Look at your hand and wiggle your fingers. Can you see how the bones of your hand move? Within the outline of the hand, draw the bones of your hand as you think they look.

3. Feel the bones of your forearm and upper arm. Is the bone at your elbow part of the upper arm or lower arm?

4. Move your arm and notice how the bones move. Within the outline of the arm, draw the bones of your arm as you think they look.

36–1   The Skeletal System

A. The Skeleton

B. Structure of Bones

C. Development of Bones

D. Types of Joints

   1. Immovable Joints

   2. Slightly Movable Joints

   3. Freely Movable Joints

E. Structure of Joints

F. Skeletal System Disorders

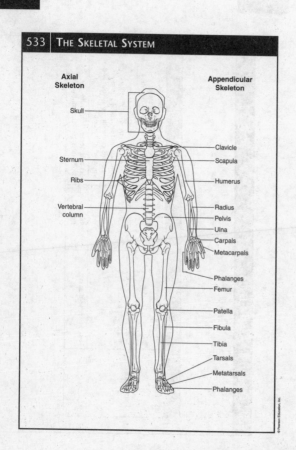

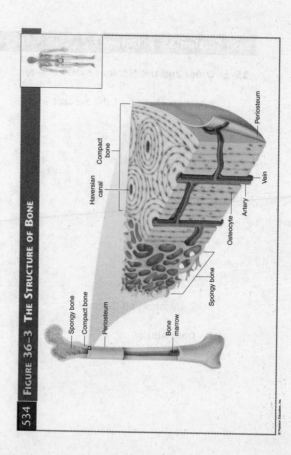

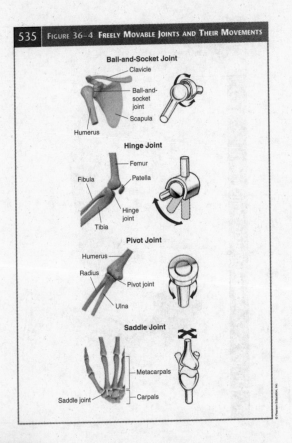

Ball-and-Socket Joint

- Clavicle
- Ball-and-socket joint
- Scapula
- Humerus

Hinge Joint

- Femur
- Patella
- Fibula
- Hinge joint
- Tibia

Pivot Joint

- Humerus
- Radius
- Pivot joint
- Ulna

Saddle Joint

- Metacarpals
- Carpals
- Saddle joint

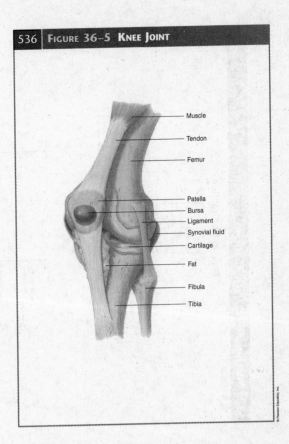

- Muscle
- Tendon
- Femur
- Patella
- Bursa
- Ligament
- Synovial fluid
- Cartilage
- Fat
- Fibula
- Tibia

537 | Section 36-2 Interest Grabber

They Can Pull But They Can't Push

Hold your arm out straight and parallel to the floor. Now, "make a muscle." As you flex your biceps muscle, notice what happens to the rest of your arm.

1. Describe what happened to your arm as you flexed your biceps muscle.

2. Using Figures 36-2 and 36-4 in your textbook as reference, draw the bones and joints of the arm and shoulder. Draw in the biceps muscle and show the places where you think the biceps muscle is connected to the bones.

3. Explain why you think the biceps muscle is attached as shown in your drawing.

538 | Section 36-2 Outline

36-2 The Muscular System

- A. Types of Muscle Tissue
  1. Skeletal Muscles
  2. Smooth Muscles
  3. Cardiac Muscle
- B. Muscle Contraction
- C. Control of Muscle Contraction
- D. How Muscles and Bones Interact
- E. Exercise and Health

Muscle Contraction

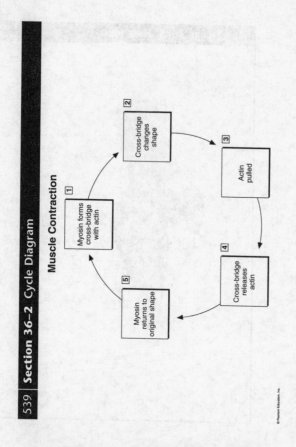

1. Myosin forms cross-bridge with actin

2. Cross-bridge changes shape

3. Actin pulled

4. Cross-bridge releases actin

5. Myosin returns to original shape

© Pearson Education, Inc.

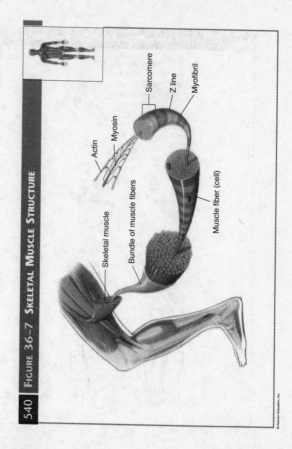

Actin
Myosin
Sarcomere
Z line
Myofibril
Skeletal muscle
Bundle of muscle fibers
Muscle fiber (cell)

© Pearson Education, Inc.

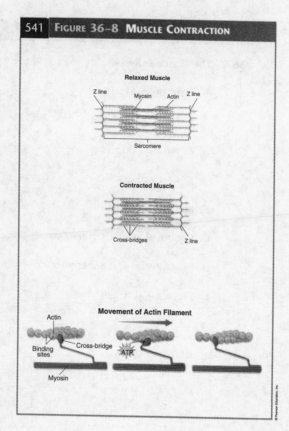

Relaxed Muscle

Z line   Myosin   Actin   Z line

Sarcomere

Contracted Muscle

Cross-bridges   Z line

Movement of Actin Filament

Actin
Binding sites
Cross-bridge
ATP
Myosin

© Pearson Education, Inc.

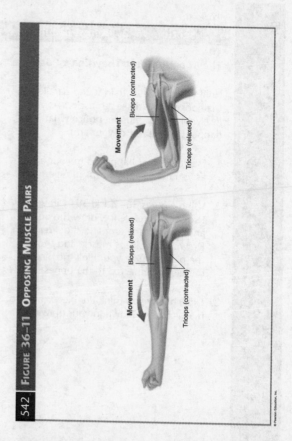

Movement
Biceps (contracted)
Triceps (relaxed)

Movement
Biceps (relaxed)
Triceps (contracted)

© Pearson Education, Inc.

Your Suit of Armor

A suit of armor protected a knight
from injuries in battle. Imagine what
it would be like to wear a suit of armor.
For one thing, it would feel very heavy.
And you'd probably make a great deal
of noise every time you moved. In some
ways, your skin is like a suit of armor.
It isn't as strong, but it has many
advantages over metal armor.

Work with a partner to make a list
of functions of the skin. It may help
you to think about a suit of armor
and compare the skin's functions
with those of armor.

ANSWERS
Students will likely list that the skin keeps germs and dirt out of the body; it can sense the body's surroundings; and it is flexible, which allows the body to move.

© Pearson Education, Inc.

36–3 The Integumentary System

A. The Skin

    1. Epidermis

    2. Dermis

    3. Skin Cancer

B. Hair and Nails

    1. Hair

    2. Nails

© Pearson Education, Inc.

Skin

is made up of the
- Dermis — which is the — Inner layer
- Epidermis — which is the — Outer layer

functions as a
- Protector against UV radiation
- Remover of waste products
- Regulator of body temperature
- Barrier to infection

© Pearson Education, Inc.

Hair
Blood vessels
Nerves
Sweat pore
Hair follicle
Sebaceous gland
Muscle
Sweat gland
Fat
Epidermis
Dermis
Hypodermis

© Pearson Education, Inc.

The Valve Detective

Veins are vessels that carry blood to the heart. Along their length, they have one-way valves to prevent the backflow of blood. With a little sleuthing, you can figure out the location of a valve or two in your veins.

1. Choose the longest vein you can see on the inner side of your wrist. Starting as close to your wrist as possible, press your thumb on the vein and slide it along the vein up your arm. Did the length of the vein remain blue?

2. Repeat this process, but in the opposite direction, moving your thumb along the vein from the far end to the end closest to your wrist. Did the length of the vein remain blue?

3. In which direction is your blood flowing in this vein? How can you tell? Can you tell where a valve is located? Explain your answer.

37-1 The Circulatory System

  A. Functions of the Circulatory System

  B. The Heart

    1. Circulation Through the Body

    2. Circulation Through the Heart

    3. Heartbeat

  C. Blood Vessels

    1. Arteries

    2. Capillaries

    3. Veins

  D. Blood Pressure

  E. Diseases of the Circulatory System

    1. High Blood Pressure

    2. Consequences of Atherosclerosis

    3. Circulatory System Health

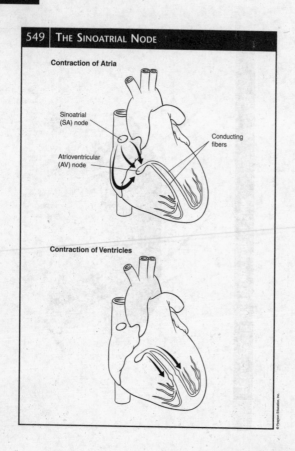

Contraction of Atria

Contraction of Ventricles

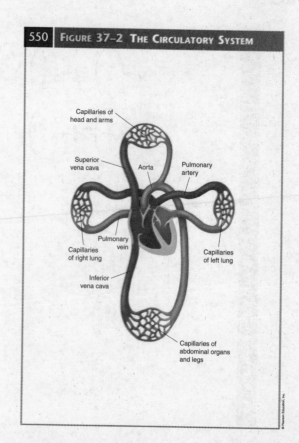

Figure 37–3 Structures of the Heart

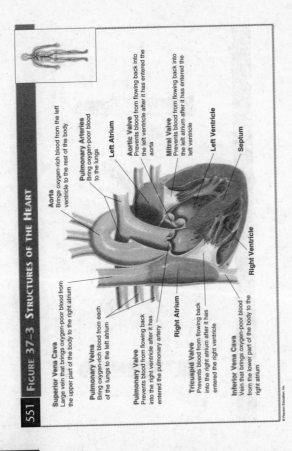

Superior Vena Cava
Large vein that brings oxygen-poor blood from the upper part of the body to the right atrium

Pulmonary Veins
Bring oxygen-rich blood from each of the lungs to the left atrium

Pulmonary Valve
Prevents blood from flowing back into the right ventricle after it has entered the pulmonary artery

Aorta
Brings oxygen-rich blood from the left ventricle to the rest of the body

Pulmonary Arteries
Bring oxygen-poor blood to the lungs

Left Atrium

Aortic Valve
Prevents blood from flowing back into the left ventricle after it has entered the aorta

Mitral Valve
Prevents blood from flowing back into the left atrium after it has entered the left ventricle

Left Ventricle

Septum

Right Atrium

Tricuspid Valve
Prevents blood from flowing back into the right atrium after it has entered the right ventricle

Inferior Vena Cava
Vein that brings oxygen-poor blood from the lower part of the body to the right atrium

Right Ventricle

© Pearson Education, Inc.

Figure 37–5 The Three Types of Blood Vessels

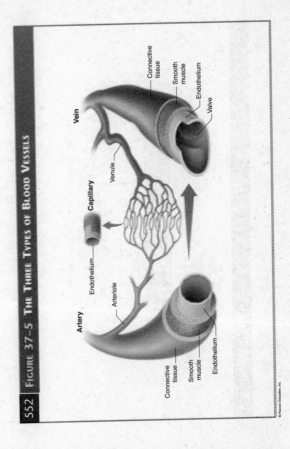

Vein

Connective tissue

Smooth muscle

Endothelium

Valve

Venule

Capillary

Endothelium

Artery

Arteriole

Endothelium

Connective tissue

Smooth muscle

Endothelium

© Pearson Education, Inc.

Section 37–2 Interest Grabber

Designer Blood

The federal government wants to find ways to make the blood supply safer for everyone who needs blood. However, no one has yet found a way to find and eliminate all disease-causing agents in the blood. Imagine that you are the head of a biotechnology company and think that you can design a safe alternative— artificial blood.

1. What characteristics would artificial blood need to take the place of real blood?

2. Do you think that artificial blood could completely replace real blood? Explain your answer.

ANSWERS
1. Artificial blood would need to be a fluid that could carry oxygen and carbon dioxide, nutrients, enzymes, hormones, and waste products.
2. No. Real blood contains living cells that combat disease. Also, real blood can form clots, preventing blood loss at cuts.

Section 37–2 Outline

37–2 Blood and the Lymphatic System

A. Blood Plasma

B. Blood Cells

   1. Red Blood Cells

   2. White Blood Cells

   3. Platelets and Blood Clotting

C. The Lymphatic System

© Pearson Education, Inc.

Blood Type of Donor	Blood Type of Recipient			
	A	B	AB	O
A	✓	X	✓	X
B	X	✓	✓	X
AB	X	X	✓	X
O	✓	✓	✓	✓

X = Unsuccessful transfusion ✓ = Successful transfusion

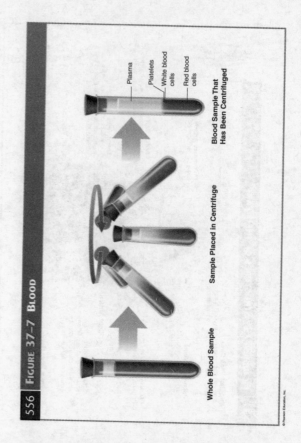

Whole Blood Sample

Sample Placed in Centrifuge

Blood Sample That Has Been Centrifuged

Plasma
Platelets
White blood cells
Red blood cells

Cell Type	Function
Neutrophils	Engulf and destroy small bacteria and foreign substances
Eosinophils	Attack parasites; limit inflammation associated with allergic reactions
Basophils	Release histamines that cause inflammation; release anticoagulants, which prevent blood clots
Monocytes	Give rise to leukocytes that engulf and destroy large bacteria and substances
Lymphocytes	Some destroy foreign cells by causing their membranes to rupture; some develop into cells that produce antibodies, which target specific foreign substances

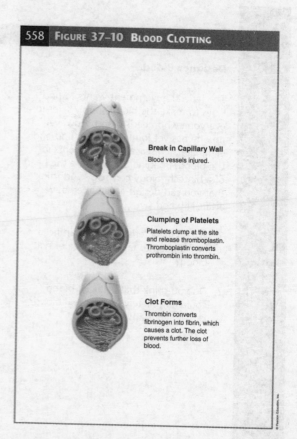

Break in Capillary Wall
Blood vessels injured.

Clumping of Platelets
Platelets clump at the site and release thromboplastin. Thromboplastin converts prothrombin into thrombin.

Clot Forms
Thrombin converts fibrinogen into fibrin, which causes a clot. The clot prevents further loss of blood.

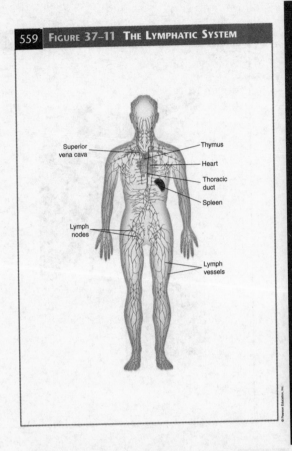

Superior
vena cava

Thymus

Heart

Thoracic
duct

Spleen

Lymph
nodes

Lymph
vessels

© Pearson Education, Inc.

Hold That Breath!

Do not perform this activity if you have any breathing problems. Working with a partner, count the number of breaths you take in 15 seconds. Multiply that number by 4 for the number of breaths per minute. Your partner will act as the timer/recorder. Repeat the procedure three times and take an average. Now, take a deep breath and hold it for as long as you can. Have your partner record your time. Repeat the procedure three times and take an average. Switch roles with your partner and repeat the procedure. Exchange data with other groups and answer the questions below.

1. What was the range of breathing rates?

2. Why are there differences in breathing rates among members of the class?

3. What was the average length of time classmates could hold their breath?

4. What factors might affect how long you could hold your breath?

5. A child having a tantrum declares she is going to hold her breath "until I turn blue!" Do you think this is possible? Explain your answer.

ANSWERS
1. The average person breathes about 16 to 24 times per minute.
2. The difference among classmates might be a result of physical conditioning and individual metabolism.
3. Most people can hold their breath for just under a minute.
4. Physical conditioning and metabolism might affect the length of time.
5. It is not possible. The child will begin to breathe again when levels of carbon dioxide reach a critical level.

© Pearson Education, Inc.

37–3 The Respiratory System

A. What Is Respiration?

B. The Human Respiratory System

C. Gas Exchange

D. Breathing

E. How Breathing Is Controlled

F. Tobacco and the Respiratory System

   1. Substances in Tobacco

   2. Diseases Caused by Smoking

   3. Smoking and the Nonsmoker

   4. Dealing With Tobacco

© Pearson Education, Inc.

Movement of Oxygen and Carbon Dioxide In and Out of the Respiratory System

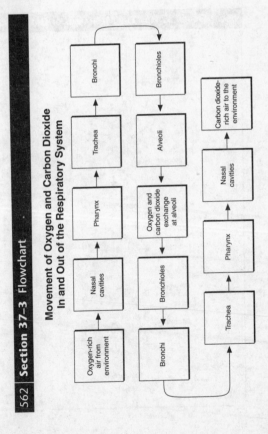

© Pearson Education, Inc.

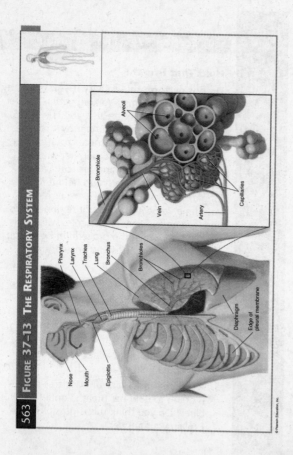

Alveoli
Bronchiole
Vein
Artery
Capillaries
Pharynx
Larynx
Trachea
Lung
Bronchus
Bronchioles
Diaphragm
Edge of pleural membrane
Nose
Mouth
Epiglottis

© Pearson Education, Inc.

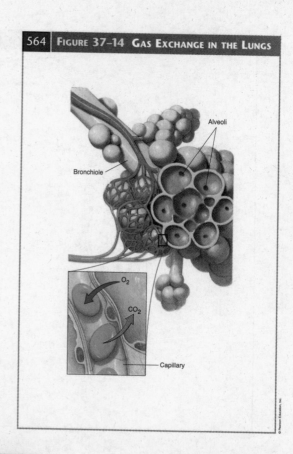

Alveoli
Bronchiole
O_2
CO_2
Capillary

© Pearson Education, Inc.

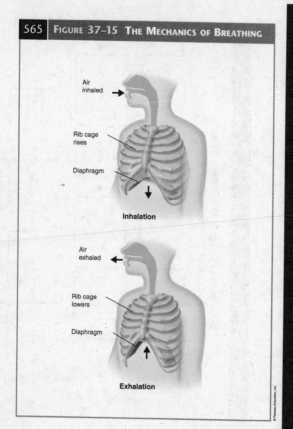

Air inhaled
Rib cage rises
Diaphragm

Inhalation

Air exhaled
Rib cage lowers
Diaphragm

Exhalation

© Pearson Education, Inc.

Good Food Sense

Nutrients are molecules that provide the body with energy and materials for growth. Three kinds of nutrients you eat are called fats, proteins, and carbohydrates—terms you may have already heard. Think about what they may mean.

1. Write a brief description of what you think fats, proteins, and carbohydrates are.

2. Which of these three nutrients do you think should make up the largest part of your diet? Which should make up the smallest part? Arrange the three nutrients in order starting from the one that you should eat the most to the one that you should eat the least.

3. Why might it be unwise to eat too much of the nutrient you listed last?

ANSWERS
1. Accept all reasonable descriptions. You may wish to have students revisit their descriptions after completing this section.
2. Carbohydrates, proteins, fat
3. Possible answer: The body needs only small amounts of fats. Fats contain more Calories than the other nutrients do.

© Pearson Education, Inc.

38–1 Food and Nutrition

A. Food and Energy

B. Nutrients

   1. Water

   2. Carbohydrates

   3. Fats

   4. Proteins

   5. Vitamins

   6. Minerals

C. Nutrition and a Balanced Diet

© Pearson Education, Inc.

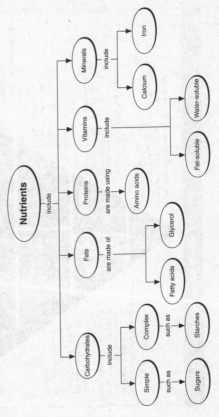

© Pearson Education, Inc.

Vitamin	Sources	Function
A (retinol)	Yellow, orange, and dark green vegetables; dairy products	Important for growth of skin cells; important for night vision
D (calciferol)	Fish oils, eggs; made by skin when exposed to sunlight; added to dairy products	Promotes bone growth; increases calcium and phosphorus absorption
E (tocopherol)	Green leafy vegetables, seeds, vegetable oils	Antioxidant; prevents cellular damage
K	Green leafy vegetables; made by bacteria that live in human intestine	Needed for normal blood clotting
B_1 (thiamine)	Whole grains, pork, legumes, milk	Normal metabolism of carbohydrates
B_2 (riboflavin)	Dairy products, meats, vegetables, whole-grain cereal	Normal growth; part of electron transport chain; energy metabolism
Niacin	Liver, milk, whole grains, nuts, meats, legumes	Important in energy metabolism
B_6 (pyridoxine)	Whole grains, meats, vegetables	Important for amino acid metabolism
Pantothenic acid	Meats, dairy, whole grains	Needed for energy metabolism
Folic acid	Legumes, nuts, green leafy vegetables, oranges, broccoli, peas, fortified bread and cereal	Coenzyme involved in nucleic acid metabolism; prevents neural-tube defects in developing fetuses
B_{12} (cyanocobalamin)	Meats, eggs, dairy products, enriched cereals	Coenzyme in nucleic acid metabolism; maturation of red blood cells
C (ascorbic acid)	Citrus fruits, tomatoes, red or green peppers, broccoli, cabbage, strawberries	Maintenance of cartilage and bone; antioxidant; improves iron absorption; important for healthy gums, tissue repair, and wound healing
Biotin	Legumes, vegetables, meat	Coenzyme in synthesis of fat; glycogen formation; amino acid metabolism
Choline	Egg yolk, liver, grains, legumes	Required for phospholipids and neurotransmitters

© Pearson Education, Inc.

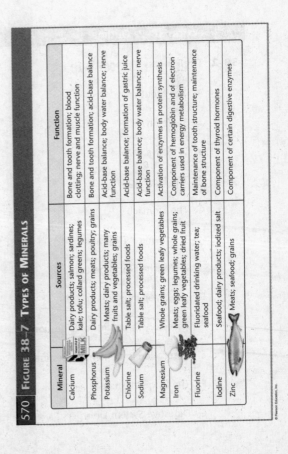

Mineral	Sources	Function
Calcium	Dairy products; salmon; sardines; kale; collard greens; legumes	Bone and tooth formation; blood clotting; nerve and muscle function
Phosphorus	Dairy products; meats; poultry; grains	Bone and tooth formation; acid-base balance
Potassium	Meats; dairy products; many fruits and vegetables; grains	Acid-base balance; body water balance; nerve function
Chlorine	Table salt; processed foods	Acid-base balance; formation of gastric juice
Sodium	Table salt; processed foods	Acid-base balance; body water balance; nerve function
Magnesium	Whole grains; green leafy vegetables	Activation of enzymes in protein synthesis
Iron	Meats; eggs; legumes; whole grains; green leafy vegetables; dried fruit	Component of hemoglobin and of electron carriers used in energy metabolism
Fluorine	Fluoridated drinking water; tea; seafood	Maintenance of tooth structure; maintenance of bone structure
Iodine	Seafood; dairy products; iodized salt	Component of thyroid hormones
Zinc	Meats; seafood; grains	Component of certain digestive enzymes

© Pearson Education, Inc.

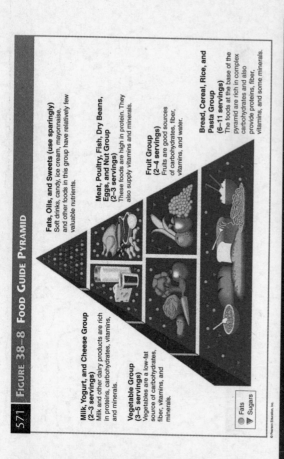

Fats, Oils, and Sweets (use sparingly)
Soft drinks, candy, ice cream, mayonnaise, and other foods in this group have relatively few valuable nutrients.

Meat, Poultry, Fish, Dry Beans, Eggs, and Nut Group (2–3 servings)
These foods are high in protein. They also supply vitamins and minerals.

Fruit Group (2–4 servings)
Fruits are good sources of carbohydrates, fiber, vitamins, and water.

Bread, Cereal, Rice, and Pasta Group (6–11 servings)
The foods at the base of the pyramid are rich in complex carbohydrates and also provide proteins, fiber, vitamins, and some minerals.

Milk, Yogurt, and Cheese Group (2–3 servings)
Milk and other dairy products are rich in proteins, carbohydrates, vitamins, and minerals.

Vegetable Group (3–5 servings)
Vegetables are a low-fat source of carbohydrates, fiber, vitamins, and minerals.

● Fats
▼ Sugars

© Pearson Education, Inc.

Dinner Is Served

Remember the last time you sat down to a dinner of your favorite foods? Recall everything that you did before you swallowed your first bite.

1. Why do you cut up your food?

2. What role do your teeth play in eating?

3. Saliva is the fluid that is found in your mouth. What role do you think it plays in eating?

ANSWERS
1. To make the pieces small enough to fit in the mouth
2. They crush the food so it is small enough to be swallowed.
3. Students will likely say that it moistens the food so it is easier to swallow. Students may also be aware that saliva contains a digestive enzyme.

© Pearson Education, Inc.

38–2 The Process of Digestion

A. The Mouth

  1. Teeth

  2. Saliva

B. The Esophagus

C. The Stomach

  1. Chemical Digestion

  2. Mechanical Digestion

D. The Small Intestine

  Accessory Structures of Digestion

E. Absorption in the Small Intestine

F. The Large Intestine

G. Digestive System Disorders

© Pearson Education, Inc.

Site	Enzyme	Role in Digestion
Mouth	Salivary amylase	Breaks down starches into disaccharides
Stomach	Pepsin	Breaks down proteins into large peptides
Small intestine (from pancreas)	Amylase	Continues the breakdown of starch
	Trypsin	Continues the breakdown of protein
	Lipase	Breaks down fat
Small intestine	Maltase, sucrase, lactase	Breaks down remaining disaccharides into monosaccharides
	Peptidase	Breaks down dipeptides into amino acids

© Pearson Education, Inc.

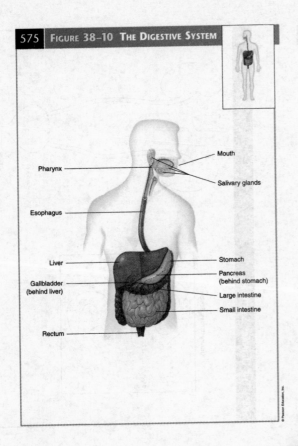

Mouth

Pharynx

Salivary glands

Esophagus

Liver

Stomach

Pancreas
(behind stomach)

Gallbladder
(behind liver)

Large intestine

Small intestine

Rectum

© Pearson Education, Inc.

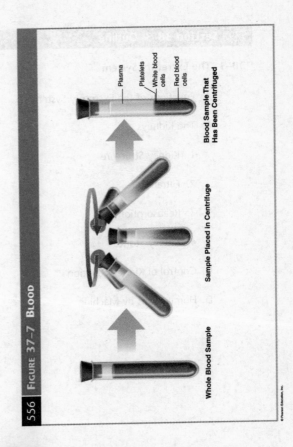

Plasma

Platelets

White blood
cells

Red blood
cells

Blood Sample That
Has Been Centrifuged

Sample Placed in Centrifuge

Whole Blood Sample

© Pearson Education, Inc.

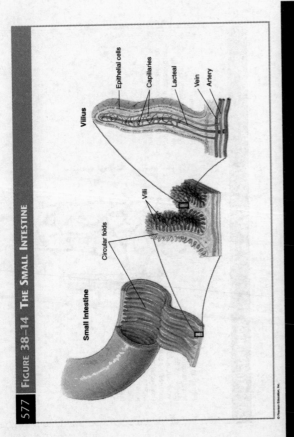

Epithelial cells

Capillaries

Lacteal

Vein

Artery

Villus

Villi

Circular folds

Small Intestine

© Pearson Education, Inc.

Your Body's Filter

Have you ever seen a water-purification
system attached to a faucet? This system
removes impurities from the water such
as arsenic or other chemicals that can be
harmful to people. As water passes through
the filters contained in the system, the
impurities are trapped on the surface of
the filters. Eventually, the water that comes
out of this purifier is free of the impurities.

1. Your body has its own system for
   filtering blood. Why might the blood
   in your body need to be filtered?

2. What organ(s) do you think filters
   your blood?

3. How do you think the filtered materials
   leave your body?

ANSWERS
1. To adjust to remove harmful blood any impurities that could be harmful.
2. Possible answer: kidneys.
3. Possible answer: as urine.

© Pearson Education, Inc.

38–3 The Excretory System

A. Functions of the Excretory System

B. The Kidneys

   1. Kidney Structure

   2. Filtration

   3. Reabsorption

   4. Kidney Stones

C. Control of Kidney Function

D. Homeostasis by Machine

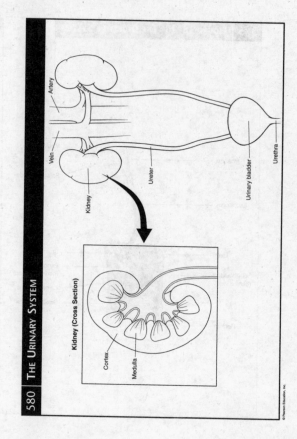

580 | **THE URINARY SYSTEM**

Kidney (Cross Section)

Artery

Vein

Kidney

Ureter

Urinary bladder

Urethra

Cortex

Medulla

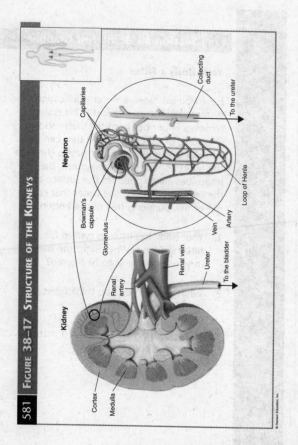

581 | **FIGURE 38–17 STRUCTURE OF THE KIDNEYS**

Nephron

Capillaries

Collecting duct

To the ureter

Bowman's capsule

Glomerulus

Loop of Henle

Vein

Artery

Kidney

Renal artery

Renal vein

Ureter

To the bladder

Cortex

Medulla

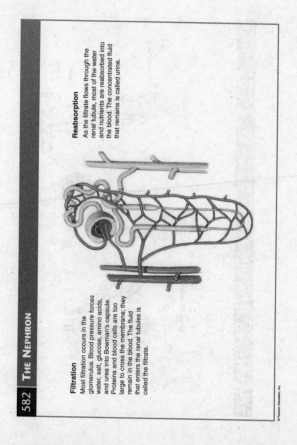

582 | **THE NEPHRON**

Filtration

Most filtration occurs in the glomerulus. Blood pressure forces water, salt, glucose, amino acids, and urea into Bowman's capsule. Proteins and blood cells are too large to cross the membrane; they remain in the blood. The fluid that enters the renal tubules is called the filtrate.

Reabsorption

As the filtrate flows through the renal tubule, most of the water and nutrients are reabsorbed into the blood. The concentrated fluid that remains is called urine.

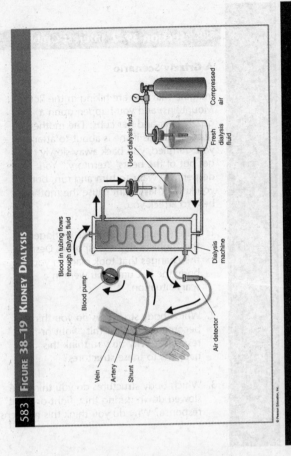

Compressed air

Fresh dialysis fluid

Used dialysis fluid

Blood in tubing flows through dialysis fluid

Dialysis machine

Blood pump

Air detector

Vein

Artery

Shunt

Fast and Slow Messages

Your endocrine (hormonal) system is the slow message system of your body. Its messages consist of chemicals released by glands into the bloodstream. Your nervous system, on the other hand, is the fast message system of the body. Its messages consist of electrical signals that travel along the membranes of nerve cells.

1. Describe a situation in which the body could use the endocrine system to deliver a "slow" message.

2. Describe a situation in which the body could use the nervous system to deliver a "fast" message.

3. Develop an analogy that illustrates this difference between these two systems.

ANSWERS
1. Slow messages include those about growth, water balance, and the proper metabolism of substances.
2. Fast messages include those about sensing and responding to environmental stimuli.
3. Possible answer: Slow messaging: mail delivered by the mail carrier; Fast messaging: e-mail

39-1   The Endocrine System

A. Hormones

B. Glands

C. Hormone Action

   1. Steroid Hormones

   2. Nonsteroid Hormones

D. Prostaglandins

E. Control of the Endocrine System

   1. Controlling Metabolism

   2. Maintaining Water Balance

F. Complementary Hormone Action

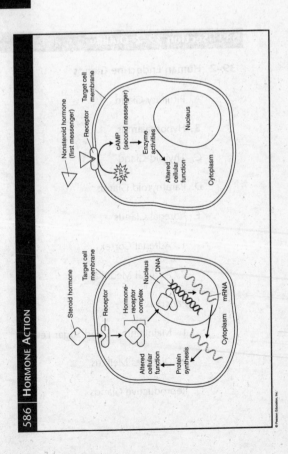

Nonsteroid hormone (first messenger)

Target cell membrane

Receptor

cAMP (second messenger)

Enzyme activities

Nucleus

Altered cellular function

Cytoplasm

Steroid hormone

Target cell membrane

Receptor

Hormone-receptor complex

Nucleus

DNA

mRNA

Cytoplasm

Altered cellular function

Protein synthesis

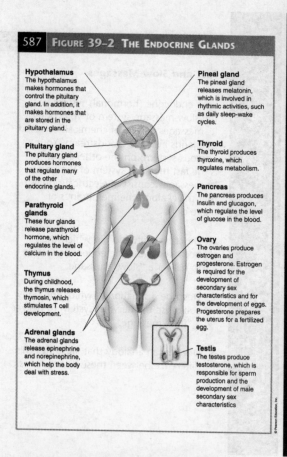

Hypothalamus
The hypothalamus makes hormones that control the pituitary gland. In addition, it makes hormones that are stored in the pituitary gland.

Pituitary gland
The pituitary gland produces hormones that regulate many of the other endocrine glands.

Parathyroid glands
These four glands release parathyroid hormone, which regulates the level of calcium in the blood.

Thymus
During childhood, the thymus releases thymosin, which stimulates T cell development.

Adrenal glands
The adrenal glands release epinephrine and norepinephrine, which help the body deal with stress.

Pineal gland
The pineal gland releases melatonin, which is involved in rhythmic activities, such as daily sleep-wake cycles.

Thyroid
The thyroid produces thyroxine, which regulates metabolism.

Pancreas
The pancreas produces insulin and glucagon, which regulate the level of glucose in the blood.

Ovary
The ovaries produce estrogen and progesterone. Estrogen is required for the development of secondary sex characteristics and for the development of eggs. Progesterone prepares the uterus for a fertilized egg.

Testis
The testes produce testosterone, which is responsible for sperm production and the development of male secondary sex characteristics

© Pearson Education, Inc.

A Grizzly Scenario

Imagine that you are hiking in the Rocky Mountains, and you happen upon a grizzly bear and her cubs. The mother grizzly looks as if she is about to attack you. Terrified, you back away slowly to get out of the bears' "territory." You desperately want to turn and run, but you know that might cause the mother bear to attack you.

1. When you are frightened, it triggers the "fight-or-flight" response. Describe the changes that took place in your body the last time you were in a scary situation.

2. Which body structures do you think become readied for this "fight-or-flight" response? Why do you think this happens to these structures?

3. Which body structures do you think are slowed down during this "fight-or-flight" response? Why do you think this happens?

© Pearson Education, Inc.

39–2 Human Endocrine Glands

   A. Pituitary Gland

   B. Hypothalamus

   C. Thyroid Gland

   D. Parathyroid Glands

   E. Adrenal Glands

      1. Adrenal Cortex

      2. Adrenal Medulla

   F. Pancreas

      1. Maintaining Blood Sugar Levels

      2. Diabetes Mellitus

   G. Reproductive Glands

© Pearson Education, Inc.

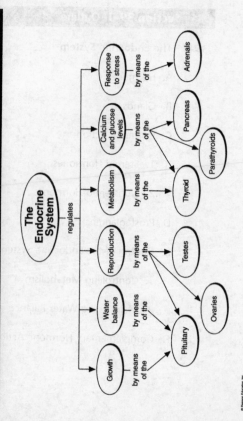

© Pearson Education, Inc.

ACTIONS OF INSULIN AND GLUCAGON

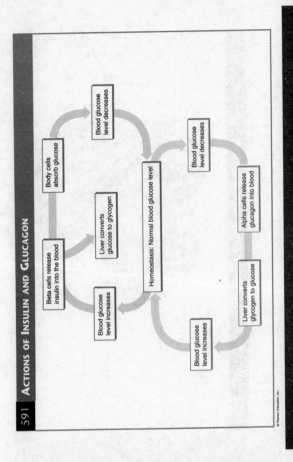

Body cells absorb glucose

Blood glucose level decreases

Beta cells release insulin into the blood

Liver converts glucose to glycogen

Homeostasis: Normal blood glucose level

Blood glucose level decreases

Alpha cells release glucagon into blood

Blood glucose level increases

Blood glucose level increases

Liver converts glycogen to glucose

ANSWERS
1. The boy's voice is much higher. The girl's voice is not much different from the adult female's voice.
2. An increase in certain hormones causes the change. This occurs as the boy matures into an adult male.
3. Since at the onset of puberty, many girls were taller than boys, but by 9th grade, more boys were taller than girls.

© Pearson Education, Inc.

A Soprano Becomes a Tenor

Many changes take place in the human body between the ages of about 9 to 15 years. Think about the changes that you have noticed in yourself and your friends in the last few years. Then, answer the following questions.

1. How does an eight-year-old male's voice compare to that of an adult male? How does an eight-year-old female's voice compare to that of an adult female?

2. What do you think causes the differences in the voices? Explain your answer.

3. Another change that occurs between 9 and 15 is a growth spurt, which is a rapid increase in height. Do you think growth spurts occur earlier in males or in females? Explain your answer.

© Pearson Education, Inc.

39-3 The Reproductive System

A. Sexual Development

B. The Male Reproductive System

   1. Sperm Development

   2. Sperm Release

C. The Female Reproductive System

   1. Egg Development

   2. Egg Release

D. The Menstrual Cycle

   1. Follicular Phase

   2. Ovulation

   3. Luteal Phase

   4. Menstruation

E. Sexually Transmitted Diseases

© Pearson Education, Inc.

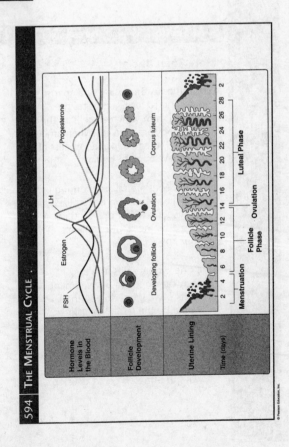

© Pearson Education, Inc.

© Pearson Education, Inc., publishing as Pearson Prentice Hall.

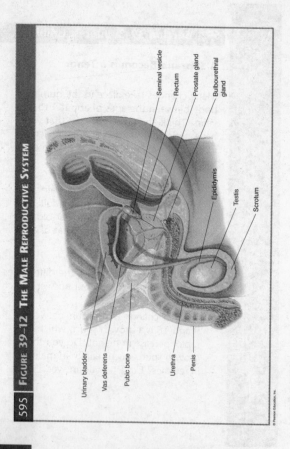

Seminal vesicle
Rectum
Prostate gland
Bulbourethral gland
Epididymis
Testis
Scrotum
Urinary bladder
Vas deferens
Pubic bone
Urethra
Penis

© Pearson Education, Inc.

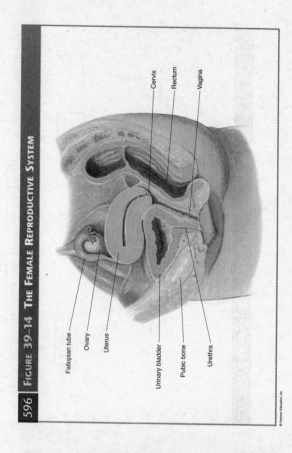

Cervix
Rectum
Vagina
Fallopian tube
Ovary
Uterus
Urinary bladder
Pubic bone
Urethra

© Pearson Education, Inc.

More Than One

Fertilization is the fusion of a sperm and an egg to form a zygote, the single cell from which all cells of the human body are derived. When an egg is fertilized, the remarkable process of human development begins.

1. If two eggs are released during ovulation, each can be fertilized by a sperm. What do you think would be the result? Explain your answer.

2. If one zygote splits into two, each can continue development on its own. What do you think would be the result? Explain your answer.

3. Triplets are three babies born at the same time. Describe three ways that triplets could develop.

ANSWERS
1. Fraternal (not genetically identical) twins would result, since they would develop from two eggs fertilized by two sperm.
2. Identical (genetically identical) twins would result, since they would develop from one egg fertilized by one sperm.
3. a. A zygote could split into three (identical triplets).
   b. Triplets could also result from two separate eggs being fertilized, with one of the eggs splitting to form two.
   c. Three separate eggs, each fertilized by a different sperm.

© Pearson Education, Inc.

39-4 Fertilization and Development

A. Fertilization

B. Early Development

   1. Implantation

   2. Gastrulation

   3. Neurulation

   4. Extraembryonic Membranes

C. Control of Development

D. Later Development

E. Childbirth

F. Multiple Births

G. Early Years

   1. Infancy

   2. Childhood

   3. Adolescence

H. Adulthood

© Pearson Education, Inc.

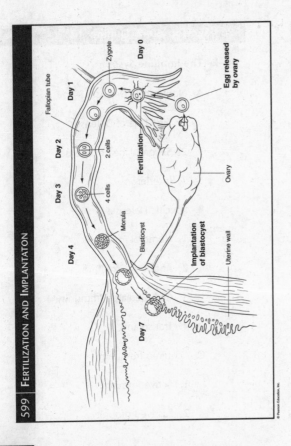

© Pearson Education, Inc.

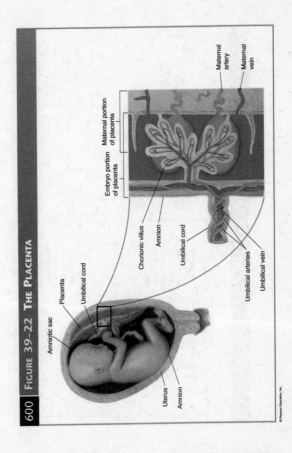

© Pearson Education, Inc.

How Do We Get Sick?

Almost everyone gets sick once in a while. Diseases are any changes, other than injuries, that disrupt the normal functions of the body. They can be inherited, caused by materials in the environment, or produced by disease-causing organisms. These organisms are called pathogens. Diseases caused by pathogens are generally infectious because the pathogens usually infect, or enter, the body of the person that gets sick.

1. On a sheet of paper, make a list of some of the infectious diseases you have had.

2. Choose one of the diseases on your list. How did you feel when you were sick with this disease? How was the disease treated?

3. How did you get the disease described in question 2? What do you think caused this disease?

© Pearson Education, Inc.

40–1 Infectious Disease

A. The Germ Theory of Disease

B. Koch's Postulates

C. Agents of Disease

  1. Viruses

  2. Bacteria

  3. Protists

  4. Worms

  5. Fungi

D. How Diseases Are Spread

  1. Physical Contact

  2. Contaminated Food and Water

  3. Infected Animals

E. Fighting Infectious Diseases

© Pearson Education, Inc.

KOCH'S POSTULATES

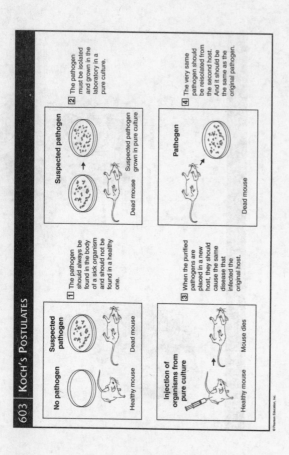

Section 40–2 Outline

40–2 The Immune System

A. Nonspecific Defenses

   1. First Line of Defense

   2. Second Line of Defense

   3. Interferon

B. Specific Defenses

   1. Humoral Immunity

   2. Antibody Structure

   3. Cell-Mediated Immunity

   4. Transplants

C. Acquired Immunity

   1. Active Immunity

   2. Passive Immunity

PRIMARY AND SECONDARY IMMUNE RESPONSES

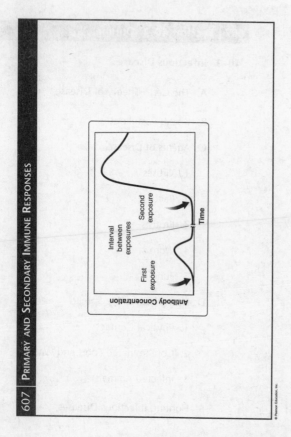

FIGURE 40–7 THE INFLAMMATORY RESPONSE

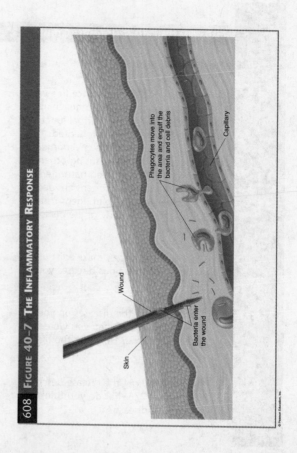

© Pearson Education, Inc., publishing as Pearson Prentice Hall.

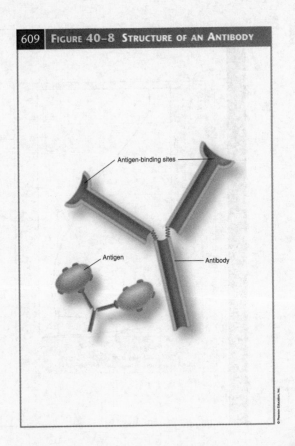

Antigen-binding sites

Antigen

Antibody

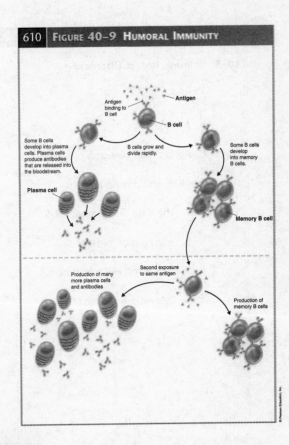

Antigen binding to B cell

Antigen

B cell

Some B cells develop into plasma cells. Plasma cells produce antibodies that are released into the bloodstream.

B cells grow and divide rapidly.

Some B cells develop into memory B cells.

Plasma cell

Memory B cell

Production of many more plasma cells and antibodies

Second exposure to same antigen

Production of memory B cells

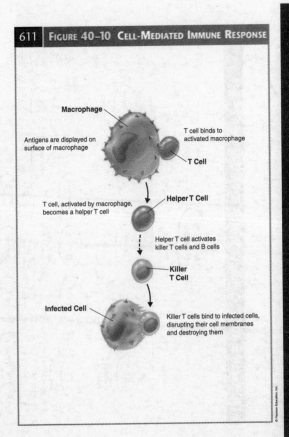

Macrophage

Antigens are displayed on surface of macrophage

T cell binds to activated macrophage

T Cell

T cell, activated by macrophage, becomes a helper T cell

Helper T Cell

Helper T cell activates killer T cells and B cells

Killer T Cell

Infected Cell

Killer T cells bind to infected cells, disrupting their cell membranes and destroying them

What Are Allergies?

Ahhhhchoo! Do you or someone you know have allergies? As you know, the immune system protects the body against invading pathogens. Sometimes, however, the immune system can make a mistake. Allergies occur when the immune system overreacts to an antigen, a substance that triggers an immune response.

Work with a partner to answer the following questions.

1. Does one of you have allergies? If so, how does your body behave when you are exposed to something to which you are allergic? If neither of you has allergies, describe the behavior of someone you know who has allergies.

2. How can you tell the difference between an allergy and a cold?

3. What types of objects are people allergic to?

4. How are allergies treated?

40–3 Immune System Disorders

  A. Allergies

  B. Asthma

  C. Autoimmune Diseases

  D. AIDS, an Immunodeficiency Disease

    1. The Virus That Causes AIDS

    2. Transmission of HIV

    3. Preventing HIV Infection

    4. Can AIDS Be Cured?

614 | **Stages of HIV Infection**

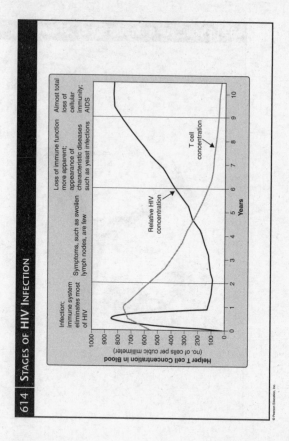

40–4 The Environment and Your Health

  A. Air Quality

    1. Carbon Monoxide

    2. Ozone

    3. Airborne Particulates

  B. Water Quality

  C. Bioterrorism

  D. Cancer

    1. Causes of Cancer

    2. Treating Cancer

  E. Maintaining Health

    1. Healthful Diet

    2. Exercise and Rest

    3. Abstaining From Harmful Activities

    4. Regular Checkups

617 | **Section 40–4** Concept Map

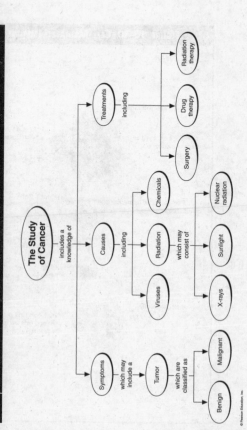